WILD FLOWERS
OF
NORTH EAST
ESSEX

Terri Tarpey and Jerry Heath

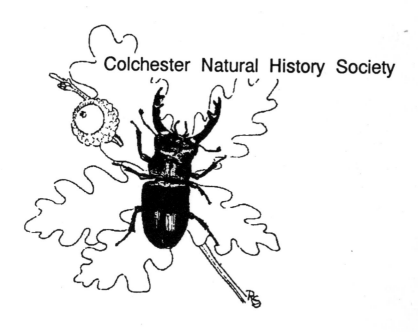

Colchester Natural History Society

Published by THE COLCHESTER NATURAL HISTORY SOCIETY
Colchester Natural History Museum
High Street
Colchester
Essex CO1 1DN

First published 1990

Printed by THE IPSWICH BOOK COMPANY
The Drift
Nacton Road
Ipswich
Suffolk IP3 9QR

ISBN   0 9516312 0 9

The cover illustration is of the Mersea Pea (Tetragonolobus maritimus)
 - J J Heath

CONTENTS

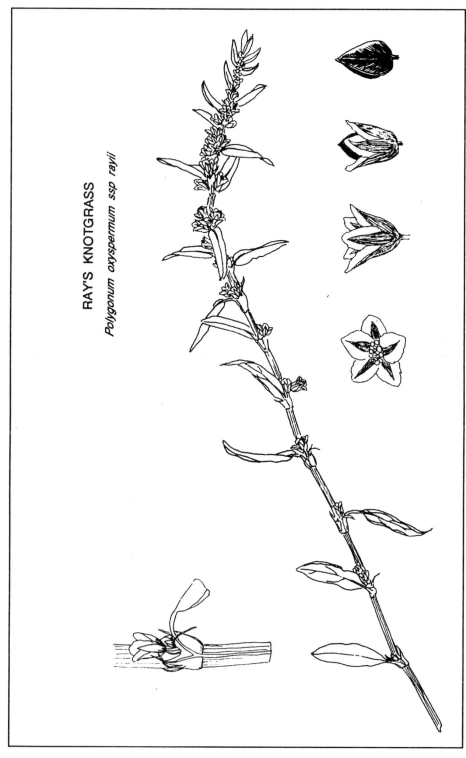

RAY'S KNOTGRASS
Polygonum oxyspermum ssp rayii

FOREWORD

As a very inactive member of the Colchester Natural History Society and one who lives outside the county of Essex, I feel honoured at being asked to write a Foreword to this splendid book. Ten years work by a team of dedicated botanists of the Society, exploring every corner of land in nineteen 10km grid-squares, has resulted in a local Flora such as has never been produced in such detail before.

I have been interested in grid-square recording for many years and I served on the Botanical Society's Committee which formulated the Mapping Scheme, which ultimately resulted in 1962 in the publishing of the **Atlas of the British Flora**, edited by Perring & Walter. For a number of years previously I had been plotting 10km grid-squares where *Clematis vitalba* grew, a plant one could spot from a car at any season; and Frank Perring tells me that the first map he ran off experimentally on the Atlas equipment was based on my *Clematis* records.

Plotting has moved from the 10km square basis to the tetrad, but here we have 1km square recording, one hundred in every 10km grid-square! It is hard to realise the painstaking survey work which the team must have achieved to produce the data for this Flora. Surveying on this scale necessitates exploring not only the interesting habitats in a 10km grid-square but also the uninteresting habitats, which every now and then produce an unexpected plant. This has been done to great effect and both botanists and wild flower lovers in north east Essex will now have a valuable guide to help them to discover the plant or flower they particularly want to see.

Much work, apart from that of the survey team, has gone into the production of this book; plotting the maps, writing the text, designing the format, checking references and reading proofs. To all who contributed I offer my congratulations on producing such a remarkably detailed Flora which will be much in demand locally for many years to come.

I would add that it is good to see the spirit of local natural history investigation and recording is still very much alive in our Society. At a time when many groups of flora and fauna are being investigated by enthusiastic amateur field naturalists, it is a tragedy that the taxonomic staff and identification facilities of the British Museum (Natural History), as it used to be called, are being drastically cut.

Parkers
Bear Street
Nayland
Suffolk CO6 4HX

E Milne-Redhead, ISO, TD, MA, FLS
May 1990

DITTANDER

Lepidium latifolium

ACKNOWLEDGEMENTS

Anyone who has been involved with a project lasting ten years and which culminates in the successful production of a scheme, system or book will know that very little can be achieved without a great deal of assistance, enthusiasm, drive and hard work. The production of **WILD FLOWERS OF NORTH EAST ESSEX** could never have been brought to fruition without all of those qualities being exhibited by numerous people and organisations.

The credit deserved by all those who actively took part in the recording work is given in the List of Recorders, but to mention by name all those who have participated in the project in other ways is an impossible task. However, in this section we would like to acknowledge a number of organisations, groups of people and individuals who have helped either with the recording of the plants or in the production of the book.

Landowners
Invariably, when we have approached landowners for permission to survey private property, we have been given every assistance and this has allowed us to achieve the almost total coverage of the whole of north east Essex.

Financial Assistance
When approached, several local organisations, authorities and companies helped by giving a grant or by providing equipment and services at reduced cost to assist with the production of this book. Without their help the publication of the book would not have been possible. We are grateful to the following for their assistance:

The John Ray Trust

Essex Naturalists' Trust
- Colchester Local Group

Strident Computer Services Ltd
Tiptree Parish Council
Aldham Parish Council
Great Horkesley Parish Council
Langham Parish Council

WATCH OVER
ESSEX

And members of the Colchester Natural History Society who either donated or raised funds for this project.

Specialist Assistance
The following people have freely given their expertise in the groups indicated:
Aquatic *Ranunculus* - Dr Sarah Webster
Rubus - Alec Bull
Rosa - Rev Gordon G Graham
Salix - Desmond Meikle
Calamintha and *Mentha* - Dr Ray M Harley
Hieracium - Jim Bevan & Dr Kenneth J Adams
Taraxacum - the late Chris C Haworth & Dr A J Richards
General assistance - staff in the Botany Section, British Museum (Natural History)

Computer Programming

An acknowledgement must go to Trev Tarpey for his computer programming; in 1981 he wrote a suite of programs to set up and maintain a database for the wild flower records. Over the last nine years these programs have withstood everything that the botanists have thrown at them - over 180,000 records. They have also survived changes in technology having been migrated from an Apple computer to one which is IBM compatible. We think it is safe to say that without these programs providing the information that the botanists needed, the recording of the flora of north east Essex would not be where it is today.

Mapping Program

The software package used with our computer database to produce printed dot distribution maps is the DMAP program written by Dr Alan Morton. Initially it was not perfected for incorporating into a Desk Top Publishing system, but Alan's quick response to our needs has enabled us to produce the excellent maps found in this book.

Illustrations

The Society is very lucky in having a wealth of diverse talents within its membership, and the beautiful line drawings included in the book demonstrate our extreme good fortune in having an artist with the expertise of Laura Lerwill within our ranks. A similar talent is displayed in Jerry Bowdrey's cartoon on page 51 which exemplifies much of the fun and humour that accompanied many of the field trips.

The Committees

Two committees were formed to assist us during the production of this book, one to concentrate the knowledge acquired during the survey into the writing of the book and the other to co-ordinate the actual production. We are grateful to the following members of the Colchester Natural History Society for giving their valuable time to the project in this way:

Bill Chisholm
Brian Corben
Joe Firmin
Chris Gibson
Basil Harley
Jeremy Ison
Ian Rose
Trev Tarpey

Further acknowledgements are due to Dr Chris Gibson for reading the manuscript and commenting thereon, to Mrs Kath Mellor for the initial proof-reading and correction of our grammar and to Mr Jerry Bowdrey for the final proof-reading of the printer ready copy, however, any errors that remain are our responsibility. Our thanks also go to Trev Tarpey who spent many hours slaving over a hot computer to put together the printer ready copy.

We have relied heavily on Gibson's **Flora of Essex**, 1862, and the work of his recorders to provide us with historical background and to Stan Jermyn's detailed recording and pioneering of dot distribution maps for the county which inspired us to undertake this work in the first place.

Lastly, our thanks must be given to the Essex Naturalists' Trust, publishers of Jermyn's **Flora of Essex**, 1974, who have kindly allowed us to quote so freely from that work.

COLCHESTER NATURAL HISTORY SOCIETY

The Society was founded in October 1953 with an initial membership of 100 and was successor to Colchester's first natural history society, which existed from 1872 to 1884. During its relatively short life the original society had several distinguished naturalists as members including Dr C R Bree, author of the nationally acclaimed **The History of the Birds of Europe, not observed in the British Isles** (1859, Groombridge & Co); Dr Henry Laver, author of the Victorian work **Mammals, Reptiles and Fishes of Essex** (1898, Essex Field Club) and contributor on mammals and fish to the **Victoria County History** (1903, Archibald Constable), as was William H Harwood, one of the best entomologists of the period, who contributed the insect section of the same publication.

The present Society owes its start to Joe Firmin and Tony Richardson, who organised the inaugural meeting with the late A Donald Blaxill as chairman, and led the early field meetings which provided the beginnings of the present valuable survey work in north east Essex. The results of this work have been published in the Society's journal, **Nature in North East Essex**, over the last thirty years. Leader of the Society's junior section in the 1950s and early 1960s was Dr John Sparks, now head of the BBC Natural History Unit and author of several wildlife books.

A special Scientific Committee was formed in 1967 and established a bird ringing scheme for north east Essex and an entomological section, led by Joe Firmin, carried out systematic surveys of selected habitats using the Society's own mercury vapour lamp and portable generator. Records from these surveys were used in the **Butterflies and Larger Moths of Essex** (1975, Essex Naturalists' Trust). Brian Goodey, and other members of the Society's current invertebrate group, have continued this pioneer work and provided several first records for Essex, particularly for **The Smaller Moths of Essex** (1981, Essex Field Club) and the enlarged **The Larger Moths and Butterflies of Essex** (1985, Essex Field Club). Society committee member Dr Ted Benton is the author of the much-praised book **The Dragonflies of Essex** (1988, Essex Field Club), and Alan Wake has produced the **Grasshoppers and Crickets of Essex, A Provisional Atlas** (1984, Essex Biological Record Centres).

The Society's contribution to the natural history and wildlife conservation in Essex can be gauged from the wide range of field activities including moth identification evenings, invertebrate surveys and of course the botanical recording. Practical conservation work on local nature reserves is also undertaken and the Society is represented on the Roman River Valley Conservation Group, the Tiptree Heath Management Committee, the Garrison Conservation Committee and the Colchester Group of the Essex Naturalists' Trust and also has several County Recorders amongst its membership.

During the winter the Society arranges popular indoor meetings, illustrated talks, identification evenings and an annual wildlife photographic competition at its headquarters in the Colchester Natural History Museum.

The Society's aim is to "increase people's awareness and enjoyment of local wildlife" and in furtherance of this, meetings are kept as informal and friendly as possible and assume no previous knowledge, just an interest in our natural environment.

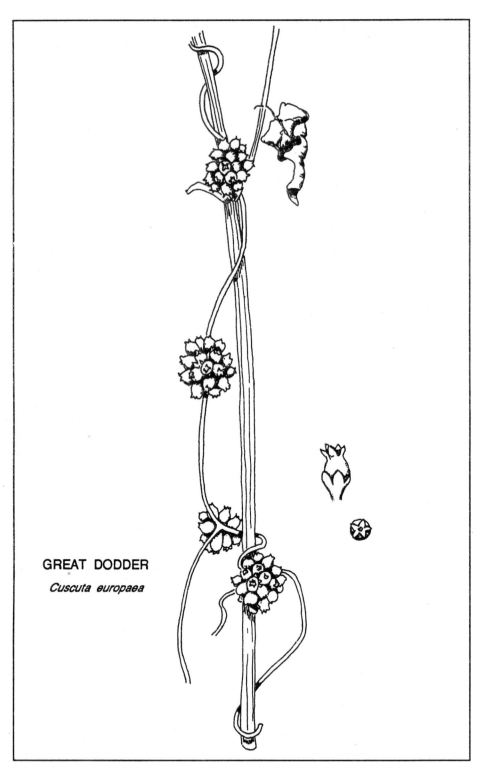

GREAT DODDER

Cuscuta europaea

AN OUTLINE OF THE PROJECT

Arthur Ransome, of **Swallows and Amazons** fame, set the beginning of one of his books, **We Didn't Mean to Go to Sea**, locally at Harwich. Because of a set of interwoven circumstances the characters in that book had a series of adventures that they never envisaged would happen to them. This project has had some of the same characteristics! In 1979 the volume of data that was to be amassed and the publication of this book could not be foreseen.

The first stone was laid by S T Jermyn when he published his book **Flora of Essex** in 1974 which meant there was now a publication to which local botanists could refer; the Flora gave sites, habitats and frequency of occurrence of each plant that grew in the county. This encouraged those interested to go and seek out either the sites mentioned in the Flora, or new ones. However, during the next few years the Colchester Natural History Society (CNHS) started to realise that the distribution and frequency given for many of the plants was no longer true due to changes in landuse and agricultural practices (Jermyn's book was the culmination of many years' work, some records dating back to 1930 or earlier).

In the late 1970s it became apparent that the botanical activities of the CNHS had grown and many records had accumulated but were 'just laying around' in members' own notes. With this in mind and with the idea of updating the records for the area covered by the CNHS it was decided to organise a system whereby north east Essex could be mapped on a parallel basis with that for the **Flora of Essex**.

The area covered by the CNHS is shown on the map overleaf and all recording is done using Ordnance Survey map references. It consists of nineteen 10km squares some of which fall partly into the sea and some partly into Suffolk, leaving 1,322 1km squares which make up 353 whole or part tetrads (a block of four 1km squares - a common unit used in botanical recording). The nineteen 10km squares are: TL 80, TL 81, TL 82, TL 83, TL 84, TL 90, TL 91, TL 92, TL 93, TM 00, TM 01, TM 02, TM 03, TM 11, TM 12, TM 13, TM 21, TM 22, TM 23.

The Essex Flora had been mapped for the common plants by 10km square whilst the rare or more localised species had been dealt with on a 1km square basis. A system was evolved by one of the authors (Jerry Heath) whereby the index of the **Flora of Essex** was used as a basis for recording additional records or deleting/amending existing records within the 10km or 1km square, according to how the species in question had been mapped in the original Flora. Each plant was listed and every record from the Flora was extracted and entered on to a series of master sheets for either its 10km or 1km square locality.

The decision was made at that time that all CNHS botanical recording would be on a 1km square basis and that **all** plants would be recorded and not just the 'more interesting ones'. This was as a direct result of collating the **Flora of Essex** records on to the master sheets as they showed obvious gaps of there being, apparently, no record within a whole 10km for some very common plants.

A spin off from the production of these master sheets was that it triggered more interest in the botanical recording and consequently more recording (there was evidently something very satisfying about having the master sheets updated as a result of one's efforts).

However, all these records created their own problem - how to cope with the volume of data.

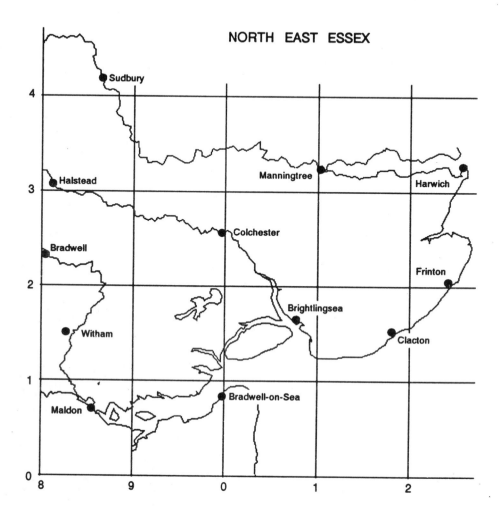

A member of the Society (Trev Tarpey) had become involved (and intrigued) by computers at work, and, with personal computers just becoming available to the home market, decided to buy one and computerise the flora of north east Essex for us. This was 1981; compared to the PCs and software available now, it is hard to imagine that the market leader at that time came with only 32K of memory and that for software, it was a case of 'do it yourself' starting with a completely blank sheet of paper - the sort of 'off the shelf' database packages that we needed had still not been developed. The whole of the micro-computer revolution was only just beginning.

The database was set up holding information on the origin and age of the record so that we could always trace the entry back to the substantiating documentation and recording. This not only allowed us to be able to establish and check the integrity of the data but would also allow us to check out old and interesting records to see if the plants were still there, and, of course, we needed to differentiate between the older records and those currently being recorded. Therefore, every plant record not only held the map reference but also details of the first time that a plant had been recorded in a particular 1km square as well as the last time it had been found at that locality.

The database, complete with all the records from the master sheets, other records extracted from the Colchester Natural History Museum's files and members' notes, was ready for the 1982 botany season. A total of just over 24,300 records had been entered on to the database. These were made up of approximately 10,700 from the **Flora of Essex**, 1,900 pre-1980 records and 11,700 post-1980 records.

At this point in time we still did not envisage the final outcome of the project, only the updating of existing records and increasing our knowledge of the wild flowers of north east Essex, but within the next two years this was to change.

In 1982 the CNHS commenced a Tuesday evening botany session. This started in order to complete the survey of the Roman River Valley (a local project) with which we were involved at that time, but the evenings proved so popular we continued them. They were held, generally within a radius of 15-20 minutes drive from the centre of Colchester, every Tuesday evening during the summer, in order to identify the wild flowers in that area. These Tuesday evenings generated more interest in the local flora and it was found that CNHS members went out, either singly or in informal groups, not only to look at and simply enjoy the wild flowers but also to record them and submit field lists.

By 1984 it was apparent that the Society's botanical activities had 'taken off' and that complete coverage of north east Essex was possible. Our objective became to gain full and even coverage over the whole of north east Essex. At this point the organisation and administration of the project took on a new dimension for now, we not only had the interest within the Society, we had the recorders to carry it out and a computer which, by now, we realised was not just a filing cabinet for our records but also a planning tool. It could analyse the records in many ways that had not been possible when the records had been kept manually and these proved invaluable in organising the botanical activities of the CNHS over the forthcoming years.

The first analysis used was the total number of species in each 1km square. By plotting these figures on to grid maps of north east Essex it could easily be seen which squares had been covered and which had not. Also squares could be allocated to specific recorders and by distributing these maps to those interested we were able to avoid duplication of effort.

The Tuesday evening outings plus the fact that most members lived in Colchester meant that the two 10km squares close to Colchester were becoming heavily recorded whilst outlying areas were remaining unrecorded - this had to be solved. The computer provided the statistics - where was the most under-recorded area in north east Essex at any point in time - and that's where our field trips were held.

Another way in which the computer helped was that before a visit was made to a site a printout could be obtained of any historical records for that area. Since the historical records were, generally, of the more interesting and localised plants it was important to take the opportunity of making a particular search in order to establish whether the plant had survived the passing of time. This was taken a stage further by collating the 1km square records originating from the **Flora of Essex** into map reference order and then annotating them with the site description given in the Flora itself. Armed with this additional information a really thorough and, in many cases, very accurate search could be made for these plants.

With the volume of work being carried out it became necessary to issue monthly updates to the maps. These updates not only included details of the squares which had been worked since the last update but also new allocations of squares, for, as recorders finished one batch of squares, they were requesting more, and it was important that this information should be communicated to other recorders.

Each winter a completely new set of maps was produced for distribution along with some facts and figures on how we were doing so far, including how many records we now had, which were the 10km squares which still needed most work, which plants had been found in north east Essex for the first time, etc. We also took the opportunity to issue any guidance notes that were felt necessary to ensure that all the recorders were working along the same lines and also to pass on some of the common mistakes that were made in the early days so that others did not fall into the same trap.

All records submitted were vetted by the main recorders, so, hopefully, all 'peculiar' records were verified and checked.

Up until 1985 we had just visited a 1km square and recorded as many plants as we could. Whilst we continued to do this right through the scheme, at the end of 1985 we had sufficient records and experience of the time it took to gain those records to be able to lay down some sort of 'Target Level', that of 200 species per tetrad was felt to be practically achievable. We would have liked this figure to be higher but whilst very active, the CNHS is not a large Society and we felt it was best to set a practical target that could be achieved in ten years. Naturally, some tetrads would not yield this number of species as they were 90% in the North Sea, or perhaps just did not have the variety of habitat required. Also, of course, there were areas where we just could not get access.

During the winter of 1988/89, a list was produced of 1km squares where we had fewer than 100 records. This list was then broken down into those squares where the majority of the square was in the sea or the habitat was very limited and the number of records could be considered typical, and the remainder - the 'hit list' for the 1989 recording season which would enable us to achieve the almost complete coverage of north east Essex.

In summary, during the ten years of this survey (1980-1989 incl) of the 1,322 1km squares in north east Essex, 1,313 (99.3%) have been visited and we have accumulated 170,928 records covering 1,123 different species or subspecies of plant (these figures exclude the specialist groups of **Dandelions** and **Brambles**). The number of records held on the database in total, including historical records (pre-1980), is 182,102.

The three following tables show the number of species per 1km square, per tetrad and per 10km square for the records from our survey, again excluding **Dandelions** and **Brambles**.

The records held have already been used locally by organisations such as the Essex Naturalists' Trust, Nature Conservancy Council and the natural history staff of Colchester Borough Council for various aspects of their work in furthering conservation and natural history in north east Essex. The Colchester Natural History Society felt, however, that, in accordance with its aim "to encourage interest in and enjoyment of the local wildlife", the information should be made available to a far wider audience and, to that end, it has published this book.

NUMBER OF SPECIES PER 1KM SQUARE

```
      | 80  81  82  83  84  85  86  87  88  89 | 90  91  92  93  94  95  96  97  98  99 | 00  01  02  03  04  05  06  07  08  09 | 10  11  12  13  14  15  16  17  18  19 | 20  21  22  23  24  25  26  27  28  29
 49   |
 48   |
 47   |
 46   |
 45   |  67 101 105 225 199
 44   | 138 169 100 158 172  53
 43   | 104 145 103 102 147 166
 42   | 100 132 166 114 140 173
 41   | 115 118 135 117 135 140 126
 40   | 142 108 109 140 116 106 119
      | 106 105 158 119 105 125 105 126   0                                                             188 179                                     1   0 124 105  93 143 121
 39   | 112 110 105 126 128 121 121 171 100                79                          86 157  97 160 118                          161 165 112 131 117 223 130 113 110 103    132 168 140 161 164 161 171 128 140 129    150 142 118 109 169
 38   | 104 100  97 134 149 123 124 120  78               112                         127 158 157 176 198 183 116                 131 143 110 135 149 158 108 122 130 151    131 157 143 147 137 134 172 187 124 144    183 142 148 105  92
 37   | 114 121 123 134 158 137 154 183  87       0 135 155 142 178           168 148 159 103 168 154 155 206 207 115 177 229     185 141 101 147 110 111 136 131 131       135 138 156 147 135 147 160 127 132 138    121 150  85 108
 36   | 129 109 101 115 107 145 154 159  57     100 109 122 162 119 142       162 136 124 171 100 109 122 162 162 119 142         152 169 136 112 115 104 141 126           136 160 145 145 156 104 129 149 129        68 130  70   1
 35   | 124 115 100 102 105 122 144 173 103      73 100 125 112 130 120 131   106 118 112 118 156 174 168 205 155 159             148 152 132 169 136 127 126 102 163 141    151 160 129 152 146 158 135 150 133 103    54  48  26  39  62  14   7
 34   | 110 154 105 144 141 110 125 104 145 115  146 129 127 148 144 127      112 114  81 128 144 127 134 147 124 126            267 132 102 188 127 126 102 163 141 111    128 133 129   0 158 130 123 100 111  18    51 118 112 123  60  90 132
 33   | 119 115 126 145 143 138 113 109 139 107  173 143 170 137 114 130      136 126 130 146 173 143 170 137 114 130           161 167 118 149 175 115 184 125 198        174 152 104 162 127 120 161 157 146 139    121 128 128  58 129  93 105
 32   | 151 149 137 121 125 120 110 128 172 122  155 171 137 115 109 120 127  143 141 158 155 169 172 168 144 206 101 113       125 170 197 112 134 168 156 160 176 162    177 152 135 161 190 133 201 125 119 102    148 130 163 136 115 147 106
 31   | 174 153 148 134 166 153 154 157 117 134  169 148 188 157 153           155 147 155 169 172 168 156 122 120 128 197      153 158 120 185 119 114 134 222 178        156 159 147 102 150 172 143 118 126 180    63 141 106 112 107 142
 30   | 120 164 143 103 142 107 132 117 115 108 157  214 149 129 134 129       121 156 159 178 156 122 120 128 197 303 171      113 176 203 212 146 111 134 158 167 194    133 121 160 162 134 135 209 107  84 144   101 148 102 105 180  43
      | 112 114  81 128 144 127 108                                                                                              114 111 187 215 166 149 155 153  96 105
 29   | 129 139 118 137 155 125 169 117 100  136 126 130 146 173 143 170 137 114 130    161 165 112 131 117 223 130 113 110 103   121 155 144 142 163 218 256 233 273 317    129 155 101 132 138 160 134 145 149  59    237 123 108 156 113
 28   | 173 118 157 114 132 176 145 138 140 121  143 141 158 155 169 172 168 144 206     131 143 110 135 149 158 108 122 130 151  135  87 156 189 152 126 207 176 109 108    144 164 113 116 109 116 136 112 111 129    78  93 103 114
 27   | 175 104 175 163 113 135 142 188 157 153  155 147 155 169 172 168 156 122 120 128  185 141 101 147 110 111 136 131 131     160 245 108 106 201  98 148  73  78  46    117 140 123 113 112 100 108 123 118 108   103 128  93
 26   | 120 164 143 103 142 107 132 117 115 108 157  121 156 159 178 156 122 120 128 197 148 152 132 169 136 112 115 104 141 126   191 190 110 116 151 106 176  52 109 149    53 135 129 106 109 109 109 133 156 122   122 100
 25   | 105 183 137 121 120 144 152 102 103 133  134 177 119 148 146 115 104 165 171 303  267 132 126 102 188 127 126 102 163 141  190 220 137 113 102 135 168  44 111 135    136 142 116 137 149 114 123 131 163 126   30
 24   | 149 142 147 174 134 123 116 145 101 162  153 214 149 129 134 129  79 137 259 170  151 167 118 149 175 115 184 125 198     170 182 166 104 107 113 184 114 155 107    111 112 139 143 116 172 168 136 133 166
 23   | 109 114 109 138 180 173 120 107 101       113 176 203 212 146 111 134 158 167 194  125 170 197 112 134 168 156 160 176 162  156 123 130 100 104 135 133 137  88  74   107 129 117 139 144 130 117 112
 22   | 126 138 118 103 165 120 147 157 132 130  114 111 187 215 166 149 155 153  96 105   153 158 120 185 119 114 134 222 178      130 107 125 104  76 151 175 113 102  58   134 117 171 142 162 114 111
 21   | 129 117 110 106 116 133 120 143 128 129  124 100 191 179 160 194 245 207 204 199   191 171 248 399 188 193 130 140 111 128  110 139 124 137 113 137 109  70  81  76   133 118 198 107 122 164 147 127 133 108
 20   | 119 123 123 105  87 103 140 145 137 139  121 155 144 142 163 218 256 233 273 317   252 257 230 224 148 187 151 193 129     128 136 121 112 146 119 135  95  90        115 133 113 124 116 116 149 101 128 108
 19   | 121 101 107 107 102 102 150 219 159 160  135  87 156 189 152 126 207 176 109 188   178 163 129 113 312 228 161 142 127 130  155 101 132 138 160 134 145 149  59       126 123 150 153 131  81 122 114 110 109
 18   | 102 104 109 109 113 113 212 119 229       160 245 108 106 201  98 148  73  78  46   124  86 107  70   0  78 194 129 144 108  144 164 113 116 109 116 136 112 111 129   136 155 123 157 184 144 106 223 104 125
 17   | 171 151 102 123 186 229 154 110 153 205   191 190 110 116 151 106 176  52 109 149   100  99  79  90  50  43 110 123 118 163  117 140 123 113 112 100 108 123 118 108   108 132  93 128 114 119 185 131 116
 16   | 109 106 141 126 130 142 107 201 158       190 220 137 113 102 135 168  44 111 135   116  78  65 101  87  62  76 132 178 178  53 135 129 106 109 109 109 133 156 122    165 111   1  94
 15   | 130 142 143 164 126 103 188 172 188       170 182 166 104 107 113 184 114 155 107   117 101 105  75  46 150 137  66 133 115  136 142 116 137 149 114 123 131 163 126   93  71 142  70
 14   | 111 112 139 143 116 172 168 136 133 166   156 123 130 100 104 135 133 137  88  74   62 103 124 105 106 154  98  51  116  92 102  73 134 119 114 129 107                79 113 112 125  86 100 118 104  97 126
 13   | 107 129 117 149 121 139 142 162 114 111   164 104 141 102 108 151  88  74 120  73   120 143 111 114 108 137  55                114  84  88 106 123 114 115  21           92  63  98  76 119 107 107  85 104 115
 12   | 134 117 171 142 162 164 147 127 133 108   130 107 125 104  76 151 175 113 102  58   178 131 155 149                            117 116 170 119 105  57                   105 110 153  67  97  85 104  95 117  86
 11   | 133 118 198 107 122 164 147 127 133 108   110 139 124 137 113 137 109  70  81  76                                             75                                          86 125 108  74 113 110 115 163 110 111
 10   | 115 133 113 124 116 116 149 101 128 108   128 136 121 112 146 119 135  95  90                                                                                            129 118 139 139  98  98  76 106 114   0  73
      |                                                                                                                                                                         142 121  85 104 143 111 108 118 104  90
 09   | 126 123 150 153 131  81 122 114 110 109   140  95  84 132 110  96 153 133  58            78 100  89                                                                      126 155 123 157 184 144 106 223 104 125
 08   | 136 155 123 157 184 144 106 223 104 125   175 138 100  98 134  82  46       91          148  86  77 107                                                                 136 110 157 152 104 104 148  57  45
 07   | 108 132  93 128 114 119 185 131 116        123                             72 121        162 100  80  50                                                                168 110 157 137 152 104 104 148  57  45
 06   | 115 114 149 103 127 138 188 175  50  56    165 111   1  94                               165 111   1  94                                                                140 139 147 146 178  62 142  70 119 139
 05   | 168 110 157 137 152 104 104 148  57  45     53  41 141  65 110  78  95 124 105          93  71 142  70                                                                  127 101 115 107  88 126
 04   | 140 139 147 146 178  62 142  70 119 139     79 113 112 125  86 100 118 104  97 126       112 103  94  91                                                                 91 102 115 107  88 126
 03   | 127 101 115 118  91 102 115 107  88 126     92  63  98  76 119 107                        112  47  54  75                                                               125 114 115 109 133 110 111
 02   | 125 114 115 109 133 110 111                105 110 153  67  97  85 104  95 117  86        115 113 102  52                                                                109 181 115 102 124 114  94  90
 01   | 109 181 115 102 124 114  94  90            86 125 108  74 113 110 111  115               105 108  71   5                                                                142 121  85 104 143 111 108 118 104  90
 00   | 142 121  85 104 143 111 108 118 104  90    129 118 139 139  98  98  76 106 114   0  73    67  74 105  81                                                                
      | 80  81  82  83  84  85  86  87  88  89 | 90  91  92  93  94  95  96  97  98  99 | 00  01  02  03  04  05  06  07  08  09 | 10  11  12  13  14  15  16  17  18  19 | 20  21  22  23  24  25  26  27  28  29
```

13

```
48 |                     |
46 | 138 252 199         |
44 | 235 215 259         |
42 | 209 237 253 126     |
40 | 189 259 196 207   0 |
---|---------------------|---------------------|---------------------|---------------------|-------------------
38 | 196 226 232 256  98 |
36 | 210 207 249 276 188 |
34 | 254 195 205 255 259 | 130         103 152 | 177 188 118         |
32 | 245 228 249 199 251 | 270 223 152 267 253 | 252 294 303 243 293 | 252         141 123 |   1 166 173 121
30 | 286 259 289 249 231 | 197 187 232 245 216 | 227 241 233 269 233 | 336 258 267 281 314 | 308 261 245 102
---|---------------------|---------------------|---------------------|---------------------|-------------------
28 | 242 282 303 293 212 | 231 252 265 259 200 | 257 227 293 174 208 | 236 236 225 237 202 | 241 217 182
26 | 252 262 221 274 219 | 252 296 320 280 270 | 287 254 224 213 231 | 217 228 226 219 226 | 220 148
24 | 270 258 215 228 246 | 322 264 243 254 426 | 366 276 251 247 261 | 238 208 258 243 184 | 136 151 132 134
22 | 216 240 289 248 210 | 232 328 263 288 260 | 298 294 251 230 288 | 249 248 259 272 232 | 239 215 201 159
20 | 199 196 204 251 222 | 221 269 320 391 396 | 370 497 311 287 260 | 268 247 258 260 249 | 208 174 249
---|---------------------|---------------------|---------------------|---------------------|-------------------
18 | 221 182 203 314 305 | 320 259 274 281 231 | 266 215 370 305 258 | 255 210 247 228 225 | 289 239 113
16 | 268 246 310 286 335 | 330 230 225 227 216 | 198 146 104 216 288 | 245 215 211 216 252 | 224  93
14 | 229 260 272 317 336 | 272 253 192 255 209 | 197 214 234 199 208 | 239 217 229 221 211 |  30
12 | 198 243 227 243 190 | 221 220 229 203 169 | 266 247 163      85 | 209 236 178 121     |
10 | 195 253 268 248 213 | 221 198 248 185 122 |
---|---------------------|---------------------|---------------------|---------------------|-------------------
08 | 252 269 261 289 193 | 264 201 197 216 111 | 210 144             |
06 | 229 221 297 287 172 | 174  69 128  67 186 | 245 138             |
04 | 253 246 229 221 183 | 152 185 173 194 185 | 171 175             |
02 | 212 202 195 192 197 | 179 191 161 180 193 | 169 127             |
00 | 254 164 206 175 169 | 192 188 164 227 156 | 161 124             |
---|---------------------|---------------------|---------------------|---------------------|-------------------
   |  80  82  84  86  88 |  90  92  94  96  98 |  00  02  04  06  08 |  10  12  14  16  18 |  20  22  24  26  28
```

NUMBER OF SPECIES PER TETRAD

```
4 | 493
3 | 575    459    526    525    479
2 | 596    746    768    577    527
1 | 676    644    647    611    409
0 | 637    500    395
--|------------------------------------------
  |  8      9      0      1      2
  | TL            TM
```

NUMBER OF SPECIES PER 10KM SQUARE

14

THE GEOGRAPHY AND GEOLOGY OF NORTH EAST ESSEX

Our climate has more in common with the continent than the rest of the British Isles with generally less than 25in (634mm) of rain in the north west falling to about 20in (510mm) along the coastal belt. Much of this rain falls in summer which, coupled with the long hours of sunshine, gives a good growing season. It is this sunshine which gives us higher summer temperatures than much of the rest of England but, being the first landfall for the cold north east winds, we have colder winters than average for other areas of southern England.

The major feature of north east Essex is the coastline, which, including the three main estuaries, is over 200 kilometres long. The majority of the coast is protected by sea walls that have cut the upper and, in many cases, the middle areas of the saltmarsh off from the sea. Formerly this reclaimed land was coastal grazing marsh rich in wild flowers but most has now been further drained and converted to intensive arable or used for urban or industrial developments. With the sea level rising (approximately 15cm so far this century), a consequence of the greenhouse effect and global warming, and the whole of south east Britain sinking (about 45cm this century) following the retreat of the last Ice Age, many areas of north east Essex will become vulnerable to flooding in the future. This subject is discussed further in the Habitat chapter under Saltmarsh as it greatly affects the future of our saltmarshes. The map of Saltmarsh and Low-lying Land gives a broad picture of the areas which are predominantly saltings (the solid squares) and land, predominantly inside the sea wall, which is less than 5 metres above sea level (the hollow squares). The accompanying map of **Common Sea Lavender** highlights the majority of 1km squares which currently contain saltmarsh.

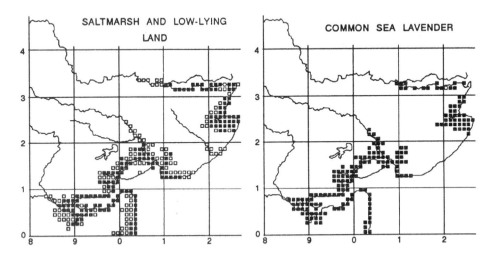

The following geology notes are derived from those in the **Flora of Essex**, 1974, supplemented by more recently published work and notes from the Geologists Association trip to the area in May 1987, plus the reports of the Soil Survey of England and Wales, now, alas, disbanded before the full publication of their work.

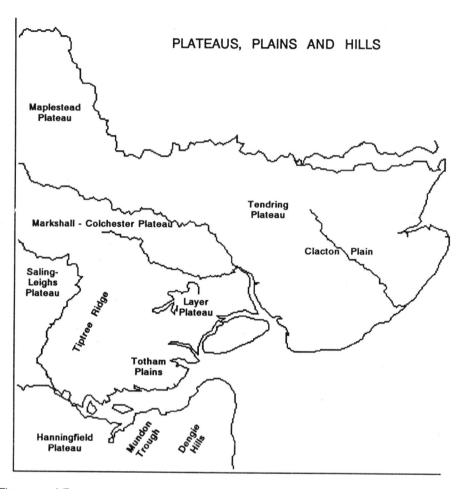

PLATEAUS, PLAINS AND HILLS

The area of Essex covered by our survey is made up mainly of level plains (the Clacton and Totham Plains and the Mundon Trough) and plateaus (Maplestead, Markshall-Colchester, Tendring, Saling-Leighs, Layer and Hanningfield), which are dissected by the rivers. Any "hills" occur at, either the junctions of the plains and plateaus, or the sides of the river channels, except for the Tiptree Ridge and the lower Dengie Hills. The height above sea level of these areas is as follows: the plains are all below 30m; the Tendring, Layer, Saling-Leighs and Hanningfield Plateaus are all between 30m-60m in our area with the Markshall-Colchester and Maplestead Plateaus being higher at 60m-90m. The Tiptree Ridge rises above the surrounding lower plateaus at 60-90m and the Dengie Hills reach a maximum height of 38m.

The northern boundary of our area is the river Stour, south of which is the Maplestead Plateau. This is separated from the Markshall-Colchester Plateau by the river Colne, which also separates this latter plateau from the Tendring Plateau. Between the Tendring Plateau and the coast lies the Clacton Plain, cut by Holland Brook. The Markshall-Colchester Plateau is bounded, in the south by the Roman River, separating it from the Layer Plateau, and further west by the river Blackwater, which separates it from the Saling-Leighs Plateau. The Blackwater also separates this latter plateau from the Tiptree Ridge, whilst the small section of the river Chelmer separates it from the Hanningfield Plateau.

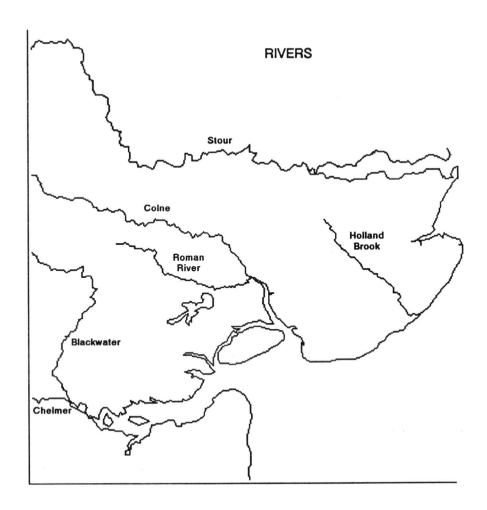

RIVERS

Stour

Colne

Holland
Brook

Roman
River

Blackwater

Chelmer

Much of north east Essex still lacks detailed modern geological maps, so the picture given here is a composite one, which hopefully gives the correct basic data, but which still leaves room for refinement of the local detail. The maps indicate the occurrence of a rock type within a 1km square, this does not mean the whole square is of that rock type, just that there is some present; several different rocks may occur in the same 1km square.

The main underlying rock is the non-calcareous London Clay which outcrops at the coast at Wrabness, Harwich, Walton, Frinton, Clacton and Mersea. Inland it influences the surface soils from the Tendring to Dengie Peninsulas in a broad

LONDON CLAY

NE-SW sweep. It thins out towards the north west of the area, its edge being marked by outcrops of its lowest layers, the Thanet Sand and Reading Beds, in the Bulmer and Sudbury area. These, being of a different make-up, are included on other maps.

Below the London Clay is the Chalk, which only reaches the surface in a few small areas in the Sudbury district.

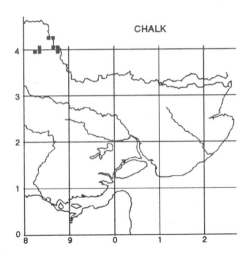

Above the London Clay in a few areas are deposits of shelly Red Crag sand, (deposited over 2 million years ago). Long known from the famous site at Walton on the Naze, it also occurs in the Beaumont-Little Oakley-Dovercourt areas as well as Wrabness, the Manningtree-Mistley area and the Dedham-Langham-Boxted area.

The river gravels form an important Pleistocene sequence in north east Essex. They start with gravel (called the Kesgrave gravel) deposited by the River Thames before the Anglian glaciation (about 300,000 years ago). At this time the Thames drained an area as far west as the present Severn basin, as is revealed by some of the pebbles in the gravel, which are from rocks found in that part of the country. During this period the Thames would have entered Essex from Hertfordshire, passed north of Colchester, on through Suffolk and Norfolk to eventually drain into the North sea. At this time the southern part of the North Sea and the present English Channel were dry land.

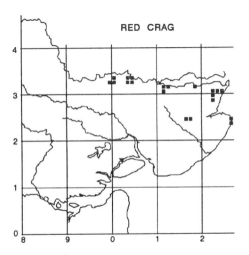

At the same time the River Medway flowed across the Dengie Peninsula and into the Tendring Plateau, depositing gravel with pebbles of Kentish and other southern rocks, before meeting the Thames in the Weeley area. The joint river passed on through the Tendring Peninsula in the direction of Oakley and Harwich, leaving behind a mixed gravel from the intermingling of the two rivers. (THAMES/MEDWAY - MAP 1).

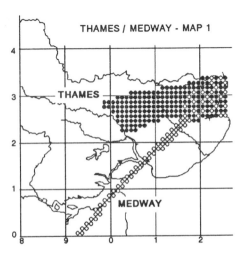

18

The valleys of the two rivers and their joint valley continued to move south until just before the Anglian glaciation; the Thames followed what is now the Colne estuary as far as about Brightlingsea, where it was joined by the Medway. The two rivers then flowed across the southern edge of the Tendring Peninsula in the direction of Holland-on-Sea. The gravels they left (called the Lower St Osyth gravel and Lower Holland gravel) were the last to be deposited by these rivers before the Anglian glaciation. (THAMES/MEDWAY - MAP 2).

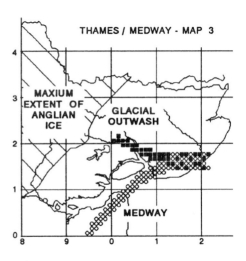

With the temporary blocking of the Thames by the ice sheet of the Anglian glaciation, the waters from the melting edge of the ice sheet spread gravel, called the Upper St Osyth gravel (because it was deposited on top of the Lower St Osyth gravel) over parts of the western half of the Tendring Plateau. At this time the Medway was still depositing its gravels on the Dengie Peninsula as it was not affected by the ice sheet. It was, however, mixing with the glacial outwash along the southern edge of the Tendring Peninsula to leave the Upper Holland gravel. (THAMES/MEDWAY - MAP 3).

The Anglian glaciation was followed by a warmer period, the Hoxnian inter-glacial, during which the Thames cut round the edge of the blocking ice sheet, captured the channel of the Medway near Southend and took it for its own. The combined rivers again left mixed deposits along a line across the Dengie Peninsula, Mersea and Clacton. (THAMES/MEDWAY - MAP 4).

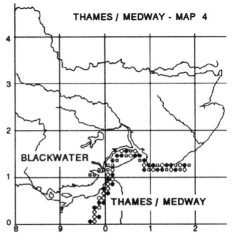

19

In a colder period towards the end of the Hoxnian and before the start of the next warm period, the Ipswichian (over 115,000 years ago), an enlarged Thames with the Medway and Blackwater as tributaries, followed a channel passing over the Dengie, Mersea and the St Osyth area leaving the Asheldham, Mersea Island and Wigborough gravels. At the same time the Blackwater was depositing the Tollesbury gravel. There is a botanical link between the Dengie and St Osyth area gravels, the grass **Loose Silky-bent** occurring commonly in both areas. (THAMES/MEDWAY - MAP 5).

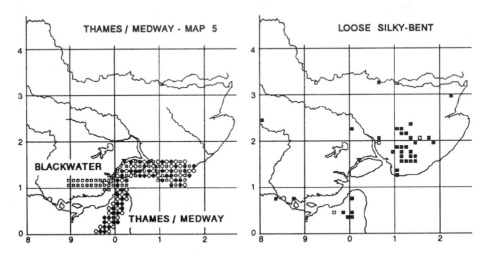

After this time the Thames moved from our area to use what is now the Crouch estuary with the Blackwater assuming much of its present course; eventually the Essex river systems we know today developed.

The Anglian glaciation left two main deposits in our area, Boulder Clay, which was deposited when the ice sheet melted rapidly and Sand, with or without gravel, which was spread by the water from slowly melting ice, mainly round the edges of the ice sheet.

At the edge of the ice sheet the melt water spread sand and gravel over parts of the county, which was supplemented, particularly in our area, by river gravels from the Thames and Medway as mentioned above. In some places, such as around Colchester, these deposits are overlain by Brickearths and, of course, the major river valleys have their own more recent gravel, which helps to complicate the soils of the region still further.

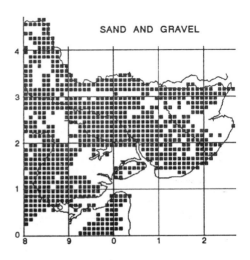

The Chalky Boulder Clay, left by the Anglian ice in the north west quarter, spreads as far south as Witham-Easthorpe and east to Wormingford-Little Horkesley. The ice is believed to have entered the area from slightly west of north bringing material from the rocks of that area, including quantities of chalk from north west Essex and Suffolk. It is because of this chalky content that it is called Chalky Boulder Clay and it also influences the wildflowers that are naturally found growing in this area. This feature is well demonstrated by comparing the distribution map for **Wild Clematis** with that for Chalky Boulder Clay.

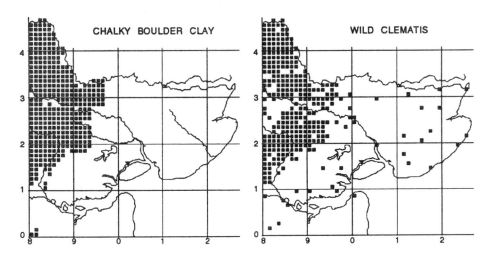

After the warmer Ipswichian period there followed the Devensian glacial period of about 110,000 years ago, when Brick-earths were deposited over much of the area. These are wind blown soils that have, in some places, been reworked by rivers and streams. Along the south side of the Stour valley (along the northern edge of the Tendring Plateau) are Brick-earths with a calcareous content. These are under intensive arable use but still have, in the weeds that grow there, species more readily associated with the Chalky Boulder Clay of the north west of our area. There are other patches of Brick-earth with a chalky influence on the Tendring Peninsula and a chalky influence can also be found where the soil is derived from underlying shelly Red Crag sands, as at Beaumont. These Brick-earths lie on top of the other sand, gravel and clays of the plateaus and form, if in a rather fragmentary way, a layer like icing on a cake.

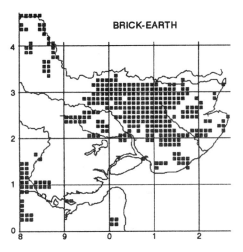

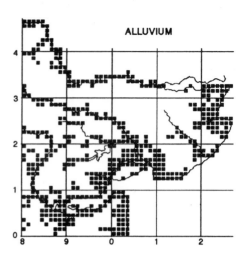
ALLUVIUM

In the low-lying coastal areas are patches of marine alluvium which vary in their makeup; that at Harwich seems, from the type of flowers that are found there, to have a calcareous content, as do patches of the fields above the Dengie Flats (these may, in fact, correspond to 'fossilised' cockleshell banks), whilst the composition of other areas is neutral to slightly acid.

In summary, the soils of north east Essex are a very mixed bag indeed, with one type of soil being overlaid by another as ice sheets formed and retreated and major rivers changed course depositing different gravels on those deposited earlier, as well as removing some of the earlier material, mixing it up and depositing it elsewhere. All of this affects the distribution of today's wild flowers. In the chart opposite, showing the Coincidence of Rock Types, the higher the number, the greater the variety of soil types in each 1km square.

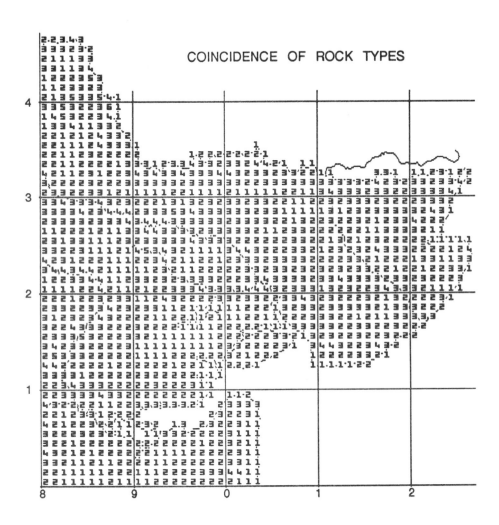

COINCIDENCE OF ROCK TYPES

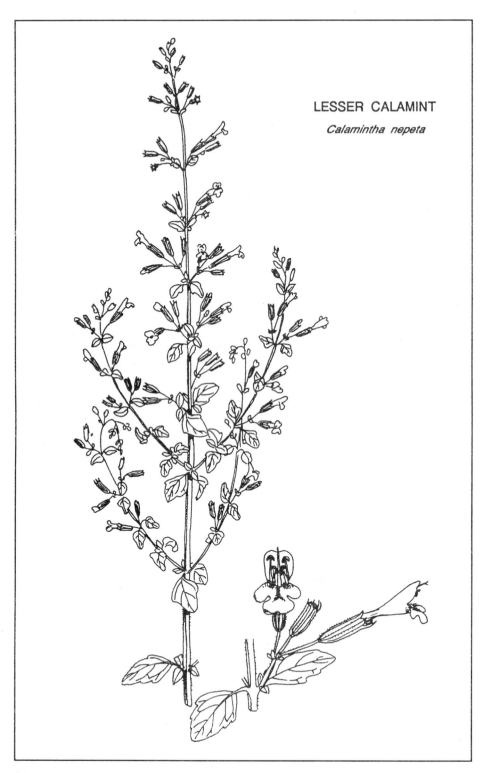

LESSER CALAMINT

Calamintha nepeta

THE HABITATS OF
NORTH EAST ESSEX

In this chapter we have covered each habitat that occurs in north east Essex and tried to give an account, not only of its current status, but also the changes that have occurred since Jermyn carried out his recording (mainly from the end of World War II to the early 1970s). The losses in some habitats have been considerable, in others not so great, but it is always a tale of loss.

However, not all is doom and gloom, many of the best remaining fragments of habitat have been recognised as such and are now protected, having become nature reserves or designated Sites of Special Scientific Interest, in many cases both. After the years of agricultural intensification, some farmers are becoming interested in conservation and beginning to maintain hedges and ditches in accordance with advice offered by the Farming and Wildlife Advisory Group. Also the introduction of the Countryside Premium and Set Aside Schemes, if implemented practically, can only bring an improvement. Other organisations that can have an impact on our countryside now have to consider environmental and conservation aspects in their work - this includes the Forestry Commission and the newly formed National Rivers Authority. Some Councils too, are now giving sympathetic management to a few special road verges which have been identified as having a significant native flora. All this may mean that the countryside might improve in the future but it will never regain its former diversity as revealed by the historical records and comments of past botanists.

For a number of habitats coincidence maps have been included. Certain plants (indicator species) occur only in a particular habitat and can therefore be used to show the location of that habitat. By plotting several indicator species for a habitat on the same map, species-rich examples of that habitat are identified when many of the plants occur together (i.e. their distribution coincides). The particularly rich areas are identified by a high number and those with a count of one are indicative of remnants of a once richer site.

Woods

From the map overleaf showing the 1km squares that contain woodland it appears that the area is well wooded, but from the coincidence map of the ancient woodland indicator species, it is clear that there are only limited areas of ancient woodland. A number of ancient woods can be identified by their high species count, for example, Chalkney Wood, the Stour/Copperas complex, Roman River Valley and the Markshall complex.

Many of our woods were planted with conifers in the 1960s, sometimes only in the centre, leaving a band of broadleaved trees round the edge. Coniferisation is often accompanied by blanket spraying of the ground flora but as there was some limited conservation outcry at the time this was avoided in some woodlands. However, even in woods where limited spraying had been agreed, the contractor often still carried out blanket spraying and several species-rich woods, particularly on the chalky boulder clays, were completely denuded of their flora. Flowers such as **Sanicle, Common Cowwheat, Common Twayblade, Early Purple** and **Greater Butterfly Orchids**, have all declined and now have very restricted distributions.

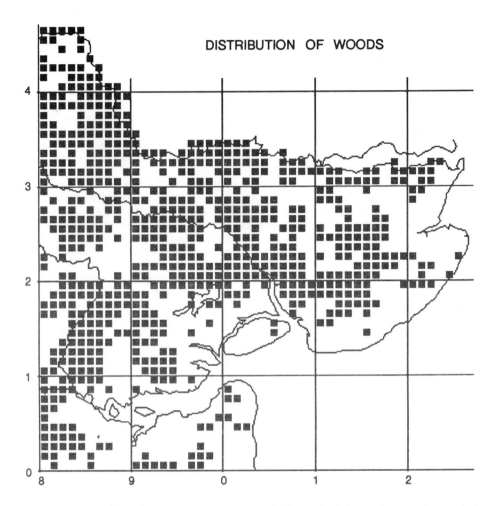

DISTRIBUTION OF WOODS

The greatest damage probably took place towards the end of Jermyn's recording period but in the intervening years game shooting and conservation interests have saved some of our woods so that most of those that had survived to the mid 1970's are still extant today. This is often reflected in the findings from our survey as the distribution of many of the woodland plants correlated reasonably well with Jermyn's recording. Neglect, however, can reduce the diversity of a wood and, in the woods where no active management has taken place, sometimes for decades, there remains only a sprinkling of their former flowers.

The storms of October 1987 have, unfortunately, been used as an excuse by some owners for clearing and replanting some of the remaining ancient woodlands in an unsuitable manner. At Pitchbury Wood, for instance, the bulldozer and a drainage scheme are likely to have made the recolonisation of the area by the more sensitive species impossible, as well as destroying a large population of Newts. There are also still some outstanding felling licences granted by the Forestry Commission in the past that call for the replanting of the wood with alien species. This has happened recently in Donyland Wood, which is part of the Roman River Site of Special Scientific Interest, when one such old licence was implemented.

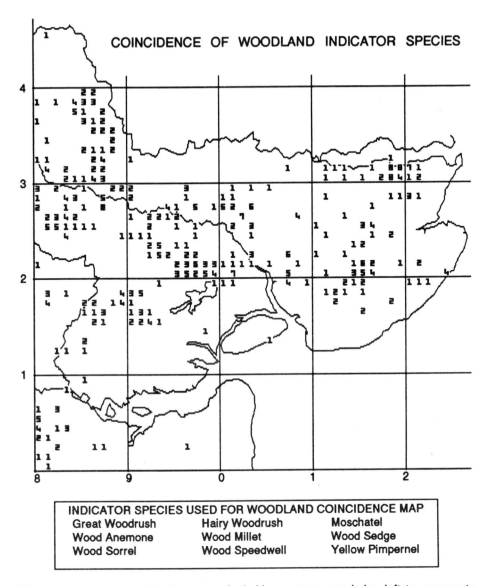

COINCIDENCE OF WOODLAND INDICATOR SPECIES

INDICATOR SPECIES USED FOR WOODLAND COINCIDENCE MAP

Great Woodrush	Hairy Woodrush	Moschatel
Wood Anemone	Wood Millet	Wood Sedge
Wood Sorrel	Wood Speedwell	Yellow Pimpernel

Within conservation woodlands, areas of windthrown trees are being left to regenerate naturally. This will provide a type of habitat that has been absent in our woods, probably for centuries, and we wait with interest to see how these areas develop.

The Forestry Commission has now gone 'green', and 'native' is in. This can be beneficial to some woodlands, for example, in Chalkney Wood conifers are now being taken out and native species planted. With luck this will enable the remnants of the native flora to recolonise the area from the section of coppice which was left as native broadleaved wood, as well as from the rides and wood edges, where the plants have survived the past herbicide spraying of the main planting area.

Many wet areas were planted with **Poplars** to produce wood for the production of matchsticks, but the market vanished with the decline of the British match industry and most of the remaining trees were damaged or blown down in the October 1987 hurricane. Other areas are planted with **Cricket-bat Willows**, those from Essex producing some of the best timber. Unfortunately some are now infected with watermark disease which makes the timber unsuitable for cricket bat production. It remains to be seen how this will affect the management of these areas.

A more recent threat to woodlands has been the introduction of war games, an activity in which two opposing sides shoot pellets of paint at each other. Whilst this could be an acceptable practice in secondary woods with a limited flora, the effect on ancient woods, particularly those with areas of wet ground, can be disastrous with the virtual elimination of the more interesting plants.

The increase in Deer is also beginning to cause problems. Their selective feeding habits can damage young coppice regrowth, particularly in the first two or three years, and prevent the seeding of **Greater Butterfly Orchids** and other plants by eating most of the young shoots or flowers. This is a particular problem for conservation bodies where conventional culling of the Deer is unacceptable to many of their members. Various alternatives are being tried, such as spreading Lion dung around newly coppiced areas (it is thought that the smell unsettles the deer). However, the effect of calcium and nutrient rich spots on the ground flora will need monitoring.

Hedges

Many kilometres of hedgerows in our area have been grubbed out in the last two decades, often with the aid of grants from the Government. This has produced large productive fields but has reduced the variety of species in an area as the hedgerow and its adjacent strip of grassland often contained remnants of the native flora. Grants are now available to put back hedges but these are species-poor, being planted in bare soil and lacking the variety of flowering plants found in our older hedges. The major species that recolonise new hedges are **Cow Parsley, Stinging Nettle, Goosegrass, False Oat Grass** and **Creeping Thistle**.

The major loss through grubbing out is where boundary hedges between fields are removed to make one larger field. At Weeley one of our recorders found a farm that had had all its hedges taken out to create one massive arable desert with the farmhouse in the middle. Soil erosion is not a problem on the heavier soils but there can be a mini dustbowl effect on large fields on the lighter soils, as has been seen in the Alresford area.

Many hedges, particularly those at roadsides are cut back to ground level, from which they will regrow if allowed to do so. Unfortunately many are then mown like a road verge and never get the chance, though the shrubs survive for a number of years in amongst the grasses.

The older type of hedgerow management of layering or coppicing to make a stock proof boundary is no longer practised in our area, the ubiquitous barbed wire fence having taken its place since it is much cheaper to install and maintain. Of the hedges that do remain, almost all are flailed or trimmed by some mechanical means which generally leads to them losing their shape and much of their wildlife interest. They are cut every year, which removes the growth that would produce flowers or fruit the following year. Also the damage from flailing makes them susceptible to fungus and rot attack, leading to their eventual demise.

Those hedges that do remain can get burnt 'accidentally' during stubble burning and, whilst they recover if left, they are often grubbed out before any regrowth can take place. The occurrence of Dutch Elm disease has also been used as an excuse to remove hedges and, on at least one occasion, a row of **Lime** trees.

On the Dengie peninsula there are hedges rich in **Elms**. This is the centre of distribution for Richens 'Dengie' variety of East Anglian Elm. These trees seem to be more resistant to Dutch Elm disease than other clones in our area. A few of these hedges have **Spurge Laurel** as a common component; on the chalky boulder clay it is more often present at woodland edges.

Hedges are richer the further west you go in our area, with the most interesting ones occurring on the Chalky Boulder Clay. These are often a mixture of **Spindle, Dogwood, Field Maple** and **Wild Clematis** as well as containing the usual **Oak, Hawthorn** and **Blackthorn**. At their bases can be found **Wood Melick** and **Hard Shield Fern**.

Hedgerows on the better draining soils can have **Polypody Ferns** growing on the shaded side, either on the bases of the hedgerow shrubs and trees, or, if the soil is suitable, forming patches on the ground amongst the moss and ground flora. During the summer months these are almost invisible in the taller vegetation and we have found that our winter surveys, after the frosts have cut back the surrounding plants, produced most of our sites for these ferns.

Heathlands

There was once a considerable area of heathland in our area (a number of villages contain the word heath in their name) but even by Gibson's time this had been much reduced and it is unlikely that we will ever again find such plants as **Marsh Lousewort, Sundew**, and **Bladderwort**.

Many of the heaths mentioned by Gibson were also recorded by Jermyn, but many others had already been brought into cultivation by the time Gibson published his book in 1862. During Jermyn's time further heathlands were lost to agriculture - Spratt's Marsh, which today would probably be recognised as warranting Site of Special Scientific Interest status, was drained and ploughed, and the last remnants of West Bergholt Heath were overgrown with scrub. Today they are lost altogether to agriculture, as is Weeley Heath. The coincidence map overleaf shows the main heathy areas remaining today (Roman River Valley, Tiptree Heath, Fordham Heath and Layer Breton Heath) as well as indicating the probable former extent of heathland.

The development of scrub on the heathlands accelerated with the reduction of grazing due to the changes in farming practices and, more importantly, the dramatic loss of rabbits after the introduction of myxomatosis during the late fifties. The scrub is now so well established that it is too big for grazing to have any real effect and deliberate scrub clearance by man is the only way to save our heathland flora and fauna. Unfortunately in the intervening years people have come to accept that heathland is an area of scrubby **Oak, Hawthorn, Blackthorn** etc., and oppose the return of the area to true heath.

Conservation bodies are having some success with Tiptree Heath where a management plan has been introduced with the agreement of most of the parties involved. This has led to an increase in the amount of **Ling, Bell Heather** and **Cross-leaved Heath** and the reappearance of **Marshwort** (*Apium inundatum*) after the absence of any records since Gibson's time. The **Heath Spotted Orchid** was also responding well to management but the plants were recently dug up and removed by an unknown thief.

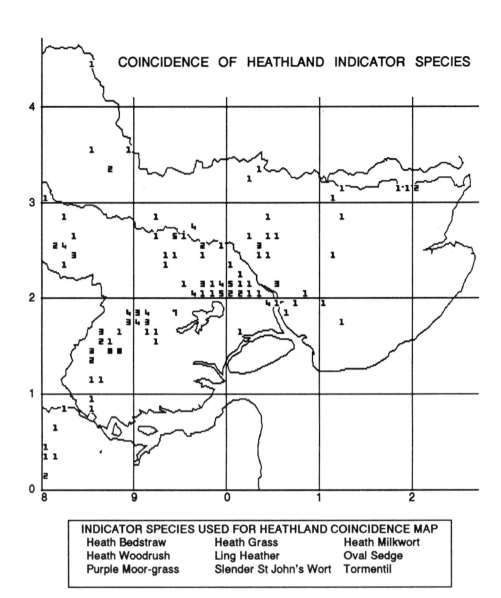

COINCIDENCE OF HEATHLAND INDICATOR SPECIES

INDICATOR SPECIES USED FOR HEATHLAND COINCIDENCE MAP

Heath Bedstraw	Heath Grass	Heath Milkwort
Heath Woodrush	Ling Heather	Oval Sedge
Purple Moor-grass	Slender St John's Wort	Tormentil

The reaction to management at Fordham Heath, which is now mainly scrub, was quite different, with an outcry at the destruction of trees, which led to the cessation of the initial work - a later reduced work programme has cleared some areas. Marker posts put in to identify a sensitive verge and protect it from mowing at the wrong time were removed at the insistence of the Parish Council. There have been proposals (thankfully rejected) to site a village hall and car park on the heath. Clearly there is much more to do here if the conservation message is to be interpreted as managing a habitat rather than just growing trees. The result of this neglect has been the loss of **Eyebright, Marsh Pennywort, Heath Milkwort** and **Purple Moor-grass** and a contraction of the area containing **Ling, Sedges, Mat Grass, Heath Bedstraw** and other heathland flowers.

Layer Breton Heath still retained its flora well into the post-Jermyn period until the village planted trees, including **Silver Birch,** on parts of the heath. As a result, the heathland is now scrub and secondary woodland with the remnants of heathland flora remaining on some of the firebreaks which have had to be cut as a safety measure.

The same depressing story can be continued: a heathland remnant at Alresford is vanishing under the combined onslaught of scrub encroachment and a gravel pit, Crockleford Heath now exists only as strips of roadside verge and Donyland Heath is now secondary woodland.

One hopeful area is Berechurch Common, planted in part with conifers, scrub covered and neglected for many years, it has recently been fenced and cleared, at least in part, and the grazing rights let. With luck the **Ling, Bell Heather, Purple Moor-grass,** Harebells, **Heath Bedstraw** and the **Hawkweeds** will spread and return at least some of the area to its former richness.

Mudflats

Another natural habitat that is under threat is that of the mudflats, though here the problem is one of rising sea levels and increasing erosion. A contributor to erosion is the commercial extraction of Lugworms by mechanical means - large areas of the upper mud are removed and sieved for worms before being returned to the seabed. This destroys not only much of the flora and fauna, but the structure of the mudflats themselves as well as the food supplies for many coastal birds. Any **Eel-grass** accidentally treated in this way is completely destroyed thus putting at risk the slight increase of this group that appears to be taking place at the moment; the returned mud is also unsuitable for **Eel-grass** recolonisation for a considerable time. So far this has taken place only to a limited extent on the Dengie flats, but any future extension of this activity could become an important factor in the degradation and erosion of this habitat.

Saltmarshes

The taking in of saltmarshes for grazing land has been practised on the Essex coast for centuries, but apart from an area on the Dengie marshes no more saltmarshes have been taken into farming since Jermyn's time. The sea walls truncate the saltmarsh, halting the succession and removing the higher marsh with its specialist plants such as **Sea Wormwood** and **Golden Samphire.** These plants then have their distribution restricted to the base of the sea wall at the appropriate level and are vulnerable to any rebuilding or repairing of the sea wall, particularly if imported soil is used or the wall faced with concrete slabs. The current area of active saltmarsh is best indicated by the distribution map of **Common Salt-marsh-grass** although this includes the occasional inland road verge and one cliff site.

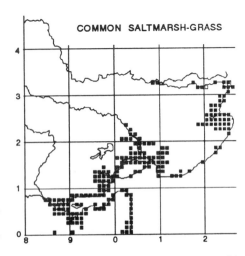

COMMON SALTMARSH-GRASS

With the sea level rising and the land sinking (it is estimated that this century the sea has risen 15cm and land sunk 45cm), the marshes are becoming dominated by the lower zone species such as the **Glassworts** and **Common Cord-grass**. We are, therefore, losing the middle zone as it has nowhere to go, the sea wall having, in most cases, already taken the upper zone away.

The greenhouse effect will make this situation worse and the future of our saltmarshes will depend upon the decisions made by the National Rivers Authority at different points along the coast - whether to protect and raise sea defences and at these points probably eventually lose all saltmarshes, or, to open up the sea wall and allow the sea in to flood what is now arable and return it over the years to saltmarsh. The latter could possibly be cost effective as, with a large saltmarsh in front of any new sea defence reducing wave damage, the defences could be constructed to a lower specification and would require less maintenance. One problem with this is that the land on the inside of sea walls is now lower than the saltmarsh outside. To create the saltmarsh inside the wall it would be necessary to build up the land, at least to the level of the lower saltings, so that a new succession of saltmarsh can develop.

Recreational damage to saltmarshes due to the construction of marinas is still a threat, but an even greater worry now are the jet-skis. These go up and down every little creek as well as jumping the saltmarshes between the creeks, causing damage to the structure of the saltings and hastening the erosion that is already taking place.

Shellbanks

There has been little change to this habitat, which is more or less restricted to Essex, except possibly in the upper reaches of the Blackwater where some shellbanks seem to have disappeared. Outside our area, Foulness is the biggest shellbank in Britain, but the one at the edge of the Dengie marshes is well developed and there are smaller ones at Dovercourt, Walton and Colne Point, amongst other sites. It is a very unusual habitat nationally and, as well as being important for nesting birds, it is in our area colonised by **Shrubby Seablite, Yellow Horned Poppy** and other plants that can also be found on sandy beaches.

Sand Dunes

Very little survives of the natural sand and shingle beaches of our area, most having vanished under holiday developments, with remnants of their flora clinging on amongst the buildings. The main site now remaining where a full dune system has developed is Colne Point, an Essex Naturalists' Trust nature reserve. Smaller areas with limited dune systems occur at Dovercourt, Crabknowe Spit, Stone Point, Mersea and Bradwell-on-Sea. These areas are all affected by erosion both from the sea (particularly Crabknowe Spit and Stone Point) and from human feet, with an even greater threat from off-the-road vehicles, which have caused damage even in the Colne Point reserve. The best areas can clearly be picked out on the coincidence map opposite.

The flowers found on these beach areas have survived at the same sites for many years, even if only in small quantity. **Yellow Horned Poppy** can still be seen in many of the places where it was known to both Gibson and Jermyn. **Sea Pea**, however, which was unknown to Gibson, found in two places by Jermyn, not refound there by us, but found at another site nearby, seems to be able to colonise suitable areas as these become available. Our major 'find' in this habitat is **Ray's Knotgrass**, a plant which Gibson forecast would be found and which we have discovered on two sites.

The erosion of our beaches by the sea, possibly increased by the removal of the offshore

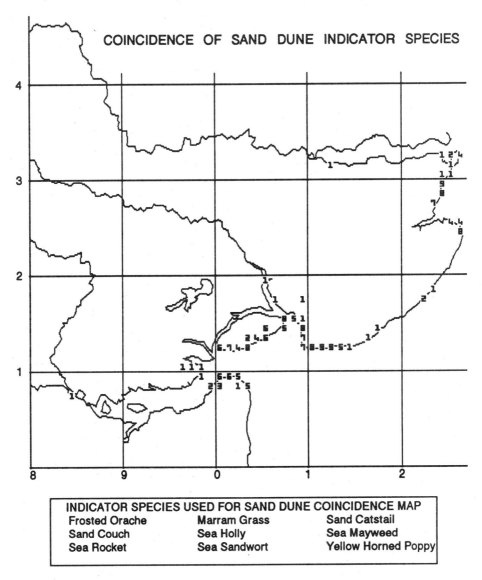

COINCIDENCE OF SAND DUNE INDICATOR SPECIES

INDICATOR SPECIES USED FOR SAND DUNE COINCIDENCE MAP

Frosted Orache	Marram Grass	Sand Catstail
Sand Couch	Sea Holly	Sea Mayweed
Sea Rocket	Sea Sandwort	Yellow Horned Poppy

sand and gravel banks to provide aggregate for the building industry, is a major problem. Away from built up areas it goes largely unnoticed - sites such as Crabknowe Spit and Stone Point, which held large areas of good vegetation and nesting birds in the 1950's and 60's, have now almost gone. In urban areas beach feeding (importing sand onto the beach) has been tried as a method of increasing the amount of sand and protecting the coastal defences. This has been successful, even if only temporarily, in increasing the beach area, as at Harwich, and in increasing the amount of sand moving along the coast and feeding other beaches. This process is costly and can be reversed by the tides in a very short time. For example, in one tide alone, an area of sand a metre wide and several centimetres deep was taken off the beach at Frinton and redeposited on the foreshore at Holland-on-Sea.

Cliffs

The cliffs of our area are not formed from hard rocks but from the softer London Clay, usually with a concrete wall along the base to reduce erosion. We have found some interesting plants on these cliffs, **Sea Purslane** is common in Clacton, as is **Sea Fern-grass**. **Sea Wormwood** and **Rock Sea Lavender** can also be found and, on one cliff, a large patch of **Bithynian Vetch**. On the Walton to Frinton cliffs **Grass Vetchling** can still be found in the same abundance as mentioned by Gibson and the cliffs have probably not changed much since his day.

To the east of Walton the natural process of erosion that had been taking place for centuries recently started to threaten properties. A new sea wall was constructed along part of the cliff and a grassy habitat created from seeding with **Rye-grass** mix; the interest of the area for the botanist and geologist has declined.

Borrow Dykes

Formed by the removal of soil for the construction of the sea walls these, often brackish water areas, were formerly part of the grazing area behind the wall. Most of this grazing has been converted to arable from which the borrow dykes receive nitrate run-off making them less species-rich. **Sea Clubrush** is the commonest plant in the borrow dykes but **Common Reed** and **Fennel Pondweed** can dominate some areas. The more uncommon plants found either in or at the edge of the dykes include **Brackish Water Crowfoot**, Soft **Hornwort, Glaucous Bulrush, Wild Celery, Parsley Water Dropwort** and Sea Hog's **Fennel**.

Wildfowlers, in order to entice the ducks, used to place seed and potatoes in the ponds on the grazing marsh but when the marsh was converted to arable these ponds were generally drained and infilled. There are no flight ponds in the saltmarsh grazing and the wildfowlers, therefore, now place the seed and potatoes into the borrow dykes. This causes eutrophication of the water, encouraging algal bloom which reduces diversity still further and could be a very serious threat to the survival of some of the rare invertebrates found in this habitat.

Grassland - Sea Walls

In most areas these have probably not changed significantly since they were upgraded after the 1953 floods. It is unfortunate that Jermyn did not record them in any detail; they would have been at that time only the edge of much larger areas of grazing land, rather than the 15 metre by over 200 kilometre strip they are today. It is not possible, therefore, to compare our records with any previous work. Further upgrading of many of the walls is currently taking place and there will be even more major works required in the future, a barrage is already proposed for the Colne estuary.

In 1953 soil from adjacent borrow dykes was used for repair of the wall but now it is often imported, bringing with it a more limited range of flora (usually weed species), as well as smothering the existing native vegetation some of which consists of nationally uncommon species. Some of the plants that can be found on the better walls are **Slender Hare's Ear, Knotted Hedge Parsley, Corn Parsley, Slender Thistle, Sea Barley** and **Stiff Saltmarsh-grass**. It is possible that the Nature Conservancy Council will be able to obtain agreement for work to be done sympathetically where the wall has a 'good' flora - this will mean that the top soil will be stripped, the wall made up, and then the top soil put back; however, this is expensive.

The changes that have taken place over the last two decades in the other types of grassland mean this long narrow ribbon has now become a habitat of major importance in north east Essex. It is often taken for granted and over-looked, even by conservationists, but many plants are now restricted to this habitat alone.

Grassland - Reclaimed Saltmarshes

This habitat has been one where major changes have taken place in Essex in the last fifty years with a reduction of at least 80%. Most of what remains are now nature reserves (Old Hall, Howlands and Brightlingsea Marshes) or Army ranges (Langenhoe) with a few areas in private hands at Tollesbury Wick, Horsey Island and a small area at Wrabness bought by residents to stop development.

From our examination of the distribution maps it was discovered that you could either use the map of a plant like **Saltmarsh Rush** to indicate likely areas of active or reclaimed coastal marsh, or, conversely, map a plant like **Ivy** which is absent from such habitat.

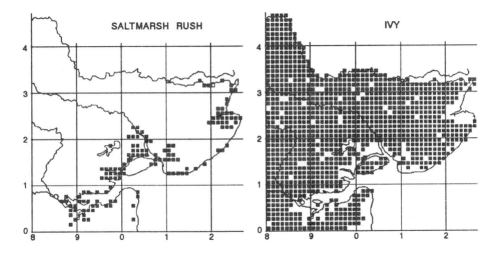

Where grazing no longer takes place, as on parts of Langenhoe, a dense layer of ground litter builds up that suppresses the low growing plants like **Strawberry Clover** and Sea **Clover**. The tall **Fescue/Saltmarsh-grass** sward also shades out **Dyer's Greenweed, Slender Birdsfoot Trefoil, Spiny Restharrow** and the ant nests which are a feature of these grazing lands. These anthills have their own special flora which includes **Upright Chickweed, Common Whitlow Grass, Changing Forgetmenot, Lady's Bedstraw** and **Mouse-eared Hawkweed** and would repay further studies - the flora of adjacent hills is often quite different. It is as yet unknown whether this correlates with the age of the founding of the colony or any other factor. Even the age of individual anthills is unknown - they can be active for many years but survive long after the ants.

The fragments of coastal grazing marshes that do remain could well be at risk from the rising sea levels as the walls that surround them will probably not be maintained due to the low economic value of the area.

Grassland - Meadows and Pastures

Our survey has shown that the flowers and grasses of meadows and pastures have all suffered a great decline. This is because our inland pastures have been nearly all lost either by conversion to arable or reseeding to 'improve' them. The latter has turned flower-rich meadows into monocultures of **Rye-grass**, which must be boring for the animals that have to eat it as well as for the botanist. In some areas the only grazing left in any amount is in horse paddocks. These are generally not best known for their wild flower content because of the eating pattern of the animals but compared to reseeded areas they usually have something in them.

As with heathland, some grazing has also been lost through neglect, going over to scrub as at Iron Latch Meadow, the story of which is given in detail in the paragraph on **Green-winged Orchid** in the main text.

Less of our damp grassland has probably survived than any other type of inland grassland. Plants like **Ragged Robin**, which had been common and generally distributed in Victorian times, were still frequent in the 1950's and 60's, but are now uncommon and generally restricted to wet flushes on the boulder clays. **Quaking Grass**, so common that Jermyn only recorded it on a 10km basis, is reduced now to just one site and that on a road verge.

Grassland - Churchyards

In many cases churchyards are pockets of old unimproved grassland, reflecting the original flora within the vicinity of the church. In Jermyn's time churchyards were cut with a scythe but mechanical mowers were being introduced (many churchyards had the old tombstones removed to allow mechanical cutting). Today in some churchyards rotary mowers and strimmers crewcut everything which keeps them tidy but has made them less interesting. It is lucky that generally no chemicals have been used so no lasting damage has been done, the plants remaining there in a vegetative state.

With the rise of interest in conservation management some churchyards are now being managed in a more sympathetic manner and the flora is returning. **Cuckoo Flower, Ox-eye Daisy** and **Lady's Bedstraw** are common here and many of our records for **Fairy Flax, Meadow Saxifrage, Pepper Saxifrage, Lesser Calamint** and **Cowslip** are from churchyards, emphasising their importance as refuges for our native flora.

Grassland - Verges

With the loss of so much other inland grassland, the many miles of road verges are now a significant refuge for many of our wild flowers and grasses. However, their importance has been over-looked in the past and the management carried out on this habitat has resulted in a degradation of the flora.

At one time the scytheman went round to cut the verges, and he could only do so much a day so the cutting was spread over a long period. He also raked up the cuttings for hay or burnt them; some verges were even grazed, for there were no motor vehicles.

As traffic flows increased in both volume and speed the hand cutting of verges became too slow and expensive, for it was necessary on road safety grounds to keep sightlines clear at all times on corners and junctions. To cope with this problem mechanical mowers were introduced, often coupled with the application of chemicals to keep the verge under control.

With the introduction of flail mowers it became possible to cut the whole verge fairly quickly and cover a large area in a day. However, apart from the sight lines, the verges are now cut less often, so the vegetation is, therefore, taller and thicker when it is cut and is just left to mulch down. This regime encourages the ranker plants and smothers the more delicate flowers and grasses.

When a verge is dug up for one reason or another then, instead of being left to colonise from surrounding flora, it is seeded. The native plants, therefore, are not given a chance to compete with the vigorous **Rye-grasses**, etc, in the stock seed mix which often comes from abroad. This vigorous growth requires regular cutting, which produces regular mulching, encouraging the coarser plants like **Cow Parsley**, **Stinging Nettles** and **False Oat-grass**, which in turn requires more regular cutting. The previous more natural flora was often lower and slower growing, requiring less maintenance than the new verge, as well as having more variety.

In some cases farmers have incorporated verges into their fields, destroying them completely and bringing the field edge right up to the tarmac.

With the help of Essex County Council some of our better verges are now protected and have cutting regimes that are sympathetic to their survival for they, like churchyards, now form an important last resort for many grassland species.

Grassland - Lawns and Municipal Amenity Areas

Individual gardeners vary in the amount of work they put into a lawn but compared to Jermyn's time there are now a lot more weed killers and lawn feeds available. Treated lawns are generally of little interest although **Slender Yellow Trefoil** and **Slender Speedwell** can be plentiful. The expansion of housing developments in our area has increased the number of lawns but, as they are generally laid with cultivated turf, their flora is of little interest. In older developments, lawns were either grown from seed or laid from native grassland turves. This latter method has resulted in some interesting lawns, including two with **Autumn Lady's Tresses** in one of which there was also Adder-stongue and **Wild Thyme**.

As far as municipal areas are concerned, other than being mown regularly the content has probably not changed much over the years except where herbicides have been used. The amount of variety in turf can often be related to when the turf was laid down - the older, the more interesting, probably coming from flower-rich meadows, the younger, originating from cultivated turf or seed have less variety. Some municipal grasslands date back to the Victorian era, for example, the lawns at Clacton seafront, though many playing fields are, of course, of much later date. Colchester Borough Council has recently stopped the use of herbicides on amenity grassland confining their use to areas such as bowling greens where a fine sward is essential.

Allotments and Gardens

There is generally a good selection of species, particularly on allotments and vegetable patches, but there are fewer allotments now than in Jermyn's time. Some of the older ones, which had a rich seedbank, occurred in the middle of towns where the land was valuable and have now been developed. Any new allotments required were made on other land, possibly arable, that was not as rich in species, having been cultivated in a different way.

The older large gardens are more interesting than the small new ones on modern estates because of both age and size. In a large garden there is room for some rough patches and it also takes a lot more work to have everything neat and tidy and in older gardens there is possibly a large and more diverse seed bank in the soil.

Gardening with native species has become more popular in recent years, and many formerly rare native species are now available from nurseries, either as pot grown plants or seeds. It will be more difficult to decide in the future if the occurrence of a species known to be rare in the area is genuine or the result of a deliberate or accidental introduction.

Arable Weeds

Many formerly common arable weeds have all but vanished from our fields. The first losses resulted from improved seed cleaning techniques but in recent years the more effective herbicides available have reduced further the number and variety of weeds. **Corn Marigold, Shepherd's Needle** were rare in Jermyn's day and **Night-flowering Catchfly** has since declined; from being "locally common on calcareous soils" according to Jermyn, it is now very rare - we found a total of less than ten plants at only two sites. Plants are usually only found in corners where the spray has missed but some farmers use a 'total' herbicide spray round the edge of the field to prevent weeds recolonising from adjacent hedges, verges, etc. and this reduces the population still further.

With the different sprays used on various crops and the recent increase in the variety of crops grown, some wild flowers are found with certain crops, e.g. Rape has to be sprayed early and as Poppies come late they have a chance with this crop as do some other broadleaved weeds.

Market garden fields are generally best for wild flowers as they are subject to a more labour intensive form of cultivation, as well as growing more broadleaved crops - onion crops are also good for a wide variety of species.

The recently introduced Set Aside Scheme for farmers has two options: one is to leave a whole field fallow but, as the seed bank is now mainly at the edges, the middle of the field is rapidly populated with coarse grasses, docks and thistles. The other option is to leave all the headlands uncultivated and allow the seed bank here to germinate and flower, thus producing a flora that has much more of interest and a greater conservation benefit. If there is a shoot on the farm then leaving the headlands also helps the game birds as it provides a variety of different seeds and insects for them to feed on.

Landscaping

The increased landscaping of new developments where grass is laid and trees planted, allows no natural recolonisation to take place producing a rather sterile environment. If soil is brought to an area and left for a time before planting takes place then, at times, an interesting flora is produced, albeit only temporarily. At one local site, where soil had probably come from Suffolk, we found **Flixweed, Tall Rocket, Spring Beauty** and *Amsinckia*.

Walls and Bridges

Electrification of the railway from Colchester to Harwich resulted in the demolition and

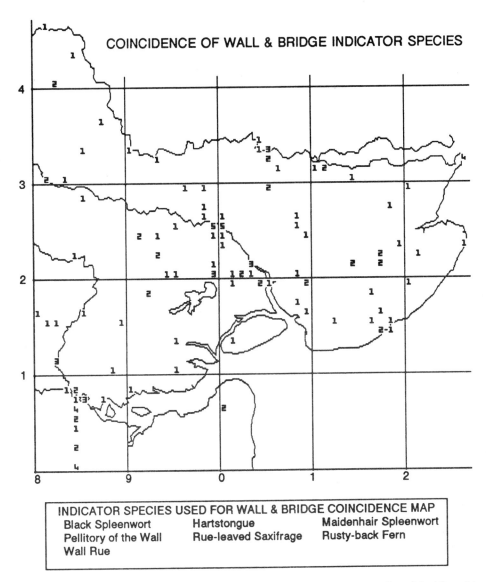

COINCIDENCE OF WALL & BRIDGE INDICATOR SPECIES

INDICATOR SPECIES USED FOR WALL & BRIDGE COINCIDENCE MAP

Black Spleenwort	Hartstongue	Maidenhair Spleenwort
Pellitory of the Wall	Rue-leaved Saxifrage	Rusty-back Fern
Wall Rue		

rebuilding of many bridges, including all those from Manningtree to Harwich. The old bridges were built with lime mortar between the bricks and were good for ferns. They have been replaced with cemented bricks and concrete structures which are not suitable for colonisation by ferns, especially at this early stage when no weathering of the structure has taken place. Should they become suitable for ferns at a later stage we will have to rely on spores coming from some distance to provide the colonists as the original colonies were lost during the demolition. The best colonies of ferns are now found on the bridges of the disused railway lines - the disused line south from Maldon is clearly shown on the coincidence map above. There were not many old walls in our area anyway so the old railway bridges are an important feature.

Where remedial work is done on a wall, this usually results in the loss of ferns and other plants, such as **Pellitory of the Wall**. The one major wall in our area is the Roman Wall at Colchester and the walls of the Norman castle in the same town. Both these structures are currently being subjected to restoration programmes, which are generally ruining this very special habitat. Where work has not yet been done there is a very interesting flora that includes **Rue-leaved Saxifrage, Lesser Calamint, Wallflower, Common Whitlow Grass, Fern-grass, Ivy-leaved Toadflax, Slender Thyme-leaved Sandwort, Red Valerian** and **Black Spleenwort** as well as rare lichens etc. Where the work has been done there is just plain wall, which, until recently, was treated with herbicide, to prevent any recolonisation by the plants that have been known from this habitat for over 150 years. Where **Sycamore** and other trees have invaded, something has to be done to protect the structure of the wall, but the damage done by the other plants is far less than that from vandalism or other causes and the loss of the flowering plants makes the wall less interesting to the general public.

Railways

There have been considerable changes in the management of the track and rolling stock since the last war. When steam trains were running the vegetation on railway banks was cut regularly by hand and the cuttings burnt, because of the risk of fire sparks from passing engines. There is no longer this risk with diesel and electric trains and the maintenance now consists of a total spray on the track and lower banks with the upper bank allowed to go to scrub. This is only cut back at long intervals when it threatens the overhead power lines. The former open habitat has been lost along with the **Wild Strawberries, Primroses**, etc, that Jermyn found so commonly.

A further threat to the banks is a machine used now, called a Ballast Cleaner - this comes along, supports the rails and sleepers, sweeps out the ballast to a depth of 2 ft, sieves it to extracts the good ballast, which is replaced, but dumps the remainder on the side of the track blanketing the ground flora. Where they cannot dump by the trackside, for example in a cutting, it is transferred to a wagon and dumped on the next available piece of bank. In places good chalky boulder clay flora has been covered with waste from these ballast cleaning operations. At Kelvedon the long established colony of **Rampion Bellflower** has been covered in rubble and ballast by British Rail during the demolition of the station building.

About 1963-66 the Beeching axe, which cut the rural network, left many disused lines where Jermyn could walk. These would still have been benefiting from the management regime in use prior to their closure. These disused lines have now been taken back into arable cultivation, or gone over completely to scrub. Even those that are now nature reserves and nature trails e.g. Maldon and Valley Walk near Sudbury, require a lot of work to keep them open and have only remnants of their former flora.

With modern high speed and quiet running trains it is very dangerous (as well as illegal) to trespass on the track as Jermyn probably did - the telephones in cabs would lead to the quick arrest of any trespasser, so we have had less chance of looking for and recording railway flora than past botanists. Most of our records come from our two members who work for British Rail and can visit this habitat in the course of their normal work. The remainder were made from train windows and platforms or bridges using binoculars.

Docks

The trade carried out at Hythe Quay and Mistley maltings has changed, with much cargo handling and the maltings gone, so the chance to find the alien plants so ably recorded by

G C Brown in the 1920's and 30's and later by Jermyn have gone for good. No longer is waste seed and the cleanings from grain dumped by the mill - it is often sent away for packeting as wild bird food and it is now under the bird table that these alien plants are regularly found.

Not only has the type of cargo changed over the years but also the method by which it is handled. Gone is the loose shipment of materials, replaced now by packaged and palleted goods, handled by fork lift trucks which require concrete hardstanding as they are unable to cope with the rough ground where many of the alien species previously grew. The cargo of fish meal, tapioca, timber, coal and granite blocks which now pass through the docks are not renowned for their alien floras!

Wivenhoe and Rowhedge still retain some areas of typical dockside but the flora consists mainly of coarse weeds of native origin along with **Oxford Ragwort** and **Perennial Wall Rocket**.

Wasteland

In Jermyn's time this would have consisted of patches of land between houses, industrial areas, railways, docks, etc, but over the last two decades these have all been infilled with developments. Our 'wasteland' is now the edges of un-made-up car parks, bits round stations, the older industrial areas and builders' yards, where garden escapes such as **Michaelmas Daisies** and **Canadian/Early Golden Rod** are found with **Rosebay, Elder, Brambles** and **Hawthorn** scrub. The new industrial estates are landscaped or have wall to wall concrete hardstanding with little room for plants of any sort.

Rubbish Tips

Since the mid 1970s waste and rubbish handling practices have altered. In Jermyn's time there were more open tips which filled more slowly with much of the waste originating from 'natural' sources (e.g. paper rather than plastic). The rubbish now comes in black plastic bags and consists of a lot of other plastics, etc, and is immediately covered in soil. This gives little opportunity for the specialities that Jermyn found to grow or, because of restricted access to these sites, for botanists to find them.

Gravel pits

Many of the gravel pits in our area are excavated almost down to the clay beneath them and are therefore liable to fill at least in part with water. A few that are on slopes or are not as deep, perhaps due to a layer of unsuitable ballast, remain dry .

The plant succession in many pits that were newly derelict in Jermyn's day, has continued to the stage where they are now covered in dense scrub, unless they have been managed for some other purpose. For example, Fingringhoe Wick has become a nature reserve, Martin's Farm at St Osyth is a landfill site, Ardleigh Pits is partly used for industrial development and Hoe Mills Quarry, in low-lying river gravels, is used for fishing.

They are by their very nature transient habitats, colonised in the bare soil stage by **Coltsfoot, Cudweeds, Canadian Fleabane, Willowherbs** and other species with readily dispersed seeds. This stage is short-lived and rapidly becomes scrub. Current planning permissions generally now require that they are brought back into agricultural use when extraction is completed but in Jermyn's day they were just abandoned and left to colonise naturally.

To the geologist the exposures in the pits represent an important source of information and those in our area are only just beginning to reveal the full facts about past geological events.

Reservoirs

The main reservoir in the area is Abberton, an important area for wildfowl, as well as an interesting site for the botanist. The main perimeter of the reservoir is concrete faced, with plants like **Golden Dock** and **Marsh Yellowcress** growing in the cracks. At the western end it has a more natural appearance, having earth banks and a much richer flora. There has been little change in the flora here since Jermyn made his records.

Ardleigh reservoir was constructed only recently and is a multi-use area with sailing and a trout fishery. The marginal flora is developing well, though the presence of *Crassula helmsii* could cause problems in the future.

Farm Reservoirs

These are a new phenomenon since Jermyn's time; the water is used to irrigate crops, usually potatoes, where it produces a marked increase in yield. It is also used as a spray to prevent frost damage to blackcurrant crops.

Where the farmers are interested in conservation, reservoirs have been built with sloping sides so that marginal vegetation can colonise. It depends on the individual farmer as to whether the margins are planted or allowed to colonise naturally. **Common Reed** and **Branched Bur-reed** are often planted and in coastal areas **Sea Clubrush** often turns up. It remains to be seen how the wild flowers of these new reservoirs develop. Some of the reservoirs have secondary uses such as fishing and duck shooting.

Many of these reservoirs are filled by water diverted from a stream by a dam but a certain minimum flow must be allowed to pass at all times, for the benefit of users downstream. The few that are built on high ground are filled by pump, either from a stream or borehole; such reservoirs often go dry in summer and have a very limited flora.

Ponds

This is another habitat that has suffered a dramatic decrease in recent years. Many ponds have been infilled, neglected or allowed to become overgrown. Some have become lost in an arable desert where, through neglect and isolation, they have become species-poor patches of willow scrub with damp hollows in the middle. Many other ponds are now drying out due to a combination of the scrub around the edge and the installation of field drainage systems which remove from the field the water that might otherwise have helped to refill the pond.

There has also been a loss of marginal vegetation where, instead of being part of grazing land as previously, the pond is surrounded by arable right up to its edge. The loss of poached edges where the animals used to disturb the bank has meant that this particular niche occupied by some wild flowers is no longer available to them and they are no longer present in many of the ponds where they used to be found. Spray drift and nutrient enrichment from the fertilizers used on the arable have also affected the marginal vegetation found today.

In last two or three years some farmers have been reinstating ponds, sometimes grant aid is available for this.

Previously, village ponds were also much neglected but the rise of interest in conservation has led to many being cleaned out. Where this has been done without guidance, replanting with material from garden centres has taken place. This has resulted in the introduction of double-flowered forms of **Marsh Marigold**, waterweeds like **Water Soldier** and *Lagarosiphon major* and variegated forms of **Reed Canary-grass**. At times bog plants such as **Cotton Grass** are also planted. It is easy with obviously introduced plants like these to leave the records off a distribution map, but where more native plants, such as **Broad-leaved Pondweed** have been introduced, the true native distribution of the plant becomes obscured.

The other side to the rise in interest in conservation has been the introduction of ducks to what have been good species-rich ponds on village greens. Unfortunately, the birds eat all the vegetation and are then fed by the local residents, the result is a foul smelling eutrophic muddy pond where only **Hard Rush** survives.

Garden ponds have become a feature of many suburban gardens and are now the most common place to find frogs and toads. These ponds are stocked with many non-native species, the surplus plants of which are often discarded into the wild e.g. *Crassula helmsii* and *Myriophyllum aquaticum*. These ponds are good for dragonflies and other invertebrates but are of less botanical interest.

Ditches

Many fields have had land drains installed in the last two decades which has affected the flora of the ditches quite considerably. When land drains are installed the water runs off the fields quickly and the ditches, in order to cope with the rapid removal of large volumes of water, have had to be deepened with oversteep sides that are mown to keep them clear of vegetation. This form of instant drainage leaves the ditches dry for much of the time as the soil of the field no longer acts as a sponge releasing the water over a longer period and evening out the flow levels. The ditches, therefore, are subject to a much greater range of wetness and dryness. Most fields are now arable to the edge of the ditch which in consequence receives nitrate run-off and is also subject to spray drift.

We can recall seeing only a handful of 'decent' ditches during the whole of our ten year survey, the rest have **Great Hairy Willowherb** as a major part of the flora sometimes with very large **Fool's Watercress**, which is at times somewhat distorted, possibly from the effect of herbicides. The other regular species are **Goosegrass, Barren Brome, Nettles, Thistles** and **False Oat-grass**.

Many more ditches have been piped and filled in to make larger fields, or where a council wants to put a footpath by a narrow country lane, the ditch is piped and the footpath laid on top.

Rivers, streams and brooks

These have all suffered from deteriorating water quality as well as over-zealous dredging and weed clearing in the recent past. As with ditches, some streams and brooks are now arable up to their edge and without grazing to keep the brookside vegetation in check,

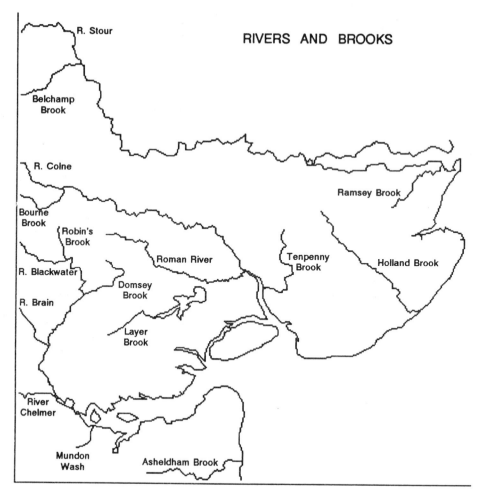

Map labels: R. Stour, Belchamp Brook, R. Colne, Ramsey Brook, Bourne Brook, Robin's Brook, Roman River, Tenpenny Brook, Holland Brook, R. Blackwater, Domsey Brook, Layer Brook, R. Brain, River Chelmer, Mundon Wash, Asheldham Brook

many now have a line of scrub along their banks. This completely shades the water, making the habitat too dark for the more interesting species to survive. The map above shows the main rivers and smaller streams on parts of which some reasonable vegetation survives.

River banks

With the increased use of land drains, leading to the loss of the marshy bits, arable fields now run right up to the **Cricket-bat Willow/Stinging Nettles** band at the edge of the river. Where arable has replaced grazing there is the loss of poached edges formerly made by cattle. It was here that some of the annual aquatics used to grow.

Whilst parts of the river would always have been steep sided, many of the rivers now have steep edges with less marginal vegetation. This is due to mechanical dredging which has, in the recent past, changed areas with sloping sides to steeper slopes with the resultant loss of the marshy edges.

Recently a new river management regime has been introduced whereby the rivers are dealt with more sympathetically in areas that have a conservation interest and the natural slope of the banks is kept. As far as is practical the work is undertaken from one bank only, with the emergent vegetation on the opposite bank being left undisturbed to help recolonisation.

Along the Stour in the Flatford-Cattawade area there probably has not been a lot of change over the years and it is here that some of the best habitat survives.

Freshwater Marshes

There has been a general loss through increased drainage and conversion to arable. In areas where the marshes were no longer grazed or cut, an increase in scrub has lead to a general drying out of the marsh with scrub **Willows** being succeeded by **Hawthorn, Oak, Elder, Brambles** and **Blackthorn** and the eventual loss of the marshland flora.

Scrub

Whilst not a specific habitat it is one that can be found on many unmanaged sites. It is more prevalent now than in Jermyn's time, the increase dating from the introduction of myxomatosis and the subsequent decline in the rabbit population. The consequent reduction in the grazing has, over the years, allowed areas of solid scrub to develop, under which nothing grows and through which even botanists cannot pass. The main habitats affected are railway banks (including disused tracks), grassland, heathland, freshwater marsh and land awaiting development for any length of time.

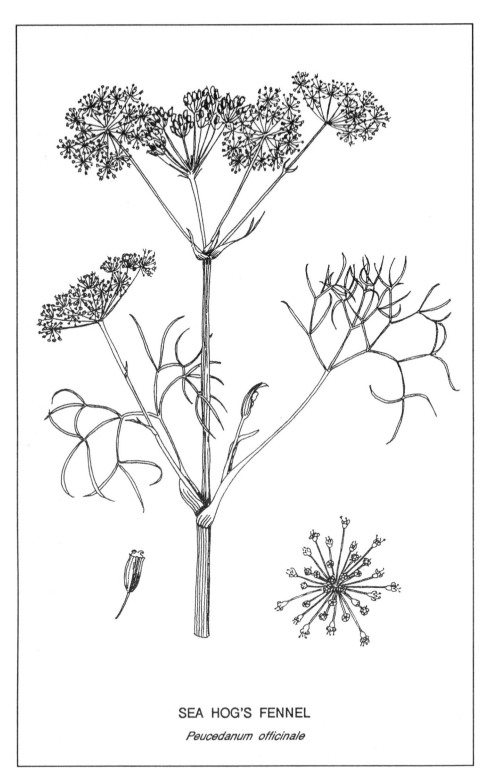

SEA HOG'S FENNEL

Peucedanum officinale

EXPLANATORY NOTES FOR THE PLANTS OF NORTH EAST ESSEX

Sequence and Nomenclature

The sequence of families follows that of **Excursion Flora of the British Isles** by Clapham, Tutin and Warburg (1981), but the species have been arranged alphabetically within each family for ease of reference; in this we follow the previous work, Jermyn's **Flora of Essex** (1974).

The scientific name for the species follows that of **Excursion Flora**, except where a species is not included, when it follows either the **BSBI Handbooks Nos 1-4** (Sedges, Umbellifers, Docks & Knotweeds, Willows & Poplars, respectively), or **Flora Europaea** (1964-1980). For clarity the authors' names have been omitted from the text but are given in the Index to Scientific Names where they are also cross-referenced to those used by Jermyn.

The English names also generally follow **Excursion Flora** but, where none is given, then those recommended by Dony, Jury & Perring **English Names of Wild Flowers** (1986) have usually been used. In some cases alternatives have been given.

Recorders and Age of Records

Gibson's recording period was up to 1861 and, whilst he included some early records, the majority are from 1800 onwards. Jermyn's recording was mainly 1930-1973 but he included some earlier records made since Gibson's publication. Our recording period is from 1980-1989 inclusive but we have made reference to records obtained between 1973 and 1979.

In both Gibson's and Jermyn's books, individual records are annotated with the recorder's name - this is common practice in standard floras. However, as most of our recording was undertaken by groups rather than individuals we have omitted these credits rather than fill the text with long lists of each groups' initials. Where it is mentioned in the text that Gibson or Jermyn recorded a particular plant, reference should be made to the original work to establish the actual recorder. The exception to this concerns the very early botanists, details being included to give an idea of the length of time that, for instance, a plant has been known from a particular site. If the actual date is known then this is given, otherwise we have used the date of publication of the relevant list. Jermyn's chapter on Past Essex Botanists should be referred to for details of their life and works, or, in the case of John Ray, **John Ray (1627-1705) Essex Naturalist** by Stuart A Baldwin, 1986. With regard to the current survey the recorders are given in a separate list and their field lists are held on file at the Colchester Natural History Museum.

Distribution, Frequency and Quantity

The maps, where given, show the exact pattern of distribution as well as frequency of occurrence. The latter can also be assessed from the number in square brackets after the scientific name - this is the number of 1km squares in which each plant has been found (the maximum number of whole or part 1km squares in our area is 1,322 of which 1,313 have been visited). It should be remembered that one dot (a 1km square) on a map could represent just one plant or a colony of many hundreds. We have tried to give some idea of quantity within the text where this is appropriate. The dot distribution maps have a hollow square for records obtained before 1980 and not refound (many are from **Flora of Essex**, 1974) and a solid square for records gained during our survey. Plants for which a map has been included are indicated with an "M" after the square brackets containing the number of 1km records.

The word "site" cannot be interchanged with the number of 1km records, for instance, Tiptree Heath is a 'site' but it falls into two 1km squares, and conversely, several 'sites' for a plant could be found in a 1km square, e.g. **Polypody Fern** where one site could be a hedge and another the roof of a building.

Some Terms and Phrases Explained

Terms such as rare, local, common, are the subjective opinion of the authors within the context of north east Essex. The term "local" is used for a plant that is restricted in its distribution by the availability of suitable habitat e.g. sand dunes. The phrase "not fully recorded" indicates that a plant has not been consistently recorded by the various recorders for the whole of the survey; this has generally occurred for introductions, relics of cultivation and garden escapes.

Our flora today consists of not just the many native species but also those which have arrived through the agency of man. A list of the terms used is given below. It is difficult to be precise in many cases and this can only be a guide as species can fall into more than one category, for instance, the **Marsh Marigold** is both native and introduced in our area. Our use of terms is with reference to north east Essex only and may not be consistent with the species' status in other areas.

Native - not introduced by man.
Introduced - intentionally planted.
Naturalised - a plant, originally either introduced or escaped, which subsequently becomes established in a self-perpetuating population.
Garden Escape - becoming established from garden plants or garden waste; these may subsequently become 'naturalised' or be only short-lived.
Casual - a plant occurring for a short time only, often germinating from spilt seed, contamination in crop seeds or verge reseeding.
Bird Seed Alien - germinating from the remains of bird food.

Both Gibson's and Jermyn's books covered the whole county. Where we have used the phrase that one or both "had no records" for a particular plant this means that they gave no records for north east Essex; they may or may not have given records for the remainder of the county.

Place Names

Our place names can all be found on the Ordnance Survey Pathfinder series of maps with the exception of Berechurch Common (TM 0021). Place names for sites given by Gibson or Jermyn are as quoted in their respective Floras, these sites may no longer be known by the names they used, or indeed, may no longer exist. In a few cases, place names quoted from the very early books of Gerard, Ray and Dale have had today's names placed alongside in square brackets, with a question mark where there is possible doubt e.g. Bandamar lading [Landermere?].

Here we would mention how, in the text, we have distinguished villages with similar names. "Bradwell" is the village on the upper reaches of the Blackwater between Coggeshall and Braintree and "Bradwell-on-Sea" is the village at the mouth of the Blackwater by the nuclear power station. "Ramsey (TL 90)" is the Ramsey adjacent to St Lawrence on the Blackwater and "Ramsey (TM 23)" is the Ramsey near Parkeston. No differentiation has been made concerning the two Great Tothams as they are adjacent to each other.

Data Archive

Machine readable copies of the database are held on the Rural Areas Database at the ESRC Data Archive of the University of Essex, the Colchester Natural History Museum and by the senior author. The paper archive, which includes a complete set of maps for all species recorded, is stored at Colchester Natural History Museum with a second copy held by the senior author. All voucher material is stored in the herbarium of the Colchester Natural History Museum.

LIST OF RECORDERS

A project of this size would not have been possible without the assistance of many people including the referees for various critical groups and specialists in other areas. The 170,928 records themselves, accumulated between 1980 and 1989, were gathered by ourselves and the following principle recorders:

Janie Berry
Bill Chisholm
Chris Gibson
Gordon Grogan
Barbara Haslam
Jeremy Ison
Alan Lyall

Jo Marshall
Tim Pyner
Ian Rose
Alan Wake
Peter Wilson
Jean Wort

We have also received records from:

Kenneth J Adams
Reg Arthur
David Bains
Dave Baker
Ted Benton
Jerry Bowdrey
Jeremy Dagley
Laurie Forsyth
Anne Guiver
Lisa Hooper
Enid Hyde
Chris Lowe

Phil Luke
Dick Mash
Rosemary Mead
Edgar Milne-Redhead
Norman Parr
Roger Payne
Kate Rowland
John Thorogood
Ruth Tucker
G A Vivian
Dr Sarah Webster

and from :

British Pteridological Society
Essex Field Club
Essex Naturalists' Trust

National Trust
Royal Society for the Protection of Birds
Witham Natural History Society

Finally, our grateful thanks to everyone who has contributed to this project and made the 99.3% coverage of the area possible.

Terri Tarpey & Jerry Heath

THE WILD FLOWERS OF
NORTH EAST ESSEX

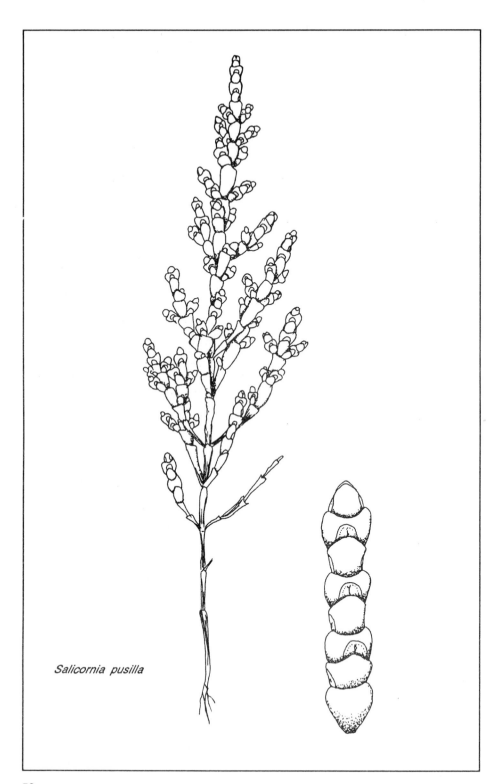

Salicornia pusilla

STONEWORT FAMILY
CHARACEAE

Stoneworts are rapidly decreasing nationally as they are very sensitive to water pollution.

Nitella opaca [1]

There were previously no records for north east Essex, but one site has now been found in a pond by Weeley Church, 1986.

CLUBMOSS FAMILY
LYCOPODIALES

Marsh Clubmoss
Lycopodiella inundata

This plant was very local in Gibson's time. Growing in boggy heaths, the only site given was Messing Heath, which no longer exists (it is on the maps by Chapman & Andre, 1777, and is now under the northern part of Tiptree). It was also recorded for Tiptree Heath in 1847 by T Bentall. Jermyn gave it as extinct in Essex and we have not refound it.

Stagshorn Clubmoss
Lycopodium clavatum [1]

The only site for this rare Clubmoss is on disturbed gravelly soil at Fingringhoe Wick Nature Reserve, where Jermyn recorded it in 1972. It is still present today.

HORSETAIL FAMILY
EQUISETACEAE

Common Horsetail
Equisetum arvense [683] M

A very common plant that can be extremely persistent and difficult to eradicate. It is often seen pushing its way through the tarmac at the road edge along country lanes, and is commonly found in arable fields, gardens, and gravel pits. It is surprisingly missing from much of the Dengie peninsula and absent from former salt-marsh and many areas of London Clay.

Water Horsetail
Equisetum fluviatile [9]

Gibson considered this plant to be common but possibly misidentified some plants. Jermyn considered it to be uncommon and our findings confirm this. Where it does occur it is quite often abundant, as in gravel pits at Brightlingsea where it grows on the sludgy mud, but its traditional sites in the shallow water of lakes, ponds and marshy, swampy areas are being lost due to land drainage and the infilling of ponds.

Marsh Horsetail
Equisetum palustre [28] M

This plant, considered common by Gibson, had declined to being only locally common by Jermyn's time. It still appears to be declining as the records are rather scattered and now very sparse in the Tendring peninsula. It is found in marshy places by

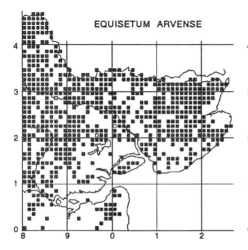

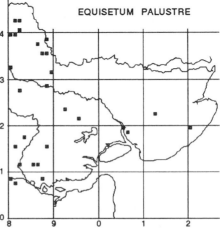

rivers and streams and in flooded gravel pits.

Wood Horsetail
Equisetum sylvaticum [1]
Gibson gave a site at Blackheath, Colchester, and Jermyn quoted Middlewick, East Donyland. Despite the intensive recording we have not refound it in this area of Colchester (these records could well be referring to the same site). We have, however, found it north of the Colne near the Greenstead Estate, growing along a stream ditch beside a wood and on adjacent damp grassland. It was in reasonable quantity covering an area approximately 10m long by 5m at its widest point.

Great Horsetail
Equisetum telmateia [87] M
Where it occurs it is usually abundant, taking over the whole area, especially in damp marshy places beside rivers, streams and ditches. It can now be found invading arable fields as farmers cultivate areas that previously would not have been ploughed. Its distribution in north east Essex correlates with the areas of clay underlying glacial deposits which is where the majority of wet flushes occur. It also seems to be found increasingly on road verges where the drainage is poor.

FERN FAMILY

Ferns have been much reduced in numbers since the mid 1800s, due to agricultural intensification and possibly climatic changes.

OPHIOGLOSSACEAE

Moonwort
Botrychium lunaria
The only record of this peculiar little fern was by Gerard in 1597 "It groweth in the ruins of a brick kiln by Colchester, in the grounds of Mr George Sayer, called Mile's End".

Adderstongue
Ophioglossum vulgatum [10] M
Never common in our area and easily overlooked growing in grassland. In damp hollows it can be found in good quantity as at the Naze, Walton. Not refound in any of the areas mentioned by Jermyn, but Gibson gave a record for Messing Heath and we have found it in Pods Wood nearby.

OSMUNDACEAE

Royal Fern
Osmunda regalis [3]
The only records we have are for obvious introductions. It was not refound in the native sites given by Gibson and Jermyn, although they were well covered in our survey.

POLYPODIACEAE

Polypody
Polypodium agg [66] M
These ferns have been found at 89 sites in 66 1km squares, with identifiable specimens collected from 67 of the sites; the other sites are either inaccessible or the fern lacked the sporangia needed for identification. *P vulgare* and *P interjectum* are found together or nearby each other at nine sites, at only one of which has a possible hybrid been found. At three further sites *P interjectum* occurs with possible hybrids. All sites (except where the fern is growing on a man-made structure or a tree) are on free draining soils usually shaded from the midday sunshine. The effect of the 1989 drought remains to be ascertained.

Polypodium interjectum [39] M
Widespread and our commonest **Polypody**, sometimes occurring in large quantities. It is more likely to be found on the ground than the **Common Polypody** but it is also found on roofs, walls and bridges. The apparent increase since Jermyn's time is due to an increased awareness of the correct identification criteria for the species. A number of specimens have a high proportion of sporangia with only one basal cell, possibly indicating back-crossing with *P vulgare*.

Polypodium X mantoniae [8]
Apparent hybrids are known from eight sites but none seem to be true *P X mantoniae* judged against accurately

named specimens from sites outside our area. They have a wide range of annulus ring number, extra large and small spores, and a range of basal cell numbers. Further work is needed to elucidate their true status.

Common Polypody
Polypodium vulgare [32] M
Not found in the southern part of our area, the **Common Polypody** is slightly less common than *P interjectum*. It is more often found on tree roots or stumps, especially in hedgerows, than the other members of this family.

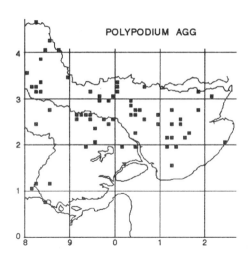

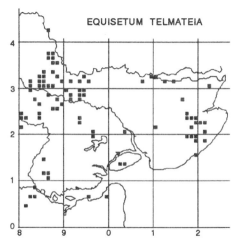

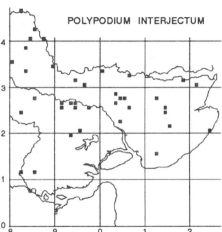

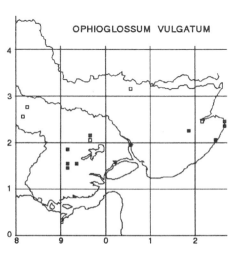

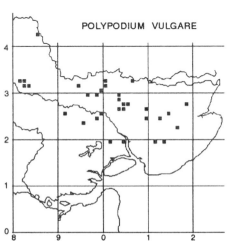

HYPOLEPIDACEAE

Bracken
Pteridium aquilinum [522] M
Common on light, free draining soils as shown by its distribution along the Tiptree Ridge. It is absent from the heavy coastal soils, but found on the Holland gravels at Holland-on-Sea. Woods, hedgerows and heaths are its native habitat but it can also be found on damp walls in the middle of Colchester and as a garden weed in North Station Road, Colchester.

THELYPTERIDACEAE

Lemon-scented or Mountain Fern
Oreopteris limbosperma [1]
Gibson gave a record for "near Kelvedon", Jermyn listed two other sites, at Tiptree Heath and Pods Wood, 1971, thus putting all the records for this fern in the same area, one which has suitable wet woods and heathy places. The plant at Pods Wood was last seen in August 1980 by the British Pteridological Society but the Tiptree Heath record was not refound during our survey. In both sites it is quite possible that it may well reoccur due to the new management of Tiptree Heath and the open areas created in Pods Wood by the storm of October 1987.

ASPLENIACEAE

The comments here apply to all the ferns in this family - they are usually found on the north or west faces of old walls and tombstones. Many of the old records were refound where the wall had remained unchanged but were usually lost where maintenance and repointing had occurred. Railway bridges are a favourite site, particularly when built from the blue engineering brick rather than the usual red. Many of the bridges on the disused railway lines around Maldon are made from these blue bricks and usually one, and sometimes, two or three different ferns from this family can be found on them.

Black Spleenwort
Asplenium adiantum-nigrum [29] M
In the west country, with the higher rainfall, this fern can be found growing in hedges as well as on old walls. It must once have occurred in the hedges in Essex as Gibson gives its habitat as "old walls and hedges" but none of Jermyn's or our records are from anything other than walls. The descendants of the plants recorded by Gibson in Dedham churchyard still survive there, as do those of many of Jermyn's records from the railway bridges south of Maldon and at Manningtree. His record for Bures station could not be refound, however, nor could his record for a Witham churchyard, although a colony was recorded on a railway bridge nearby.

Wall Rue
Asplenium ruta-muraria [19] M
Many of the sites for this plant in our area are of one or two very small, shrivelled specimens although some colonies of ten, or occasionally, even twenty or more plants can be found on a favoured wall. It seems to survive at these sites for many years if the wall is left alone - we have refound many of Jermyn's sites including those on railway bridges at Maldon, Bures station, bridge at Mistley and Walton Tower.

Maidenhair Spleenwort
Asplenium trichomanes [16] M
Always in less quantity than the two previous species but in similar situations and quite often growing with them. The only unusual habitat was a single plant found growing from wooden supports at the side of a pond at Colchester.

Rusty-back Fern
Ceterach officinarum [1]
Always very rare in Essex as a whole: Gibson gave no records for the north east of the county and Jermyn only one, which we have not been able to refind. However, we have found another site, on a bridge over a disused railway line at Wickham Bishops. It is a good colony, holding 17 healthy plants.

Hartstongue
Phyllitis scolopendrium [40] M
Thinly scattered, usually on damp brickwork such as walls underneath leaking guttering and the sides of soakaways as well as on tombstones in churchyards. It can also be found in damp shady places -

Friday Wood, wood at Mistley, Loshes Meadow by streambank, Great Holland Pits (it has been known from this site for many years and it is still common in the scrub there). The specimens found in north east Essex are invariably small and depauperate compared to those found in the wetter parts of Britain.

ATHYRIACEAE

Lady Fern
Athyrium filix-femina [15] M
A rare fern of damp shady woods where it is usually found in ones and twos, except

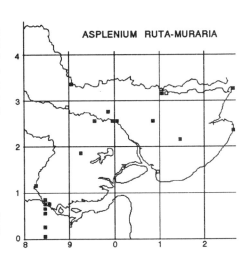

ASPLENIUM RUTA-MURARIA

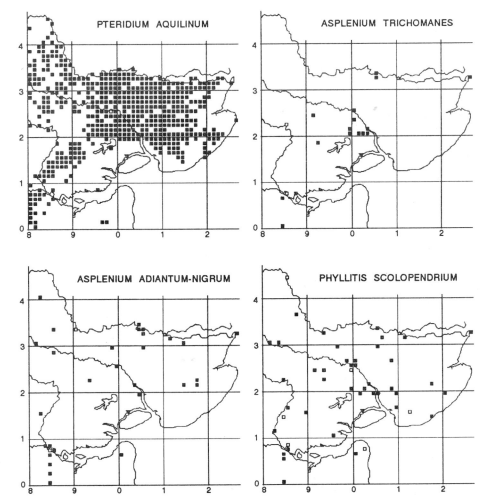

PTERIDIUM AQUILINUM

ASPLENIUM TRICHOMANES

ASPLENIUM ADIANTUM-NIGRUM

PHYLLITIS SCOLOPENDRIUM

for one site by a shady stream in Friday Wood where it occurs in good quantity.

ASPIDIACEAE

Scaly-male Fern
Dryopteris affinis [6]
A plant that grows in wet flushes by streams. It is very infrequent but possibly overlooked. It also hybridises with the **Male Fern** which causes difficulties with positive identification. At Rowhedge Pits, for instance, a few **Scaly-male Ferns** grow amongst a lot of **Male Ferns** mixed in with many hybrids. The hybrid also occurs at Stour Wood.

Narrow Buckler Fern
Dryopteris carthusiana [15] M
Uncommon and decreasing in damp woods, wooded streamsides and wet heathy places. Always found in small quantity (1 or 2 plants), it is still present in Chalkney and Pods Woods where it has been known since Gibson's time. We have also refound Jermyn's sites at Fordham Heath and Fingringhoe Wick Nature Reserve.

Broad Buckler Fern
Dryopteris dilatata [157] M
Widespread and occasionally abundant in ancient woodlands occurring on the better drained soils. Where this is a slope we have sometimes found **Lady Fern** in the wet areas at the bottom, with **Broad Buckler** half-way up and **Male Fern** on the drier parts at the top. **Broad Buckler** can also be found growing on dead logs and on the shady side of tombstones.

Male Fern
Dryopteris filix-mas [334] M
Common and well distributed, except in the coastal strip, it can be found on walls, in ditches, streamsides and woods. It now also frequently spreads from cultivated plants growing in gardens.

Hard Shield Fern
Polystichum aculeatum [15] M
Uncommon, and always just one or two plants, usually growing along the side of a ditch under a hedgerow or at the edge of a wood. It is most frequently found around Twinstead.

Soft Shield Fern
Polystichum setiferum [23] M
Local in woods and damp shady places. It can be abundant in ditches which are nutrient rich from agricultural run-off but usually just single plants occur. It is relatively frequent in the Stour/Copperas Wood complex.

BLECHNACEAE

Hard Fern
Blechnum spicant [6]
Rare and in small quantity, growing on the well-drained edges of ditches or banks, deep in woodland. The largest colony is in Friday Wood.

AZOLLACEAE

Water Fern
Azolla filiculoides [20]
Local and sporadic, sometimes as a throw-out from garden ponds. It may occur one year in incredible quantity, for example, in 1989, Holland Brook and its tributaries were filled from bank to bank to a depth of several inches. However, just as suddenly as it appears, it will disappear only to occur at another site, or, after an absence of several years, reappear at a previous locality.

PINE FAMILY
PINACEAE

None are native in our area but they are widely planted as ornamental trees, in shelter belts and forestry plantations. The list is incomplete as not all garden and park species have been recorded. At least 50 different species, varieties and cultivars can be found in garden centres, but they rarely produce seedlings.

Noble Fir
Abies procera [2]
Introduced. Occasional trees are planted for ornamental and landscaping purposes.

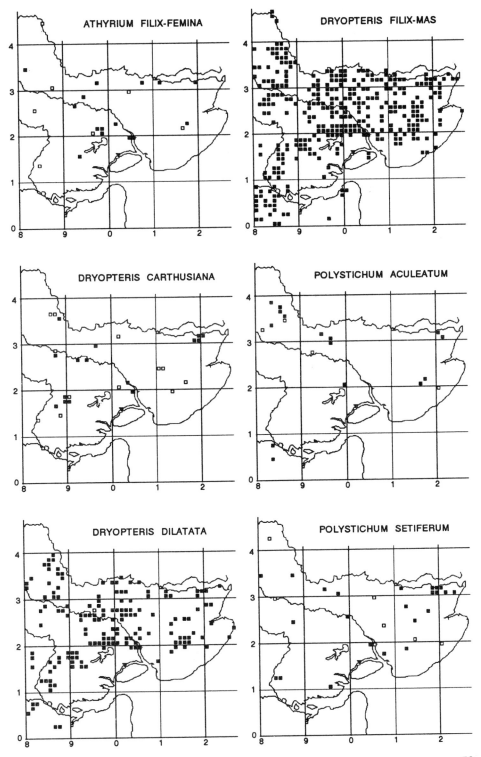

ATHYRIUM FILIX-FEMINA

DRYOPTERIS FILIX-MAS

DRYOPTERIS CARTHUSIANA

POLYSTICHUM ACULEATUM

DRYOPTERIS DILATATA

POLYSTICHUM SETIFERUM

Cedar of Lebanon
Cedrus libani [1]
Introduced. Rare, a few trees planted for ornamental and landscaping purposes.

European Larch
Larix decidua [27]
Widespread. Usually found in plantations which are quite frequently planted in ancient woodlands when they are coniferised, but sometimes found singly in large gardens and parks. A few records included here may refer to the following two species.

Larix decidua X kaempferi [1]
Introduced but not often met with, possibly under-recorded.

Japanese Larch
Larix kaempferi [1]
Planted, rare, but possibly overlooked.

Norway Spruce
Picea abies [11]
Introduced. Usually in plantations but sometimes grown as a crop for Christmas trees on various sites, including allotments.

Sitka Spruce
Picea sitchensis [4]
Uncommon and invariably found in a plantation.

Austrian and Corsican Pines
Pinus nigra [18]
Introduced. We have recorded all varieties as *P nigra*. More often met with singly, or as a line of trees providing a shelter belt along the edge of a recreation area or park, than as a plantation tree. It is also found in large Victorian gardens.

Monterey Pine
Pinus radiata [1]
A few trees planted for ornament.

Weymouth Pine
Pinus strobus [1]
The occasional tree can be found planted for ornament.

Scots Pine
Pinus sylvestris [211] M
Frequent and widespread, it is, however,

not a native tree in Essex. It can be found singly, in shelter belts or as a plantation tree. It does regenerate from seed in a few places, but it is not the invasive problem here that it is just across the border in Suffolk because we have so little seminatural habitat for it to invade. Seedlings are most successful on light sandy soils.

Douglas Fir
Pseudotsuga menziesii [6]
Generally found in ones and twos where occasional plantings have occurred.

CYPRESS FAMILY
CUPRESSACEAE

Monterey Cypress
Cupressus macrocarpa [3]
The occasional planted tree has been found.

Juniper
Juniperus communis
Gibson mentions that it grew on Donyland Heath in his time (Rev W P L Garnons collected specimens on 2nd April 1829), although he suggests that it might have been planted. It was last found on Donyland Heath in 1912 by G C Brown, nearly 90 years after it was first recorded. By Jermyn's time it no longer occurred in Essex and we have not refound it at Gibson's site during our current survey.

Western Red Cedar
Thuja plicata [2]
Occurs as a plantation tree in two woods.

YEW FAMILY
TAXACEAE

Yew
Taxus baccata [175] M
Widespread. Almost invariably in churchyards, but occasionally met with in woods and large gardens. Seedlings can often be found growing from deep leaf litter close by their parents. The columnar **Irish Yew** is common in churchyards and it is interesting to note that the self sown seedlings in the grounds of the Colchester Natural History Museum (All Saints Church) do not

have the columnar habit of the nearby trees, but the spreading nature of those in the park opposite.

BUTTERCUP FAMILY
RANUNCULACEAE

Monkshood
Aconitum napellus
In Gibson's time this plant was very local in Essex, occasionally being found in woods and hedges. Jermyn found it only as a casual or garden escape in Essex but had no records for the north east. We have found one plant but the identification has not been confirmed and some other species or garden variety is possible.

Pheasant's Eye
Adonis annua
No recent records. A very rare casual, recorded only once this century in north east Essex - Turner Road, Colchester, c1920. In Gibson's time, although very local, it did turn up occasionally as a cornfield weed; the only record he gave for our area was at Pattiswick.

Blue Anemone
Anemone apennina [2]
Planted as a 'naturalised' plant in parklands.

Wood Anemone
Anemone nemorosa [106] M
In those ancient woodlands in which it occurs it is usually plentiful, carpeting the ground in the spring to make a fine show. Woods are one of the few habitats where there has not been too much loss in the past two decades and the current distribution of the **Wood Anemone** reflects this, being much the same as it was for Jermyn. This plant does well growing under coppiced **Sweet Chestnut** and the classic site for **Wood Anemone** in Essex is at Stour Wood, where a wide range of variation in petal numbers (5-10), colour (white to reddish purple on the back of the petals) and size can be seen.

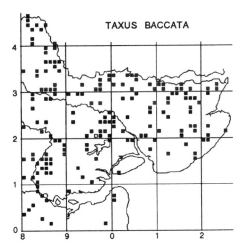
TAXUS BACCATA

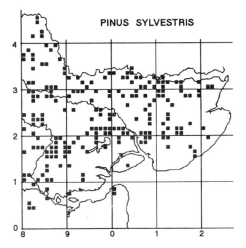
PINUS SYLVESTRIS

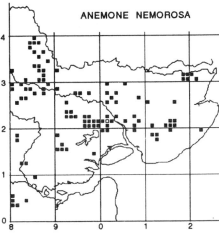
ANEMONE NEMOROSA

Columbine
Aquilegia vulgaris [1]
A casual of garden origin that is infrequently met with.

Marsh Marigold
Caltha palustris [59] M
Decreasing in its native habitat of marshy places by rivers, streams, lakes and ponds, due to the drainage of these places, although it can still be plentiful under alder carr in the north west of our area. It is still widely distributed as it is readily available in garden centres and is now commonly planted in village ponds which have been the subject of a restoration scheme.

Wild Clematis or Traveller's Joy
Clematis vitalba [316] M
The distribution map clearly shows its preference for calcareous soils but otherwise there are odd scattered records where the soils, perhaps for some man-made reason (e.g. Colchester Roman Wall, railway lines), are suitable. A further example of this is the distribution within the old town of Maldon where the **Clematis** grows in part along a parish boundary where the outcrop of calcium rich Maldon Till (between 25 and 30m OD) occurs.

Larkspur
Consolida ambigua [15]
Casual or garden escape of short-lived duration. Frequently occurs on verges where top soil has been dumped.

Winter Aconite
Eranthis hyemalis [11]
Often planted in quantity and carpeting the ground very early in the year.

Stinking Hellebore
Helleborus foetidus
This plant would never have been anything but very rare in our area, Gibson gives one record for Kelvedon which he thought might be a garden escape, and Jermyn one record for Borley in 1952. We have not found it at all.

Mousetail
Myosurus minimus [53] M
Jermyn considered this plant to be rare and sporadic in its occurrence but we have found during our survey that it has a wide but scattered distribution. It favours the heavy soils, particularly where they are waterlogged in winter, turning up in field corners which have missed the farmer's sprays, and frequently in the hard packed soil of gateways. It travels well on botanists' boots! It turned up in the garden of one of the authors where the mud had been knocked off her boots into the flower bed, and although more plentiful some years than others, it has appeared every year since 1981.

Love-in-a-Mist
Nigella damascena [2]
A bird seed alien and garden escape.

Meadow Buttercup
Ranunculus acris [600] M
Common and well distributed. Although never abundant it is frequently found on well-drained grassland including road verges.

Corn Buttercup
Ranunculus arvensis [11]
Now rare, and still decreasing. Its distribution compared to that given by Jermyn is even more scattered. Sporadic in its occurrence, there are usually only two or three plants at the edges and corners of arable fields where the chemical sprays have missed. It was also found on recently disturbed soil on a golf course where a bank had been built but will soon disappear as the permanent ground cover closes in.

Goldilocks Buttercup
Ranunculus auricomus [42] M
Not common, but more frequently met with where there is a calcareous influence in the soil, otherwise scattered. Most frequently found in churchyards and damp shady hedgerows.

Bulbous Buttercup
Ranunculus bulbosus [342] M
The earliest of the typical Buttercups to flower, it is apparently not as widespread as the **Meadow Buttercup** but this may be due to it being easily overlooked once it has flowered. Growing in any general grassland such as verges, churchyards and lawns, except that there are quite large

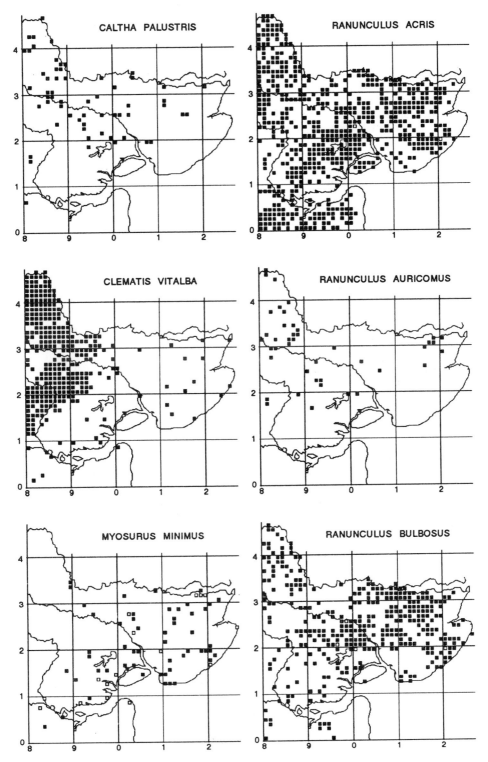

CALTHA PALUSTRIS

RANUNCULUS ACRIS

CLEMATIS VITALBA

RANUNCULUS AURICOMUS

MYOSURUS MINIMUS

RANUNCULUS BULBOSUS

areas, usually on heavy soils, such as parts of the Dengie peninsula, from which it is missing altogether.

Lesser Celandine
Ranunculus ficaria ssp bulbifer [10]
Ranunculus ficaria ssp ficaria [425] M
Common and widespread, growing by streams, in ditches, soggy areas, woods and damp hedges. In places it can be abundant, forming large patches. *Ssp ficaria*, with the larger yellow flowers, is by far the commoner of the two subspecies, tending to grow in the more open situations; *ssp bulbifer* with smaller flowers which set little seed, prefers shaded conditions such as underneath a hedge. It is probable that this subspecies is overlooked as it tends to appear a little bit later, dying back almost immediately its bulbils have been set, thus becoming hidden by the surrounding vegetation.

Lesser Spearwort
Ranunculus flammula [38] M
A plant predominantly of wet flushes in meadows and grassy areas although it also occurs in marshy and muddy margins of ponds and streams. A plant that has obviously declined due to the loss of meadows and pastures since the Victorian era when Gibson found it common and "generally plentiful" in our part of Essex. A century later Jermyn considered it to be "uncommon but widespread", a situation that our findings would confirm.

Greater Spearwort
Ranunculus lingua [9]
Introduced into lakes and ponds.

Small-flowered Buttercup
Ranunculus parviflorus [3]
Very rare and still decreasing since Jermyn's time - there are now only three known sites, despite the intensive coverage of our study. Two of the sites are on dry ridges and banks on coastal grazing marshes and the third is at the Essex Naturalists' Trust reserve at Great Holland Pits.

Creeping Buttercup
Ranunculus repens [1229]
Very common, widespread and locally abundant.

Hairy Buttercup
Ranunculus sardous [93] M
Traditionally considered the buttercup of estuarine grazing marshes, these are now mainly arable fields in north east Essex. Our survey has found it in quite a number of inland areas, usually in short turf but sometimes on tracks. Usually only one or two plants are found except one year at Cattawade when the whole of the marsh was a blaze of yellow with **Hairy Buttercup** flowers after the soil had been disturbed.

Celery-leaved Buttercup
Ranunculus sceleratus [280] M
Common and well distributed in ditches and ponds throughout the area. It seems able to tolerate a high degree of pollution in the water and so is quite often one of the last plants to die out in what to botanists are extremely nauseating conditions.

Water Crowfoots
The aquatic members of the Buttercup family have been grouped together. Our thanks go to Dr Sarah Webster for her help in identifying many of our specimens of this difficult group.

Common Water Crowfoot
Ranunculus aquatilis [25] M
Possibly over-recorded in the past but still the commonest Water Crowfoot in freshwater ponds and streams.

Brackish Water Crowfoot
Ranunculus baudotii [28] M
Frequent in ditches and borrow dykes near the sea. Not always easy to identify as it probably hybridises with other species. It requires a slight salty influence in the water.

Stiff-leaved Water Crowfoot
Ranunculus circinatus [3]
Rare. Mostly found in flooded gravel pits or farm reservoirs and occasionally in ponds.

Ivy-leaved Water Crowfoot
Ranunculus hederaceus [6]
Rare and usually in small quantity. This Crowfoot is associated with the head-

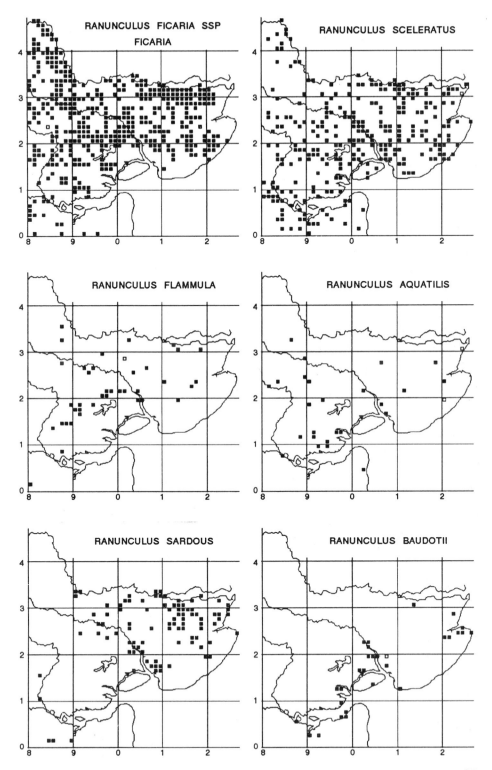

RANUNCULUS FICARIA SSP FICARIA

RANUNCULUS SCELERATUS

RANUNCULUS FLAMMULA

RANUNCULUS AQUATILIS

RANUNCULUS SARDOUS

RANUNCULUS BAUDOTII

65

waters of springs and wet flushes along springlines. This plant was seen one winter frozen solid in ice that had formed in deep ruts caused by army vehicles in Friday Wood but it seemed to suffer no ill effects, flowering the following year.

Pond Water Crowfoot
Ranunculus peltatus [14] M
This plant has never been common in our area but seems to have maintained its restricted distribution in lakes and ponds.

Short-leaved Water Crowfoot
Ranunculus trichophyllus [7]
Rare in ponds and ditches, sometimes in slightly brackish water near the coast.

Common Meadow Rue
Thalictrum flavum [13]
A plant of wet meadows, ditches and riversides it could once be found along the Stour, Colne and Blackwater. It is now reduced to a few sites on the Stour at Cattawade, Boxtedhall and Sudbury and to one site on the Blackwater at Maldon. All our other records are introductions from gardens and parks.

BERBERRIS FAMILY
BERBERIDACEAE

Barberry
Berberis vulgaris [6]
Gibson wrote that this shrub was becoming increasingly scarce as it was "being extirpated in many places, in consequence of the current opinion that it produces blight in wheat crop". Modern research has, however, failed to find **Black Rust** on **Barberry** in Britain and it is believed to be spread each year by windblown spores from the continent. Of the six records we have, it is apparently native at only two of the sites, the rest being introductions.

Barrenwort
Epimedium alpinum [1]
Introduced with garden waste. Only one record.

Oregon Grape
Mahonia aquifolium [22]
Introduced and frequently planted in large

gardens and parks. It readily generates from seed spread by birds in their droppings.

WATER LILY FAMILY
NYMPHAEACEAE

Yellow Water Lily
Nuphar lutea [62] M
A plant of slow-moving rivers and which still occurs in good quantity on the Stour, Colne and Blackwater. Away from these main rivers it is found as an introduction to lakes and ponds.

White Water Lily
Nymphaea alba [25]
Even in Jermyn's time he considered that it still occurred as a native in the area, but all our records are ornamental introductions to lakes and ponds.

HORNWORT FAMILY
CERATOPHYLLACEAE

Rigid Hornwort
Ceratophyllum demersum [28] M
The more common of the two Hornworts, widely scattered in freshwater ponds, ditches, canals and flooded gravel pits.

Soft Hornwort
Ceratophyllum submersum [18]
This Hornwort prefers the salinity of brackish dykes of estuarine marshes. As with the previous species, it often dominates to the exclusion of all other waterweeds.

POPPY FAMILY
PAPAVERACEAE

Greater Celandine
Chelidonium majus [58] M
A plant of the old cottage garden that now occurs as a naturalised plant near houses and on waste ground. It has grown by the river at Middleborough in Colchester for many years.

Californian Poppy
Eschscholzia californica [2]
A casual escape from gardens or where

garden refuse has been thrown by the roadside. Usually short-lived, seedlings have been found, however, suggesting that it could become naturalised.

Yellow Horned Poppy
Glaucium flavum [16] M
On sandy and gravelly beaches around the coast, rarely in quantity. Generally in the same sites as found by both Gibson and Jermyn, it has not been refound on the upper reaches of the Blackwater at Stansgate and Osea Island.

Welsh Poppy
Meconopsis cambrica [2]
A rare introduction in our area which is

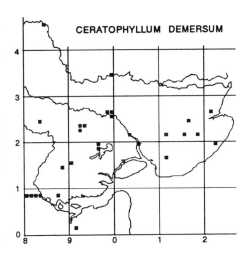

CERATOPHYLLUM DEMERSUM

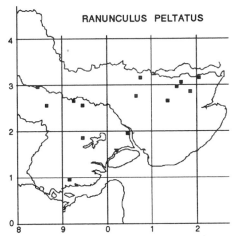

RANUNCULUS PELTATUS

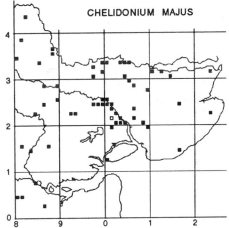

CHELIDONIUM MAJUS

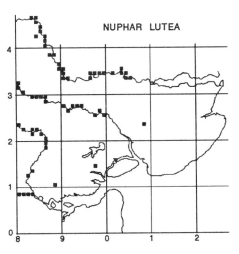

NUPHAR LUTEA

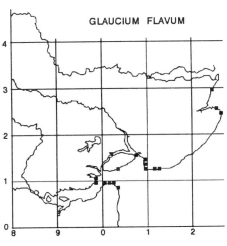

GLAUCIUM FLAVUM

usually found in towns.

Long Prickly-headed Poppy
Papaver argemone [26] M
Not common and always in small quantity, preferring the lighter soils. It is found mainly at the edge of arable fields where it has been missed by the chemical spray, but also occurs on railway banks, footpaths and track edges.

Long-headed Poppy
Papaver dubium [35] M
Gibson's records show that this was common over most of our area in his day, growing in cornfields and on waste ground. Jermyn considered it uncommon but well distributed, which still seems to be the case.

Round Prickly-headed Poppy
Papaver hybridum [3]
This poppy has always been rare in our area, Gibson giving two sites at Walton and Harwich and Jermyn one at Alresford. Our survey has turned up three sites, one at Manningtree and two at Elmstead.

Babington's Poppy
Papaver lecoqii [9] M
A poppy of waste ground, rubbish tips and soil heaps, which can in consequence turn up almost anywhere. It appears to be increasing.

Common Poppy
Papaver rhoeas [758] M
This is the traditional cornfield Poppy. Although still very common it no longer grows in amongst the cereal but along the edges or in corners where the farmer's sprays have missed. Occasionally a field will be seen full of poppies when the spray did not 'take' because of adverse weather conditions at the time. The sprays used when Rape is grown also allow the poppies to come back. Flash appearances of poppies often occur during road construction when the soil is disturbed. This indicates that in traditional arable farming areas there must be an enormous seed bank in the soil and that poppy seeds are long-lived and durable. This is also shown by the lack of records around Tiptree and south of Maldon; these areas, due to their soils, have had a slightly different regime of pastoral farming in the past, thus the seed bank of this arable plant has not had so long to develop.

Opium Poppy
Papaver somniferum [64]
A short-lived casual that occurs as a throw-out from gardens on refuse heaps by the roadside and other tip sites.

FUMITORY FAMILY
FUMARIACEAE

Climbing Corydalis
Corydalis claviculata [46] M
This plant requires old woodland on sandy soils where it can be locally abundant. It is sometimes found in old established hedgerows. Many of our old woodlands are now nature reserves or SSSIs and this habitat has not, therefore, been devastated as some others have in recent years. Comparison of the results of our survey correlates well with sites given by both Gibson and Jermyn, the main losses being Tiptree Heath (where it could still be refound) and Spratt's Marsh (which is now an arable field).

Yellow Corydalis
Corydalis lutea [55]
Escapes well from gardens but usually only to the outside of the garden wall and never far from human habitation.

Bleeding Hearts
Dicentra spectabilis
Introduction. This was found once, in 1975, at West Bergholt.

Tall Ramping Fumitory
Fumaria bastardii
A rare colonist. Jermyn recorded it once at Little Holland but we have not found it during our current survey.

White Ramping Fumitory
Fumaria capreolata
      ssp babingtonii [32] M
Considered rare by Jermyn, our survey has revealed many more sites, particularly around Great Oakley and Ramsey (TL 23). It seems to have two growing habits; either

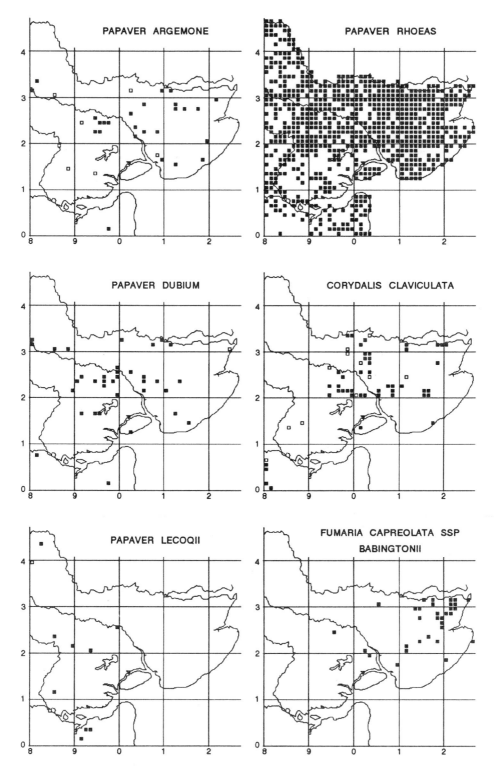

69

right at the bottom of a hedge so that it can then scramble up and over the hedge, or, at field and track edges where it grows prostrate.

Common Fumitory
Fumaria officinalis
   ssp officinalis [232] M
Fumaria officinalis ssp wirtgenii [4]
Common as a weed of gardens, allotments and the edges and corners of arable fields. Generally widespread but favouring the Tendring area with its free draining soils. Jermyn said that this Fumitory was locally abundant on calcareous arable land but our distribution map shows it avoiding the areas of chalky boulder clay. The subspecies *F officinalis ssp wirtgenii* has not been fully recorded.

Small White Fumitory
Fumaria parviflora [1]
This Fumitory was first recorded in Essex by Gibson in 1841 in an allotment field in the north west of the county. There have never been any records for the north east, it traditionally being a plant of cultivated fields on a chalky soil which occurs mainly in the north west of Essex. In 1988 a few plants were found growing along a field edge at Weeley. During the 1970s the Essex Naturalists' Trust had experimented with trying to recreate a traditional corn field in the area and we wondered if these flowers could have originated from this, but it turned out that that experiment had taken place in a field a couple of kilometres away. Whether these plants were native or introduced we do not know and any information on them would be gratefully received. (See also next species).

Small Pink Fumitory
Fumaria vaillantii [1]
This Fumitory grows in similar places to the previous species (chalky arable fields), and again had never been recorded in the north east of the county, until a few plants were found growing alongside those of the previous species at Weeley.

CABBAGE FAMILY
CRUCIFERAE

Garlic Mustard
Alliaria petiolata [926] M
Common over the whole area except on the heavy clays of the coastal belt. It grows on the edges of ditches, the bottom of hedgerows, edges of woods and beside fences, indeed, anywhere where it has some shade and can avoid the full glare of the sun.

Small Alison
Alyssum alyssioides
Once found in clover fields near Coggeshall, 1851.

Thale Cress
Arabidopsis thaliana [332] M
An early flowering plant common on walls, banks and disturbed ground on the drier, free draining sand and gravel soils. Often overlooked later in the season and probably under-recorded.

Tower Mustard
Arabis glabra
Both Gibson and Jermyn regarded this plant as rare. Gibson gave six localities, Jermyn two, the latest of which was in an old gravel pit near Colchester in 1952-53. It has not been found during our present survey.

Hairy Rockcress
Arabis hirsuta [1]
This plant had not been recorded anywhere in Essex in Gibson's time; he thought it possible that it would be found and subsequently it was. Jermyn gave four sites for the north east but stated that it was rare and decreasing. Usually associated with the dry chalk soils, our only site is an old gravel pit at Great Totham, 1985.

Horse Radish
Armoracia rusticana [587] M
Common on road verges, farmyards, gateways, allotments and railway tracks, always near habitation. Gibson interestingly considered this plant as "rather local" - was this plant, in Victorian times, still mainly within the confines of the kitchen garden?

Medium-flowered Wintercress
Barbarea intermedia [5]
This plant, not known to Gibson, and only on scattered sites in small quantity to Jermyn, has been found on five occasions - generally just single plants invariably associated with introduced tipped soil.

American Wintercress
Barbarea verna [6] M
A casual introduction that turns up from time to time in tipped soil. In Gibson's time it was an escape from cultivation, but Jermyn had no records and considered it lost to Essex. Wintercress seed is still available from nurserymen which probably accounts for our records.

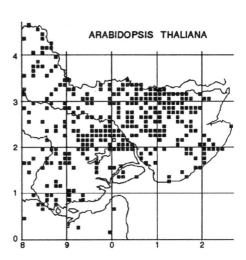

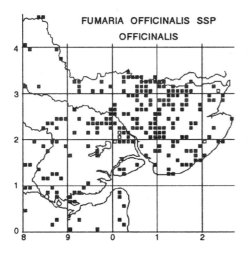

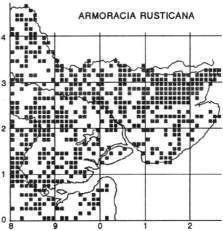

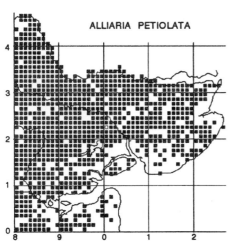

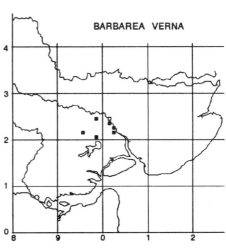

71

Common Wintercress
Barbarea vulgaris [337] M

Common in damp ditches and woodland edges as well as river and streamsides on the heavier clays. Jermyn gave four sites for *var arcuata* but it has not been separately treated in our survey.

Hoary Alison
Berteroa incana

A casual introduction that was recorded from Hythe Quay, Colchester, between 1905 and 1920, but not since.

Brassica juncea

Only recorded once, in malting refuse at Hythe Quay in 1927, when the type of cargo and cargo handling methods were very different from today.

Rape
Brassica napus [164]

Now a common crop in our area, the effect of EEC subsidies, being visible as yellow fields early in the year. Consequently it appears commonly along field edges and on roadside verges as a casual weed. Although much seed is spilt during transportation it does not, as yet, seem to persist. Our records for this plant are incomplete. Gibson considered it to be "rather local" indicating that it was not a commonly planted crop in Victorian times.

Black Mustard
Brassica nigra [123] M

Common in coastal areas along sea walls, field borders and ditches, but local inland, generally by stream and ditchsides. Inland, its distribution has contracted, probably due to it no longer being cultivated as a crop. As a result casual introductions from this source have ceased, leaving us with a distribution showing mainly its native habitat.

Wild Turnip
Brassica rapa [5]

Ssp *rapa*, which is the cultivated **Turnip**, occurs occasionally as a relic of cultivation, and ssp *campestris*, the **Wild Turnip** with the non-tuberous tap root, occurs by river and streamsides. Jermyn showed it to be widespread, but, although not fully recorded during our survey, we have very

few sites. This could indicate that the current management of river and streamsides has altered the distribution of this plant.

Sea Rocket
Cakile maritima [23] M

Lost from the higher reaches of the Blackwater (as was the **Yellow Horned Poppy**, which grows in the same habitat) and the Stour, but still present and locally plentiful at its traditional sites on sandy shores at Bradwell-on-Sea, Mersea, Colne Point, Walton, Dovercourt and Harwich. The distribution map for this plant could equally be the map depicting the sandy and shingly beaches of north east Essex. At Harwich in recent years the beach has been built up with additional sand and this has created ideal conditions for **Sea Rocket** which has become dominant over a long stretch of the foreshore.

Shepherd's Purse
Capsella bursa-pastoris [1099] M

An abundant and very variable weed over the whole area, growing on any patch of bare soil. The only habitat from which it is absent is the grazing marshes of Old Hall and Langenhoe and the saltmarshes of Hamford Water.

Large Bittercress
Cardamine amara [27] M

Decreasing due to the drainage of its habitat. Typically found in shaded willow or alder carr where a stream spreads out into a marshy area of black peaty soil, which will come straight over the top of one's boots. It occurs mainly within the chalky boulder clay area.

Wavy Bittercress
Cardamine flexuosa [182] M

Commonly found in shady wet ditches, often in woods. Its absence/scarcity from large areas can be correlated with a lack of suitable streams combined with the 'manicured' ditches now often associated with intensive farming.

Hairy Bittercress
Cardamine hirsuta [268] M

Often abundant on old walls it is found most commonly as a garden weed of the

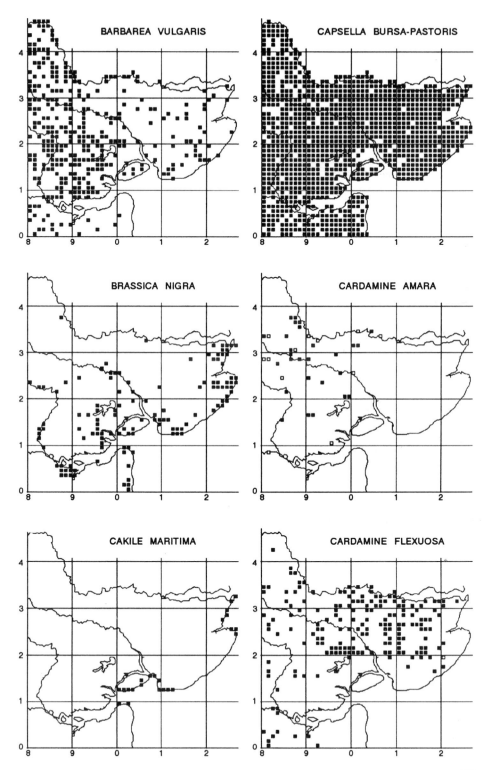

lighter soils, on which it can reach plague proportions, exploding its pods and scattering its seeds throughout most of the year, but particularly when being weeded! However, it can be a useful green vegetable for salads in mild winters.

Cuckoo Flower
Cardamine pratensis [129] M
Locally common on damp grassland, wet banks and damp open woods, except the relatively acid London Clays. Where it occurs in managed grassland, such as in churchyards and council open areas, it is often mown before having a chance to flower and persists in the vegetative state for many years.

Hoary Cress LEPIDIUM - (Stace)
Cardaria draba [417] M
This plant was introduced to Britain only about 1809 and gradually spread into Essex from the London area, mainly after the turn of the century and between the two World Wars. It is now common and locally abundant especially on road verges and sea walls, although it is largely absent from the boulder clay.

Wallflower
Cheiranthus cheiri [3]
The yellow-flowered variety was known by Gibson from the Roman Wall and Castle at Colchester from 1830 onwards and, although still present, its numbers are much reduced by the restoration work that is taking place. Elsewhere it is the result of casual introductions from garden throwouts. Not fully recorded.

English Scurvy Grass
Cochlearia anglica [39] M
Scattered on all the saltmarshes around the coast.

Danish Scurvy Grass
Cochlearia danica [35] M
The peculiar distribution i.e. virtually all records inland, is a result of *danica's* very early flowering (March) and the saltmarsh recording being conducted later in the season when this plant has flowered and disappeared from view. It probably occurs

on many of our saltmarshes. Some saltmarsh plants, and *danica* is one, have been able to 'travel' inland, their seeds being carried by vehicles and deposited along the roadsides as well as probably arriving in the grit and salt spread on the roads in winter. Here they have been able to germinate and flourish in the narrow band of bare soil at the edge of the carriageway where the salty spray from passing vehicles has killed the more vigorous plants that would normally crowd out this type of invader. An area such as this along the central reservation of the A12 *danica* has made its own, it can only be described as abundant, looking like a fine covering of snow in March and early April. It appears to prefer the parts of the A12 that were the first to be 'dualled', where the central reservation was constructed of soil and grassed. It does not grow along the stretches built later where several inches of shingle were used to provide the barrier between carriageways. This is clearly demonstrated along the new Colchester bypass where not a single plant of *danica* can be found. With crash barriers now being installed along much of the A12 it will be interesting to see how this plant survives the upheaval. Jermyn makes no mention of any inland records indicating that it is a 'recent' phenomenon although it has been known from the A12 since the mid 1970s, and more recently from the A133.

Common Scurvy Grass
Cochlearia officinalis [12] M
Not as common as the **English Scurvy Grass** and generally occurring at the bottom of sea walls rather than on the saltmarsh itself. It is typically a plant of upper saltmarshes, but in Essex the sea walls have truncated the saltmarsh zonation, and the higher marshes have been reclaimed. Thus, the only place left for *officinalis* is the sea wall, giving it a much restricted distribution along a narrow habitat.

Hare's Ear Mustard
Conringia orientalis
Dale (1732) recorded this plant from cornfields and cliffs near Harwich, but it has not been recorded since.

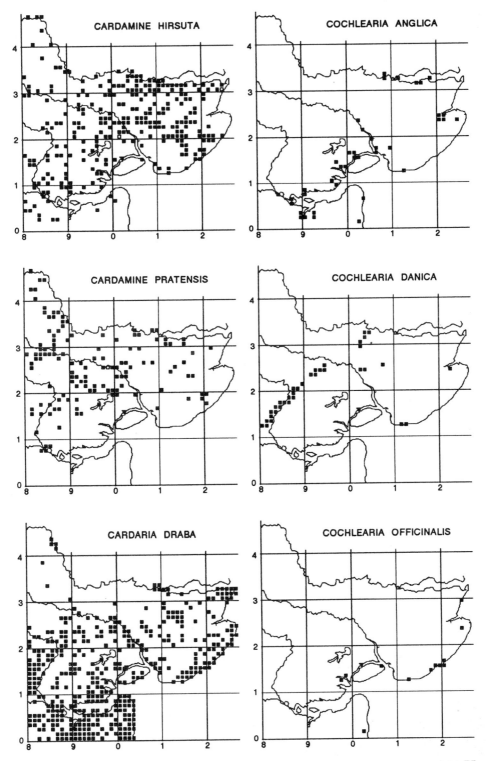

Lesser Swinecress
Coronopus didymus [54] M

Locally common but with a scattered distribution. It is generally an urban plant occurring more frequently in gardens, allotments and cracks in pavements than in arable fields. When being weeded it gives off a lovely fresh cress smell.

Swinecress
Coronopus squamatus [733] M

Common in arable fields, cart tracks and gateways, where it appears oblivious to the trampling. It seems to do especially well where nitrogen enrichment has occurred, e.g. near manure heaps.

Sea Kale
Crambe maritima [19]

Increasing on coastal shingles and sand. Gibson thought it lost to the county as it had not been recorded anywhere in Essex since 1640. Jermyn had three sites, those at Bradwell-on-Sea and Walton in the 1960s and at Great Oakley in 1971. We have not only refound it at all Jermyn's sites but also at Harwich, Colne Point and Mersea Island. There is a good colony of this plant at Landguard Point, Felixstowe, and with the development at Felixstowe Dock from the 1960s onwards, the consequent dredging required to create and maintain the berths and deep water channels for the dramatic increase in shipping, it could be that the tidal flow has altered just enough for the seeds of this plant to be swept from there onto the Essex coastline.

Flixweed
Descurainia sophia [5]

Although common in parts of Suffolk on the lighter soils, here it is nearly always a casual introduction brought in with tipped soil. It could possibly be native at Pentlow, where it was found in field edges in two 1km squares, as the soil there is very light, over a chalk outcrop.

Annual Wall Rocket or Stinkweed
Diplotaxis muralis [32] M

Scattered, generally in urban areas in dry situations. It is often found at the bottom of walls and fences or between cracks in paving stones. Despite being called **Annual Wall Rocket**, this plant can occur as a biennial or, indeed, a perennial growing from a large tap root down deep in the soil. However, its other English name of **Stinkweed** is extremely apt!

Perennial Wall Rocket
Diplotaxis tenuifolia [17] M

A plant of neglected waste areas at edges of car parks, stations and industrial sites. Except for Clacton, all the records occur in towns which have ports - Colchester, Harwich, Brightlingsea, Manningtree (Mistley) and Maldon. Some earlier records for Maldon were not refound but Maldon has redeveloped its older derelict areas into modern industrial estates during the last decade, which could account for this. Also Jermyn's record from Mistley maltings was not refound; redevelopment has been taking place here too, with several of the maltings being demolished.

Erophila conferta

Originally grown in the greenhouse at Layer Marney Tower from seed collected on the Island of Rhodes in 1934, it escaped into the garden by 1938 and persisted for many years. It was still present in 1970 but has not been seen during the 1980s.

Common Whitlow Grass
Erophila verna [80] M

Flowering in March and April this plant can be found on walls, between paving slabs, gravel paths, railway tracks and other sites where there are free draining but poor soils. The only completely natural habitat where it can be found regularly is the top of anthills on grazing marshes.

Eruca vesicaria ssp sativa [2]

Found twice in our survey - as a bird seed alien in Colchester, 1985, and, in 1987, as an arable weed when several plants were found along a field edge at Tiptree.

Treacle Mustard
Erysimum cheiranthoides [45] M

Occasional on the lighter soils on disturbed verges, allotments and corners of fields that have been missed by the sprays. It is reasonably common around Dedham village and Dedham Heath, occurring in many of the fields through this area.

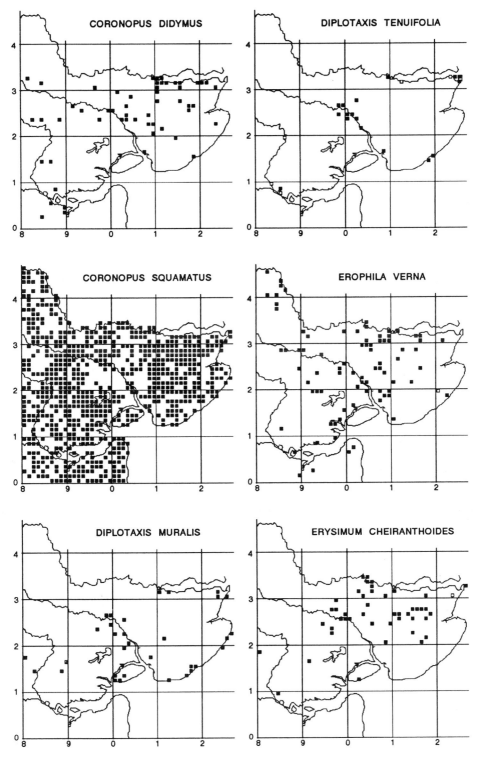

CORONOPUS DIDYMUS

DIPLOTAXIS TENUIFOLIA

CORONOPUS SQUAMATUS

EROPHILA VERNA

DIPLOTAXIS MURALIS

ERYSIMUM CHEIRANTHOIDES

Dame's Violet
Hesperis matronalis [6]
A garden escape that can establish itself by riverbanks and streamsides.

Hoary Mustard
Hirschfeldia incana [1]
Common in south and metropolitan Essex having spread quite quickly in recent years from rubbish tips in the south of the county, but it has only just found its way to our area. Our first and only record is from a tip at Great Totham, 1985. It will be interesting to follow the future spread of this plant in our area.

Wild Candytuft
Iberis amara
Never native to Essex, it was occasionally introduced in the past with seed, as it was in 1843 in cornfields near Pattiswick Church.

Garden Candytuft
Iberis umbellata
A short-lived garden casual that occurs from time to time, Jermyn had two records for it during the 1960s but we have not maintained records.

Woad
Isatis tinctoria
Once widely cultivated for the dye that could be extracted for use by the clothmakers, it is now a very rare casual - West Mersea, 1944, and Wivenhoe, 1970, are the only records. It is still grown on a small scale in north Essex to dye wool for handicraft use.

Field Pepperwort
Lepidium campestre [24] M
Scattered and occasional on the acid sand and gravel soils where it occurs on dry banks and railway tracks.

Smith's Pepperwort
Lepidium heterophyllum [8]
A rare native occurring in dry, gravelly and sandy places. It is commonest in the Roman River Valley Conservation Zone on the gravelly plateau above the Valley but otherwise only the odd scattered site has been found.

Dittander
Lepidium latifolium [81] M
Nationally a very localised plant, **Dittander** is mostly found around the rivers and estuarine marshes of the East Anglian towns of Ipswich and Colchester, indeed it is probably at its most abundant in Britain along the Colne in the ungrazed marshes around Wivenhoe. Often referred to as 'growing on saltmarshes' we have only found one such site during our survey. Its habitat in north east Essex falls into two categories: sea walls and brackish marshes in the upper estuaries, and waste places - gravel car parks, railway stations, railway tracks and banks, builder's yards, etc. It has persisted and still flourishes along the Colne in Colchester where, due to the introduction of flood-gates downstream, the river is no longer tidal.

Narrow-leaved Pepperwort
Lepidium ruderale [47] M
Generally scattered on bare ground along sea walls, it can sometimes occur abundantly in places, especially in cracks between concrete facing slabs. Inland only scattered plants are found, mainly on disturbed soils on verges.

Garden Cress
Lepidium sativum [1]
Found as a casual introduction, relic of cultivation or bird seed alien (Colchester, 1985) but not fully recorded.

Sweet Alison
Lobularia maritima [1]
Garden escape; not fully recorded. At the site recorded, it was growing as a cornfield weed along the edge of a field.

Honesty
Lunaria annua [26] M
Another garden plant found along roadsides where it has been discarded or become naturalised from nearby gardens, as on the Roman Wall, Colchester.

One-rowed Watercress
Nasturtium microphyllum
Since the publication of Jermyn's Flora much work has been done on the identification of the different species of Watercress and their hybrid, and more

precise definitions produced. Our survey has revealed no records which comply with the updated criteria, and a question mark must be placed on the records for this species, and its hybrid with **Common Watercress**, given by Jermyn; however, further searching may reveal its presence.

Common Watercress Rorippa (Stace)
Nasturtium officinale [204] M
Common and locally plentiful, sometimes choking small ponds and watercourses. It also occurs in ditches, streams and shallow edges of slow-moving rivers. Please note it should not be picked and eaten from any of our polluted watercourses.

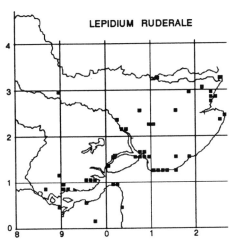

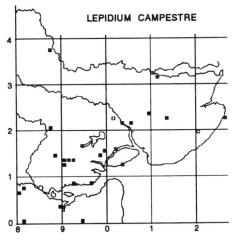

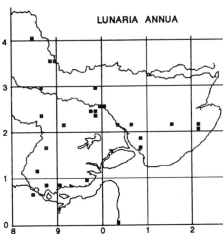

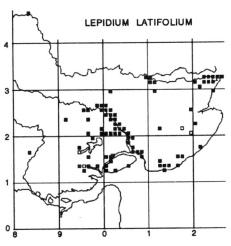

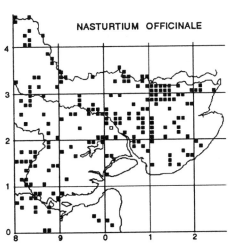

Wild Radish
Raphanus raphanistrum [364] M

Common as an arable weed along the edges of fields and in allotments on the lighter loamy and sandy soils, but avoiding the heavy clays. It occurs in yellow and mauve flowered forms but these have not been recorded separately.

Garden Radish
Raphanus sativus [1]

A relic of cultivation that turns up occasionally on roadsides, disused allotments and waste places but we did not record our sightings of this plant. Our only record is a bird seed alien (Colchester, 1985).

Bastard Cabbage
Rapistrum rugosum [3]

A casual of tips and waste places. One plant at West Mersea had germinated along the high tide mark where it had obviously been washed ashore along with the Sunflower, Tomato and Wheat growing with it.

Greater Yellowcress
Rorippa amphibia [11] M

Not refound at Jermyn's location at Langham on the Stour but it is common further downstream just above Cattawade and still occurs plentifully at Abberton Reservoir. It is perhaps worth noting that Abberton Reservoir can be fed through the water network from the Stour, as Anglian Water had to do following the long hot summer of 1989. The excess winter water on the Ouse Washes in the Fens, instead of being released into the sea, is fed through the water network into the upper reaches of the Stour and then, from the pumping stations on the lower reaches, through to Abberton. There are no historical records of this plant from the Abberton area before the reservoir was built (although that does not mean that it did not occur there) and it is interesting to ponder whether Greater Yellow Cress arrived in the reservoir via the water network. If it did, what will turn up after the major pumping operations of the winter of 1989? The only other site for this plant is in the reservoir on Quietwaters Golf Course - close enough to Abberton for the seeds to have arrived with the wildfowl that frequent both sites.

Marsh Yellowcress
Rorippa palustris [22] M

Commonest at Abberton Reservoir, growing in between the concrete slabs, at Ardleigh Reservoir and in places along the Stour. Other scattered records are from the damp muddy edges of streams and ponds, poached by grazing stock, where it seems to like growing in the squelchy hoofprints.

Creeping Yellowcress
Rorippa sylvestris [26] M

Although very common in the south of the county, here it is scattered and found generally in urban sites, such as gardens, parks and nurseries.

White Mustard
Sinapis alba [15]

Odd scattered plants have been found on disturbed road verges probably as an escape from cultivation - the seeds of this plant are used to make mustard.

Charlock
Sinapis arvensis [602] M

Common, widely distributed, occurring on any bare soil, often in abundance.

Tall Rocket
Sisymbrium altissimum [5]

A casual introduction with tipped soil. The only stable site is around Harwich where it grows by walls, fences and on any rough piece of land, including the newly reclaimed land by Bath Side.

Hedge Mustard
Sisymbrium officinale [1024] M

Common over the whole area, on arable land, gardens, roadsides, hedgebanks and car parks; the only habitats where it cannot be found are the saltmarshes around Walton and the grazing marshes at Langenhoe and Old Hall. It is also a little less abundant on the lighter chalk soils. Jermyn gives four records for *var leiocarpum* but we have not recorded its varieties during our survey.

Eastern Rocket
Sisymbrium orientale [8]

An introduction of urban waste places that, according to Jermyn, had "considerably extended its range in the past decade and

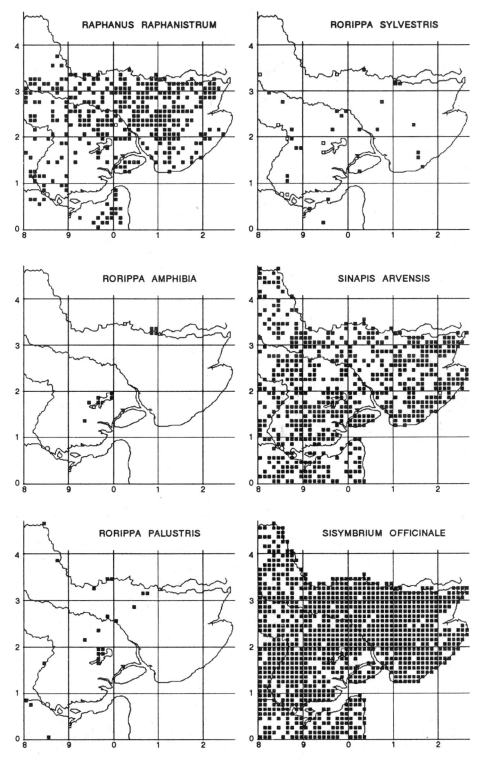

is still increasing". He had recorded it in nine 10km squares. We have found it in six squares in only four areas; Colchester, Manningtree/Mistley, Harwich and Maylandsea on the Blackwater. All are associated with boats, either large or small, but whether this is relevant to the distribution of this plant is not known.

Shepherd's Cress
Teesdalia nudicaulis
A plant of light sandy soils often occurring around rabbit burrows in Suffolk. Gibson notes it from Langham and Wivenhoe Parsonage but there have been no records in modern times.

Garlic Pennycress
Thlaspi alliaceum [2]
An introduction which has a stable population near Beeleigh Abbey on the Blackwater. It has been known from here since 1950 and was refound during our survey.

Field Pennycress
Thlaspi arvense [348] M
Common on field edges, allotments, vegetable plots, gardens, and other disturbed ground on the free draining sands, gravels and brick-earth soils. Where it appears to occur on the boulder clays its distribution actually correlates with the valley gravels which run through the area. It also avoids the London Clay.

MIGNONETTE FAMILY
RESEDACEAE

Wild Mignonette
Reseda lutea [25] M
On the chalky boulder clay, it is probably native, occurring on suitable dry grassy banks and verges. Elsewhere, however, it is probably introduced except in the Harwich area where it commonly occurs on railway tracks and dry gravelly places.

Weld
Reseda luteola [242] M
Reasonably frequent on disturbed soil on grassy verges, sea walls, car parks and railway tracks.

Garden Mignonette
Reseda odorata
An uncommon casual of garden origin. Jermyn had recorded it only once, in Colchester, and whilst we have not found any sites during our survey, one was found in Colchester in 1978, which was lost to development the following year.

VIOLET FAMILY
VIOLACEAE

Field Pansy
Viola arvensis [581] M
Common in arable fields, particularly on free draining soils, where it is one of the few plants that survives the chemical sprays used by farmers. Very variable in size and flower colour.

Heath Dog Violet
Viola canina
Never common in our area, occurring only on heathy places. Both Gibson and Jermyn knew it from Tiptree Heath, Gibson from Blackheath, Colchester, and Jermyn from Fordham Heath. It has not been refound at any of these sites.

Viola flavicornis
Once reported from short turf in Markshall Deer Park, 1938.

Hairy Violet
Viola hirta [10] M
Grassy banks, verges and hedgerows on the chalky boulder clay are its native habitat; other sites are introductions, generally arising from garden escapes. Gibson states that it was plentiful in his time near Burton's Green, but our nearest locality is several kilometres from there. However, we have found it north of Witham, which relates quite well to his Rivenhall site. Jermyn's locality at Wrabness was not refound.

Sweet Violet
Viola odorata [108] M
Commoner on the chalky boulder clay with many other scattered records from escaped garden plants. Hedge banks, dry verges and churchyards are its usual habitats.

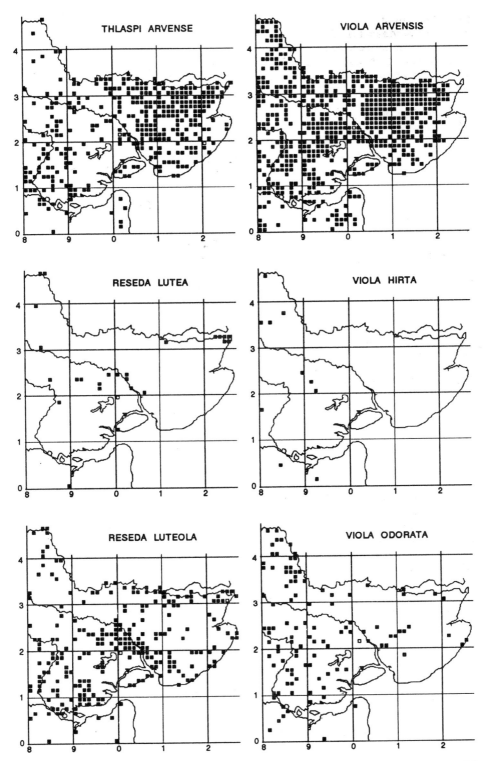

Early Dog Violet
Viola reichenbachiana [38] M

Fairly frequent on calcareous soils in suitable habitats such as woods, coppices, shady hedgerows and banks, very occasional elsewhere.

Common Dog Violet
Viola riviniana [123] M

More common than the last species. Whilst occurring in much the same habitat, it is able to tolerate a wider range of soil types, although still avoiding the heavy London Clay and the coastal belt generally.

Heartsease or Wild Pansy
Viola tricolor

We have not found this species during our survey and there are no Essex specimens in the herbarium of the Colchester Natural History Museum. There has either been a marked decline in this species or it has been incorrectly recorded in the past. Of the two possible recent reports one referred to a plant seen on a road verge, which was probably a garden variety, and one from a lettuce field which appeared to be a hybrid between **Field Pansy** and a garden Pansy.

MILKWORT FAMILY
POLYGALACEAE

Heath Milkwort
Polygala serpyllifolia [6] M

Uncommon due to the lack of suitable habitat, grassy places on free draining sandy heaths. It is now found only in the Roman River Valley Conservation Zone and on Tiptree Heath. We were unable to refind it on Layer Breton or Fordham Heaths.

Common Milkwort
Polygala vulgaris

In the past there has been much confusion between this and the last species. An examination of the herbarium in Colchester Natural History Museum revealed that the older specimens had been misidentified. This, plus our inability to find **Common Milkwort**, despite careful searching, leads us to believe that this species does not, and possibly never has, occurred in north east Essex.

ST JOHN'S WORT FAMILY
HYPERICACEAE

Tutsan
Hypericum androsaemum [4]

In Gibson's time **Tutsan** appeared to be a native plant occurring in several places in our area, but, by this century, it had become a casual occurring only as a garden escape.

Rose of Sharon
Hypericum calycinum [2]

Planted on banks near houses, in parks and shrubberies from which it escapes and becomes naturalised. Not fully recorded.

Hairy St John's Wort
Hypericum hirsutum [104] M

Fairly common on the soils with a chalky influence occurring on verges, grassy banks, hedgerows and railway banks. Scattered in smaller quantity on other soils.

Trailing St John's Wort
Hypericum humifusum [37] M

Found in short turf on heathy, sandy areas or in gravel pits, it is common in the Roman River Valley Conservation Zone but scattered elsewhere. At Oliver's Orchard in the Roman River Valley it grows under the fruit trees and seems to survive the spraying, its deep tap root sending up new shoots to replace those decimated by the chemicals.

Imperforate St John's Wort
Hypericum maculatum

None of Jermyn's sites have been refound. We can trace no mention of this plant occurring in north east Essex prior to Jermyn and are wondering whether this could have been a case of mistaken identification. Forms of **Common St John's Wort** with only a few translucent glands in the leaves have been found.

Common St John's Wort
Hypericum perforatum [599] M

Common and widespread, preferring the better drained soils, where it grows on grassy verges and banks, at the top of ditchbanks and rough grassland generally.

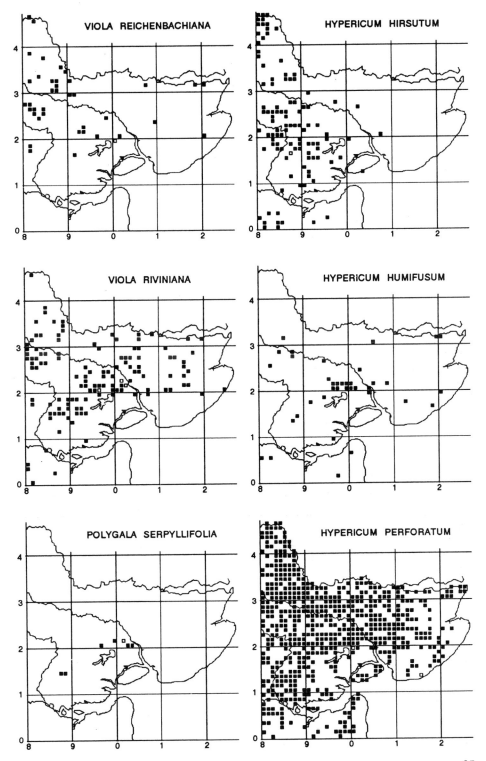

VIOLA REICHENBACHIANA

HYPERICUM HIRSUTUM

VIOLA RIVINIANA

HYPERICUM HUMIFUSUM

POLYGALA SERPYLLIFOLIA

HYPERICUM PERFORATUM

85

It will tolerate the boulder clays but is noticeably absent on the heavy acid clays.

Slender St John's Wort
Hypericum pulchrum [27] M
Its liking for dry sandy and gravelly soils is demonstrated by its distribution which follows the Tiptree Ridge which appears to have once been the site of a bank of the River Thames before it took its present course. Many of Jermyn's sites on smaller areas of suitable soils have not been refound - these may very well have been brought under the plough today.

Square-stemmed St John's Wort
Hypericum tetrapterum [74] M
Fairly scattered but always by water, either river, stream or wet ditchsides.

ROCKROSE FAMILY
CISTACEAE

Common Rockrose
Helianthemum nummularium [1]
A plant associated with chalk soils of the north west of the county, it had not previously been recorded for our area until found in 1988 in the 'chalkiest' area in the north east near Pentlow where six plants were found growing on a roadside verge.

TAMARISK FAMILY
TAMARICACEAE

Tamarisk
Tamarix gallica [51] M
Frequently planted near the sea and well established between Jaywick and Walton and at Dovercourt and Brightlingsea, scattered elsewhere.

SEA HEATH FAMILY
FRANKENIACEAE

Sea Heath
Frankenia laevis [2]
Very rare, now only occurring on sandy and shingly mud in the higher zone saltings at Colne Point Nature Reserve. First found in Essex in 1677 by John Ray at marshes at Thorrington, it was subsequently found "in

maritime places, near the bridge between Marnwood and Mersea Island", 1732, and by the Rev W L P Garnons at Wivenhoe in 1825. It was found at Walton by different botanists c1855, 1864 and lastly in 1896. It has possibly been known from Colne Point since c1910, the location at that time being given as "between Clacton and Brightlingsea"! However, its presence was confirmed there in 1951. Other sightings of this plant have been recorded from Bradwell-on-Sea in 1932, Brightlingsea in 1953 and Thorrington Marshes c1955. We consider this latter record could be a mistake as there is no longer any suitable habitat in this area and has not been for a very long time.

PINK FAMILY
CARYOPHYLLACEAE

Corn Cockle
Agrostemma githago [2]
So common in cornfields throughout the county in Gibson's time that localities were apparently too numerous to quote. Jermyn mentions that it had been recorded from a few localities in the early part of this century in other parts of Essex, but considered it probably extinct. We have found one site where **Corn Cockle** has been introduced. **Corn Cockle** is a common component of wild seed mixes now available at local nurseries, but it should be pointed out that these should only be grown in gardens and not released into the wild. Whilst well-intentioned, some introductions can cause havoc, upsetting the delicate balance of the native plants (see *Crassula helmsii*).

Slender Thyme-leaved Sandwort
Arenaria leptoclados [82] M
Scattered and well distributed, growing on bare dry walls, between paving and concrete slabs, gravel drives, or other such places where there is a minimum of soil. It can occasionally be found on coastal sand. We have found this species to be more common than the next, which is the opposite of Jermyn, although he does mention that there may have been some confusion between the species.

Thyme-leaved Sandwort
Arenaria serpyllifolia [40] M
This Sandwort prefers the shady side of
the wall, often growing out of a moss
carpet, where there is a little more mois-
ture. It can also be found along the edges
of arable fields and in the gravel edges of
country lanes, kept moist by road run-off.

Field Mouse-ear
Cerastium arvense
Generally associated with light chalky soils
in other areas, this plant would always
have been rare in north east Essex, and
Jermyn gave only two sites, that of Berechurch Common and Lawford Hall. Both
these localities have been searched

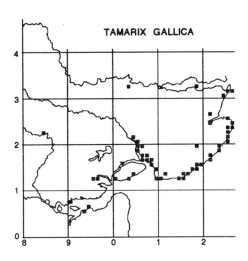

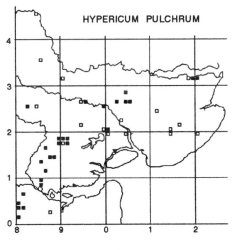

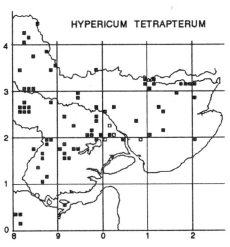

thoroughly but to no avail.

Dark Green Mouse-ear
Cerastium diffusum [8]
Always uncommon, it has declined. Jermyn listed fifteen sites, all coastal except one, ranging from Bradwell-on-Sea to Harwich. We have found it at only four localities, all of which were given by Jermyn. All the refound sites were coastal (West and East Mersea, Colne Point, St Osyth Beach area and Holland-on-Sea) in short turf on light sandy soil.

Common Mouse-ear
Cerastium fontanum
ssp glabrescens [917] M
Very common and widespread in rough grassland, verges, lawns (where it withstands mowing by growing prostrate), and bare ground.

Sticky Mouse-ear
Cerastium glomeratum [258] M
Less common than the last species, preferring the sandy, gravelly drier areas such as gravel pits, tracks and banks. It often travels with tipped gravel.

Little Mouse-ear
Cerastium semidecandrum [9] M
A tiny plant that flowers early in the season and which is usually only found when the recorder is on hands and knees. Jermyn gave thirteen 10km square records although he considered it uncommon. We have found it in only six 10km squares, a decrease of more than 50%. Whilst some sites could well have been missed, we do not feel that this would account for this level of decrease. It requires very dry sandy banks or very short, rabbit grazed, sandy coastal turf.

Snow-in-Summer
Cerastium tomentosum [8]
A garden escape that becomes naturalised on banks and waste places. There are two closely related gardens species *C tomentosum* and *C biebersteinii*, but we have not differentiated between them in our records.

Deptford Pink
Dianthus armeria
Gibson gave 26 records for the whole of Essex (6 for the north east) but by the 1970s only one remained (in the south of the county). We have not found any sites for this plant despite the intensive coverage.

Maiden Pink
Dianthus deltoides
Native in other parts of Britain but only a rare casual of garden origin in this area. Gibson had one record and Jermyn three (all in the 1960s). No sites have been found during our survey.

Sea Sandwort
Honkenya peploides [31] M
Locally plentiful on sand and shingle in the coastal areas. It has disappeared from the upper estuarine areas since Jermyn's time, no longer occurring on the upper reaches of the Blackwater or Stour, which correlates with losses for other plants requiring the same habitat e.g. **Yellow Horned Poppy.**

Lychnis coronaria [1]
A garden escape that turns up from time to time on waste and tipped areas by roadsides. Not fully recorded.

Ragged Robin
Lychnis flos-cuculi [38] M
A plant of wet flushes in damp grassland, most frequent on the boulder clays. Common and generally distributed in Victorian times and still frequent according to Jermyn, it is now uncommon; the decline due to loss of suitable habitat with the draining and/or ploughing of the meadows and wet marshy areas.

Fine-leaved Sandwort
Minuartia hybrida
Only once recorded for our area, in a rough gravelly field near Ramsey Fleet (TL 90) in 1947, the site being subsequently destroyed by the 1953 floods.

Three-nerved Sandwort
Moehringia trinervia [170] M
Common and locally plentiful in long established copses and woods, where it

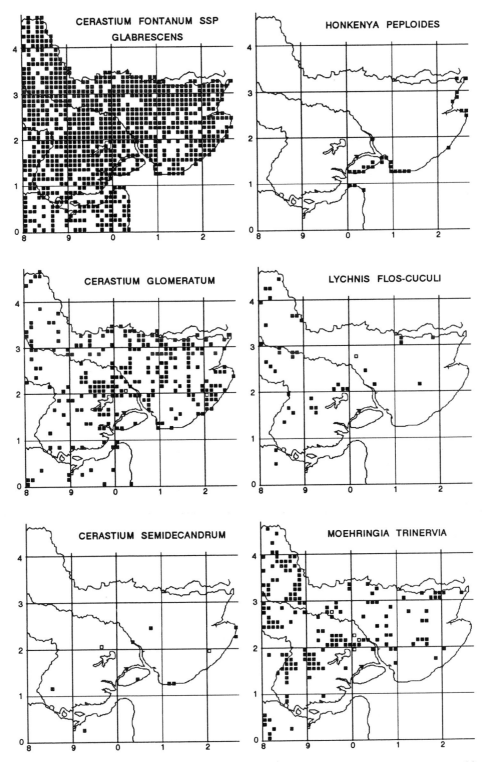

CERASTIUM FONTANUM SSP GLABRESCENS

HONKENYA PEPLOIDES

CERASTIUM GLOMERATUM

LYCHNIS FLOS-CUCULI

CERASTIUM SEMIDECANDRUM

MOEHRINGIA TRINERVIA

89

often grows through leaf litter in deep shade.

Upright Chickweed
Moenchia erecta [6] M
Now very rare. Not refound at any of Gibson's or Jermyn's sites, we have found it at four others, all on old traditional grazing marshes. At Langenhoe Marshes it occurs on the dry banks of the Victorian sea walls, which are now part of the grazing marsh itself, as it does at Old Hall where it also, like the site at Brightlingsea Marshes, is found on the top of the large ant hills which dot the former marsh. The fourth site at Alresford near Plumpton's Farm, found in 1981, has since been ploughed.

Water Chickweed
Myosoton aquaticum [58] M
Common along the freshwater parts of the Stour and Blackwater and in the Roman River Valley, but very occasional elsewhere. Lost now from the Tendring Hundred where Jermyn found it well distributed and locally common. Its typical habitat is wet and marshy places by rivers and streams, including **Poplar** and **Cricket-bat Willow** plantations.

Four-leaved Allseed
Polycarpon tetraphyllum
This once turned up in a greenhouse at Layer Marney Tower, but we have not come across it during the survey.

Fringed Pearlwort
Sagina apetala ssp apetala [88] M
Annual Pearlwort
Sagina apetala ssp erecta [56] M
Both subspecies occur in similar habitats on walls, between paving and concrete slabs, around manhole covers, and dry gravelly paths. **Fringed Pearlwort** appears to be the more common of the two but it is interesting to note that there are very few 1km squares where both subspecies occur. This possibly indicates that, once one subspecies had been found, we have perhaps not examined enough further specimens to establish if the other subspecies also occurred.

Sea Pearlwort
Sagina maritima [4]
Very rare. All Jermyn's records were on coastal sands, at Ramsey (TL 90), Colne Point, Lee-over-Sands and Walton. The only site we have refound is that at Colne Point, which was the latest of his records (1968). Additionally it has been found at Brightlingsea on two sites, one growing in very short coastal turf, the other between the cracks of the concrete sea wall, and at Dovercourt it was found growing at the bottom of a hedge by the putting green!

Knotted Pearlwort
Sagina nodosa
Jermyn had one record which he thought might be an introduction, Lawford Hall, 1951.

Procumbent Pearlwort
Sagina procumbens [381] M
Common, widespread and generally urban in its distribution, growing in lawns, paths, cracks in concrete, pavements and on old walls.

Soapwort
Saponaria officinalis [26] M
Naturalised on road verges where it can persist for many years. Both single and double-flowered forms can be found, the latter indicating its garden origin.

Annual Knawel
Scleranthus annuus [34] M
No longer common, it occurs on arable

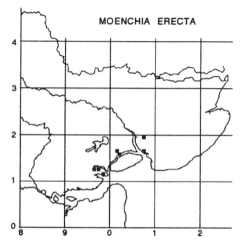

MOENCHIA ERECTA

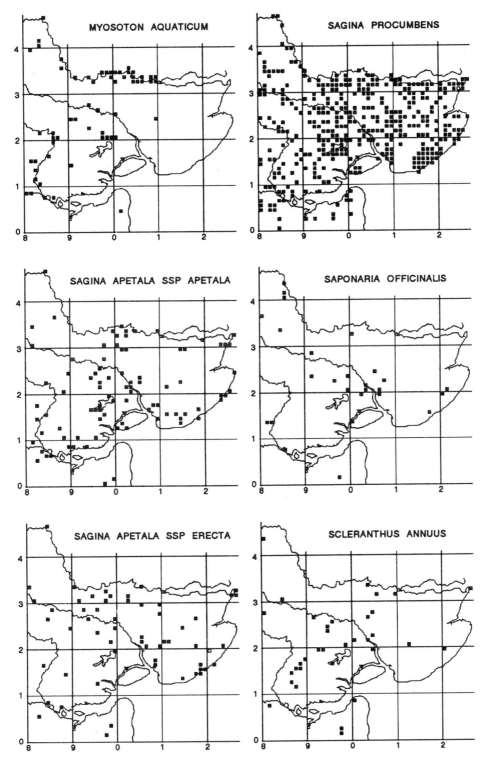

91

fields on sandy, gravelly and other free draining soils. It was found once growing on a gravel drive.

White Campion
Silene alba [698] M
Common along field borders, and verges on the free draining soils, the map clearly indicates its dislike of the heavy clays.

Silene alba X dioica [237] M
Probably under-recorded, this hybrid will occur wherever both parents grow in close proximity.

Sweet William
Silene armeria
A garden escape even in Victorian times, when it was recorded between Colchester and Berechurch. Neither Jermyn nor ourselves have maintained records.

Red Campion
Silene dioica [640] M
Very common over most of the area in woodland rides, glades and edges, hedgerows and ditchbanks. However, it is very scarce on the Dengie peninsula and in a swathe round the coast from Tollesbury to Dovercourt, but whether this is due to the proximity of the coast, or the lack of woodland cannot be determined.

Small-flowered Catchfly
Silene gallica
Gibson considered it very local in sandy and gravelly fields, giving eight sites, the bulk of them being either in the Colchester area or around Manningtree, with the exception of one record at Grinstead [Greenstead?] Green, near Halstead. It was subsequently found at Hythe Quay in 1913 but this would have been a casual occurrence. Jermyn had found it only once, at Wrabness on a railway bank in 1961. We have not found it during our survey.

Sea Campion
Silene maritima [15] M
Local on shingle spits and beaches. Many of the other sand and shingle sea shore species have been lost from the upper reaches of the Blackwater but this is not the case with **Sea Campion**. However, its only other sites are East Mersea and the Colne Point area.

Night-flowering Catchfly
Silene noctiflora [3]
We have found just two sites covering three 1km squares, all in arable fields on a light chalky soil. One site contained about six plants growing with **Shepherd's Needle** at the edge of a **Sugar Beet** field, whilst the other was just a single plant at the edge of a ploughed field. Gibson gave no records for the north east of the county considering it 'rather local' for the whole of Essex (it is commoner on the chalks of north west Essex). Jermyn, however, listed ten 10km squares, so, like many arable weeds, the **Night-flowering Catchfly** has declined drastically in the last twenty years.

Bladder Campion
Silene vulgaris [46] M
Common on banks and verges on the chalk in the very north west of our area, it is only a casual introduction or garden escape elsewhere. Several of the sites where it has been found have been infill sites, the tipped soil presumably coming from a chalk area. It is occasionally found on the sea shore on old shell banks where the calcium in the shells provides the alkaline soil that it requires.

Corn Spurrey
Spergula arvensis [71] M
Gradually declining, we have found it in only twelve 10km squares compared to Jermyn's eighteen. It grows in the edges of fields where the sprays have missed, on free draining soils avoiding all clays.

Spergularia bocconii
Recorded as a casual from Hythe Quay, Colchester, c1920 and 1938-40.

Lesser Sea Spurrey
Spergularia marina [162] M
A plant of the higher saltmarsh, which, in our area, is often foreshortened by the sea walls. Common on the inland side of sea walls where there is some seepage through the walls making the soil slightly brackish, sometimes carpeting the ground between the wall and the borrow dyke. It has also been found by the side of Mersea Road,

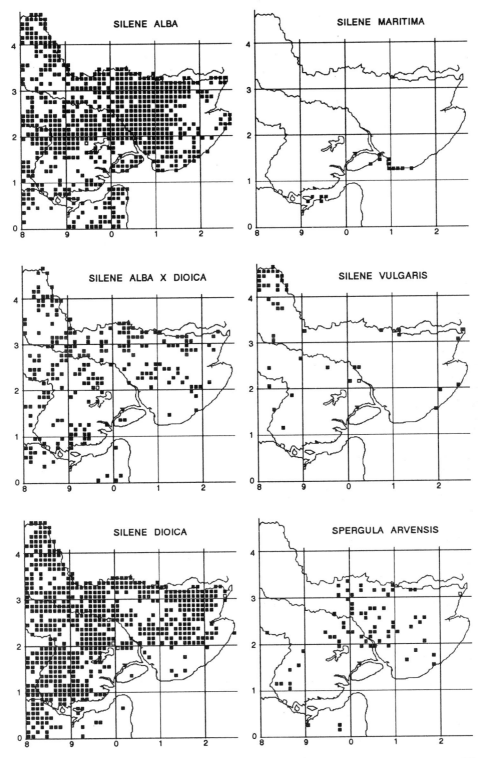

SILENE ALBA

SILENE MARITIMA

SILENE ALBA X DIOICA

SILENE VULGARIS

SILENE DIOICA

SPERGULA ARVENSIS

Colchester, where the seed had been transported by vehicles. The other inland site at Abberton Reservoir could well have arisen from bird droppings, possibly of Wigeon, which graze saltmarsh turf and grasses.

Greater Sea Spurrey
Spergularia media [160] M
Not quite as widespread as the previous species, preferring the saltmarsh itself, where it is still a common plant.

Sand Spurrey
Spergularia rubra [108] M
Reasonably frequent on sandy tracks and in gravel pits as well as some coastal sites where the soil is suitable, such as the north bank of the Blackwater (the sea wall has been capped with gravel). It can be found in most places where sand and gravel have been tipped to create or maintain a track indicating that it probably moves from site to site with the ballast.

Bog Stitchwort
Stellaria alsine [62] M
Occasionally met with in wet woodland rides, its star-like flowers peeping out of the damp grass. Jermyn considered it "common in marshy places, water meadows, wet flushes, by rivers and streams" but this habitat has been very much reduced due to drainage and changes in land use. Whilst it still occurs in these habitats the map clearly shows that it is commonest in the Markshall complex of woods and the Roman River Valley Conservation Zone, both areas where there has been little change to the habitat since Jermyn's recording.

Lesser Stitchwort
Stellaria graminea [334] M
Common and well distributed in old grassland, remnants of which are found most frequently nowadays in churchyards.

Greater Stitchwort
Stellaria holostea [763] M
Very common in most hedgerows, banks, woodland edges and verges. It does, however, avoid the coastal belt and much of the Dengie peninsula.

Common Chickweed
Stellaria media [1127] M
Abundant on any bare and disturbed soil in fields, verges and, most commonly, gardens.

Greater Chickweed
Stellaria media ssp neglecta
Recorded from two fields near Halstead and at Kelvedon in Victorian times, and only found since at Alphamstone in 1913 by G C Brown.

Lesser Chickweed
Stellaria media ssp pallida [8]
Rare but possibly overlooked. All our records come from dry banks on light soils.

Cow Basil
Vaccaria pyramidata [1]
An unusual bird seed alien that occurred in 1980 at Colchester.

PURSLANE FAMILY
PORTULACACEAE

Blinks
Montia fontana
    ssp chondrosperma [15]
Uncommon and once apparently more widespread than it is now, although it is possibly overlooked (a predominance of records around Colchester could be due to the suitable habitat, or the intensity of surveying near our home base). It occurs

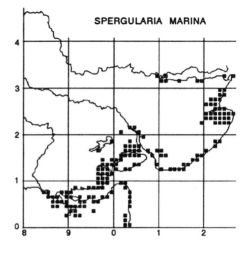

SPERGULARIA MARINA

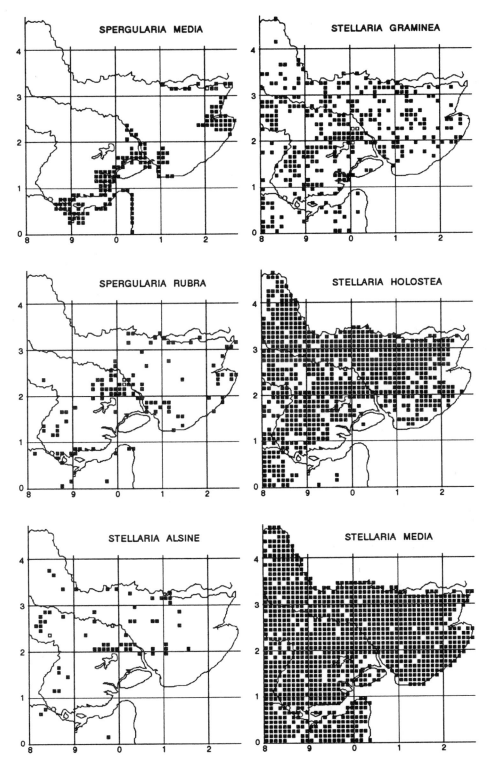

SPERGULARIA MEDIA

STELLARIA GRAMINEA

SPERGULARIA RUBRA

STELLARIA HOLOSTEA

STELLARIA ALSINE

STELLARIA MEDIA

where water lies on closely packed gravel soils.

Spring Beauty
Montia perfoliata [53] M
Introduced as a garden plant by Victorians, this is now part of our flora, being well established on light sandy soils in hedgerows, banks and along footpaths. The distribution clearly shows its garden origins with the clusters of records around Colchester, Brightlingsea, Sudbury and Dedham-Manningtree.

Pink Purslane
Montia sibirica
Introduced but rare as a garden escape. Jermyn recorded it once in 1967 at Lexden Heath.

AIZOACEAE

Hottentot Fig
Carpobrotus edulis
An introduction that became naturalised on shingle at Walton but was killed off by the severe frosts during the winter of 1970/71. (Preston & Sell, *Watsonia* **17.3**, (1989), query the identity of this plant as *C glaucescens* is found in Suffolk).

AMARANTH FAMILY
AMARANTHACEAE

White Amaranth
Amaranthus albus [1]
A casual recorded only once from the rubbish tip at Maldon. Gibson had a record of *A blitum* from Elmstead Market (pre-1849) which is probably this species.

Amaranthus bouchonii
A casual recorded by Jermyn from an arable field at Bradfield.

Green Amaranth
Amaranthus hybridus [2]
The only previous record for our area was in 1960 at Ardleigh, but it was found twice within a week in 1989. The first was by a manure heap adjacent to a derelict pig farm and the second site was on a farm track near to some pheasant rearing pens. It is possible that the long hot summer of

1989 encouraged the seed to germinate.

Common Amaranth
Amaranthus retroflexus [3]
Jermyn had recorded this at Hythe Quay on one occasion and it was subsequently recorded from Bradfield (1959), Ardleigh (1960), where it was growing with *A hybridus*, and at the Old Cattle Market, Middleborough, Colchester, (1978). During the survey it was found at Fingringhoe Mill (1983) originating from the seeds handled at the' mill, Colchester from bird seed (1986), and lastly at Maldon rubbish tip (1989).

GOOSEFOOT FAMILY
CHENOPODIACEAE

Babington's Orache
Atriplex glabriuscula [19]
Its range has contracted since Jermyn's time and its stronghold is now the confluence of the Colne and Blackwater and Mersea Island. It prefers growing on the driftline on sandy beaches.

Garden Orache
Atriplex hortensis [2]
A garden escape found occasionally.

Frosted Orache
Atriplex laciniata [32] M
Found on most of our sandy beaches, it grows along the driftline where organic matter has been deposited by the high tides.

Grass-leaved Orache
Atriplex littoralis [219] M
A plant of the upper saltmarshes frequently found at the bottom of the seaward side of the sea wall. It also travels inland carried by vehicles and can be seen occasionally on bare road verges which are subject to salting in the winter. Very rarely it has been found as an arable weed growing with other members of this family.

Common Orache
Atriplex patula [624] M
Common and well distributed occurring in arable fields, gardens and disturbed ground on verges.

Spear-leaved Orache
Atriplex prostrata [540] M

Very common near the coast. It is a natural component of the upper saltmarsh turf and is frequently found at the base of the sea walls where its leaves occasionally take on a purplish hue. It is also common on disturbed ground, bare patches on road verges and edges of arable fields.

Axyris amaranthoides

A casual that was once recorded from the Hythe Quay, Colchester in 1927 when the cargo and cargo handling methods were very different from today. The grain in those days also contained many more impurities.

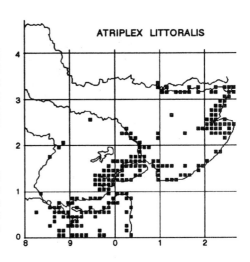

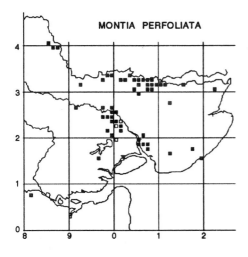

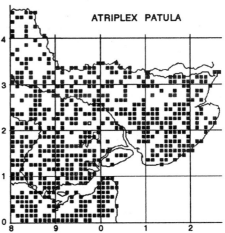

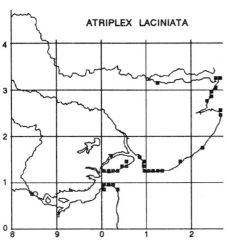

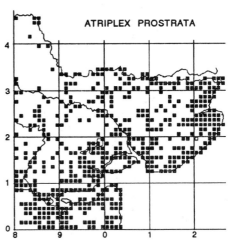

Sea Beet
Beta vulgaris ssp maritima [231] M
Common on the seaward side and the top of sea walls, as well as the sea cliffs from Clacton to Walton. It is capable of growing in the cracks between concrete blocks when the sea wall has been faced with these.

Sugar Beet
Beta vulgaris ssp vulgaris [2]
Not fully recorded as it is such a common crop in our area and the majority of sightings are from obviously dropped beet which have re-rooted.

Fat Hen
Chenopodium album [938] M
Very common on almost any bare soil as in gardens, arable fields, and allotments. The only habitat where it seems to be absent is old grazing marshes as at Langenhoe and Old Hall.

Good King Henry
Chenopodium bonus-henricus [4]
Once grown as a kitchen crop, it was frequent and widespread, although seldom in quantity, according to Jermyn. Prior to our survey it was found at Maldon (1955), St Osyth (1976) and Witham (1979). Our survey revealed only four sites, all adjacent to farm yards.

Small Red Goosefoot
Chenopodium botryodes
Always rare, we have not been able to find any sites for this plant during our survey. Both Gibson and Jermyn had records for Mersea Island, and Jermyn had also found it on the Blackwater at Stangate, Mayland Creek and Tollesbury Wick Marshes.

Fig-leaved Goosefoot
Chenopodium ficifolium [55] M
Scattered, but not uncommon, it can be found on disturbed soil on verges, tipped soil heaps and, frequently, on manure heaps.

Oak-leaved Goosefoot
Chenopodium glaucum
Rare according to both Gibson and Jermyn; recorded in Victorian times at West Mersea and Kirby and in 1972 in a beet field at Witham. We have no records for this plant.

Maple-leaved Goosefoot
Chenopodium hybridum [9]
Occasional, usually introduced with seed but also on rough waste ground.

Nettle-leaved Goosefoot
Chenopodium murale [1]
A casual of rubbish tips and waste places it was apparently more common in the last century. Jermyn had recorded it twice; in the kitchen garden of Layer Marney Tower (1945), and Maldon tip (1968). We have found it once at Great Totham Pits (1983).

Grey Goosefoot
Chenopodium opulifolium
Recorded once from Colchester in 1937.

Many-seeded Goosefoot
Chenopodium polyspermum [338] M
Widely distributed, it can be locally common in beet fields, allotments, strawberry fields, market gardens and pick-your-own places.

Chenopodium pratericola
Recorded from waste ground at Salcott (1956) and Manningtree tip (1973) but not found during our survey.

Quinoa
Chenopodium quinoa [1]
A recent introduction, being grown on farms to provide food for game birds. It will be interesting to see if this Goosefoot becomes part of our flora.

Red Goosefoot
Chenopodium rubrum [215] M
To coin (and adulterate) a well-known phrase - "where there's muck there's **Red Goosefoot**". This plant can be found anywhere where there is a muck heap, or highly enriched disturbed ground such as farmyards or heavily poached gateways to cattle fields.

Chenopodium rubrum
var pseudo-botryodes [1]
Jermyn found this variety in the wet mud of dykes in drained estuarine marshes at Tollesbury, Manningtree-Lawford and

Parkeston areas. We have only one confirmed identification from the edge of a dried up pond on Horsey Island, 1989.

Chenopodium suecicum
A casual of waste places that was found at Hythe Quay, Colchester, in 1930. There have been no further records.

Upright Goosefoot
Chenopodium urbicum
Another casual, **Upright Goosefoot** was recorded by Gibson at Messing and Layer Marney, but there have been no records this century.

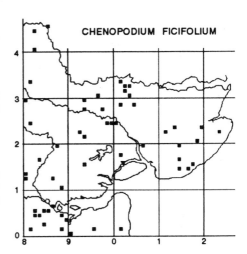
CHENOPODIUM FICIFOLIUM

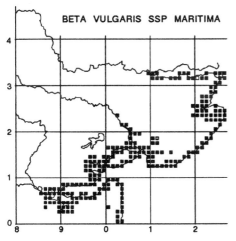
BETA VULGARIS SSP MARITIMA

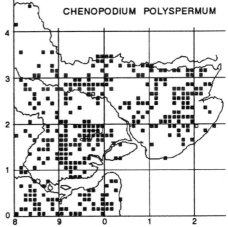
CHENOPODIUM POLYSPERMUM

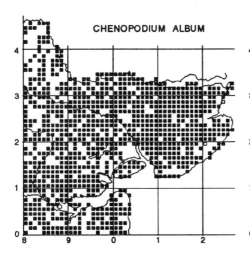
CHENOPODIUM ALBUM

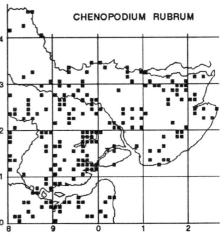
CHENOPODIUM RUBRUM

Stinking Goosefoot
Chenopodium vulvaria
A plant that lives up to its name (it has an atrocious smell), but which has not been noted in north east Essex since 1920. It appears not to have been uncommon in Gibson's time as he gives five sites - Maldon; allotment fields Kelvedon; Feering, by the side of garden paths; Messing; under a wall at Harwich - it was last seen here in 1891.

Sea Purslane
Halimione portulacoides [213] M
Common on saltmarshes and also on the cliffs at Clacton and Frinton. It prefers the middle to upper zone of the saltmarsh and can be found along the top of the creek edges and at the bottom of the sea walls. It disappears from a marsh when this is grazed.

Burning Bush
Kochia scoparia [1]
Jermyn's comment remains unchanged "Formerly much grown in gardens and found as an outcast on rubbish tips". Our only record for this plant is Maldon rubbish tip, 1989.

Glassworts - Salicornia
A group of plants that grow along our coasts and on the bare mud of the saltmarshes that have been causing botanists identification problems for many years. In Gibson's time, only two species were recognised; the **Perennial Glasswort** was one, leaving all the annuals lumped together. By the time Jermyn was recording these annuals had been split into five species (*S dolichostachya, S europaea, S fragilis, S pusilla* and *S ramosissima*). During our survey these five were reduced to three with *dolichostachya* being combined with *fragilis, europaea* with *ramosissima*, and *pusilla* remaining distinct. Glassworts can only definitely be identified at the very end of the summer, in late September and October, and it has not been possible to cover the many miles of saltmarsh to fully record these species.

Salicornia dolichostachya [61] M
This Glasswort, with the long tapering branches, is found in the lowest zone of the saltmarsh, frequently growing on the sides of the creeks cutting through the marsh. It occurs on all our saltmarshes.

Perennial Glasswort
Salicornia perennis [87] M
The **Perennial Glasswort** requires a mature saltmarsh. It occurs on stable areas that are slightly raised from the surrounding saltings and which usually have a slightly higher content of sand at that point.

Salicornia pusilla [29] M
Restricted to mature and stable saltmarshes with a high content of sand and gravel in the mud. This Glasswort grows on the bare sandy mud, not seeming able to cope with competition. It is the most delicate of our Glassworts and disperses its seed by dropping its segments onto the bare mud so that they form a scattered ring around the parent plant.

Salicornia ramosissima [108] M
Our commonest Glasswort occurring in the short turf on the top of the marsh and also on sandy and gravelly spits. It occurs on all our saltmarshes.

Prickly Saltwort
Salsola kali ssp kali [8] M
Uncommon on sandy beaches. It has maintained its distribution reasonably well having been refound at the majority of Jermyn's sites, only the East Mersea site not being rediscovered. One plant turned up on a verge on the Mersea to Colchester road growing alongside two other seaside plants, **Sea Hard Grass** and **Lesser Sea Spurrey**.

Spinach
Spinacia oleracea
We have not maintained records for this vegetable which can occasionally be found growing on tips, waste ground and disused allotments.

Common Seablite
Suaeda maritima [195] M
Very common on all our saltmarshes, it is usually at its most abundant on the marsh closest to the sea wall. It can also be found in the borrow dykes on the inland side of the sea wall where there is seepage of

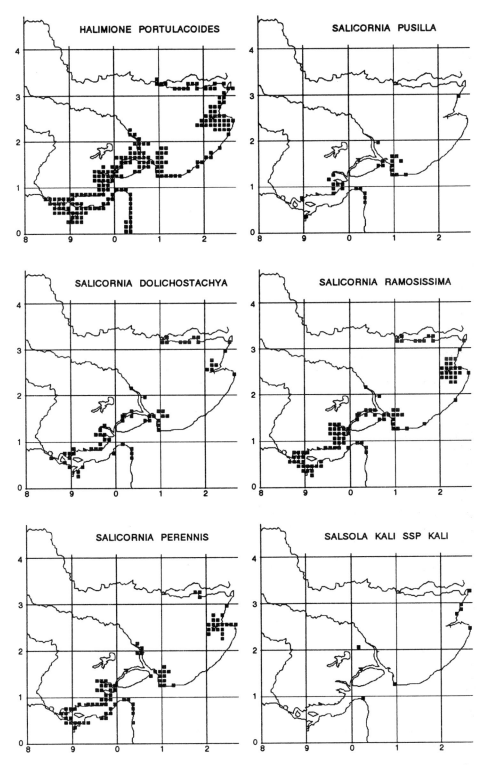

HALIMIONE PORTULACOIDES

SALICORNIA PUSILLA

SALICORNIA DOLICHOSTACHYA

SALICORNIA RAMOSISSIMA

SALICORNIA PERENNIS

SALSOLA KALI SSP KALI

101

brackish water through the wall.

Shrubby Seablite
Suaeda vera [102] M
This Mediterranean plant reaches the northern limit of its distribution in Lincolnshire, and in Britain occurs mainly around the East Anglian coast. The major British population is in Essex. It grows on the seaward side of sea walls, on the back edge of shingle spits and can cope with moving shingle where it grows up through the ridge. There are very large populations on Osea Island, at East Mersea and Colne Point.

PHYTOLACCACEAE

Phytolacca latbenis [1]
A casual, possibly spread in bird droppings. It has been present at the same site for three years. Under-recorded, as many early records of *P americana* are incorrect and should be referred either to this or the two other species of *Phytolacca* that have been found in Britain.

LIME FAMILY
TILIACEAE

Small-leaved Lime
Tilia cordata [91] M
Native and introduced with planted trees scattered over the area. Gibson stated that this tree was "abundant in woods at Halstead and truly wild". The current distribution shows that it is commonest today in the Halstead area, where it can be found in good quantity in all the old woods, and occasionally in hedges. Elsewhere, a few trees can be found in each of the ancient woodlands, such as Stour/Copperas Woods, High Woods, Pods/Layer Wood area, but it is more often found as a hedgerow tree. It is a tree that coppices well and withstands the 'annual flail' of our hedges, growing into a thick leafy shrub with large gnarled stem and branches.

Large-leaved Lime
Tilia platyphyllos [13]
Planted, it is introduced for scenic effect in parks, old gardens and churchyards. The church at Tolleshunt Knights has several fine specimens.

Common Lime
Tilia X vulgaris [263] M
Common and widespread. Planted in large gardens, parks, churchyards, along roadsides, often in the form of avenues.

MALLOW FAMILY
MALVACEAE

Abutilon theophrasti [2]
A casual that is an occasional contaminant of seed. In 1989 it was found growing in a field of Potatoes.

Hollyhock
Alcea rosea [2]
An uncommon garden escape, it is generally short-lived, but will occasionally survive for four or five years. Roadsides and waste places, near houses.

Marsh Mallow
Althaea officinalis [4]
A very rare native. It was known to Gibson from the sea walls of the Stour between Wrabness and Manningtree, and at Harwich. It was subsequently recorded in this area in 1887, and Jermyn found it in the marshes below Copperas Wood in 1971. It still occurs along the Stour from Copperas Woods to Manningtree but in very small quantity. It is at its best where the woods come right down to the saltmarsh, the Mallow growing in the high grassy marsh just in front of the overhanging trees.

Hibiscus trionum
An uncommon casual that, like *Abutilon theophrasti*, occurs as a contaminant of seed. It was found growing in a lettuce field in 1976. Seed of this plant is now available at garden centres and it will be interesting to see if it turns up with greater frequency in the future.

Tree Mallow
Lavatera arborea [16] M
Gibson gave no records for this plant in our area, indicating that all our current sites must be from introductions. Jermyn recorded it from Holland Cliffs in 1961, and coastal dunes at Little Oakley in 1970. This

latter site has not been refound, but its range now includes the cliffs and coast from Jaywick to Walton. It has also been found on the coast at Parkeston, Brightlingsea and West Mersea, and inland at Marks Tey.

Lavatera olbia [1]
Introduced on the cliffs at Frinton (1984).

Lavatera trimestris
Jermyn recorded this short-lived casual in 1967 at Mistley on Brook's seed trial grounds.

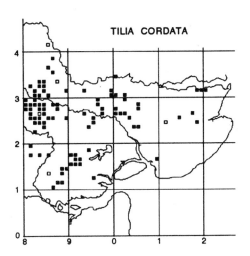

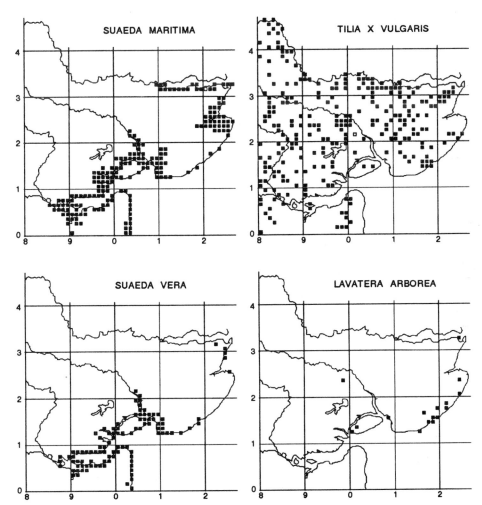

Musk Mallow
Malva moschata [69] M

Decreasing and now infrequent. It prefers a well drained site resulting either from the prevailing soil type or the slope of the land. It often grows on grassy banks, usually at or near the top. These banks are regularly subject to cutting, the rank grasses being left to mulch down, and it could be this regime which has caused the decline of this delicate, pink mallow, as it encourages the more vigorous plants and grasses with which the **Musk Mallow** cannot compete. A plant grown, under ideal conditions, in the garden of one of the authors, gave a magnificent show growing to 4 ft high, in contrast to those in the wild, which usually only manage to reach a foot in height at most.

Dwarf Mallow
Malva neglecta [153] M

Well distributed but seldom in quantity. **Dwarf Mallow** is invariably found in gateways to farmyards and around farm buildings.

Least Mallow
Malva parviflora

It was found in 1927 at Hythe Quay, Colchester, where so many other casual aliens used to occur due to the shipment of grain through the port. The only other record was by Jermyn at Aldham in 1962 as a very rare colonist of arable land.

Small Mallow
Malva pusilla [1]

A plant not known to Gibson, that occurs as an introduction on arable land and around farm buildings. Jermyn had found this Mallow on five occasions, the sites well scattered over north east Essex. It has been found only once during our survey, growing beside a barn at Foxearth in 1988.

Common Mallow
Malva sylvestris [1055] M

Very common, coping with all soil types and differing habitats, from lawns and grass verges, to disturbed soils, field edges and waste areas.

FLAX FAMILY
LINACEAE

Pale Flax
Linum bienne [1]

Previously only once recorded for north east Essex, by Rev W L P Garnons at Thorpe (1842), it was found during our survey growing in the grassland of the cliffs at Frinton. There were several plants covering an area of about 3 sq ft.

Fairy Flax
Linum catharticum [4]

Considered common by both Gibson and Jermyn, and, indeed, locally plentiful in suitable habitats by Jermyn. We have found just four sites. Its preference is for grassland on a calcareous substrate and the loss of so many old pastures must account for its decline. Two of our records are from churchyards (Bradwell and Bradwell-on-Sea) highlighting such places as being in many areas the only remaining sites where old and unimproved grassland can be found.

Cultivated Flax
Linum usitatissimum [9]

A short-lived escape from cultivation, usually occurring on disturbed road verges where the seed has been spilt. It also occurs as a bird seed alien. Once commonly grown for its fibres for linen, it disappeared from our fields for many years, but is now enjoying a come-back for the production of linseed oil.

Allseed
Radiola linoides [1]

Gibson knew this plant from Tiptree and Bergholt Heaths. The latter heath no longer exists and it was thought to have become extinct on Tiptree Heath but the disturbance of part of the heath in an attempt to make a football pitch created the right conditions for this plant to flourish again. It occurs, dependent upon the weather conditions, in varying quantities each year in damp depressions on the heath.

GERANIUM FAMILY
GERANIACEAE

Common Storksbill
Erodium cicutarium [95] M
In other parts of Britain this species often forms part of the plant community of coastal sands, but in north east Essex, other than West Mersea, it appears to be singularly missing from this habitat. Our inland records occur in old sand and gravel pits, edges of gravel paths, tracks and car parks. It also occurs on verges and banks but it does not seem to be able to compete with more vigorous plants and is usually found where the other vegetation is sparse. It has, however, occurred for a number of years in several lawns on the Riverside Estate, Colchester, rarely flowering due to the mowing. It also grows in the gaps between the kerbs on this estate. Jermyn's record of *ssp dunense* at West Mersea in 1952 is now regarded as a misidentification.

Musk Storksbill
Erodium moschatum
Not recorded since Gibson's time, when it was considered to be a garden escape; he gave one record for Dedham. This shows how the changes in garden fashions, as new species become popular and old ones are discarded, can also affect the plants that are found beyond the garden fence.

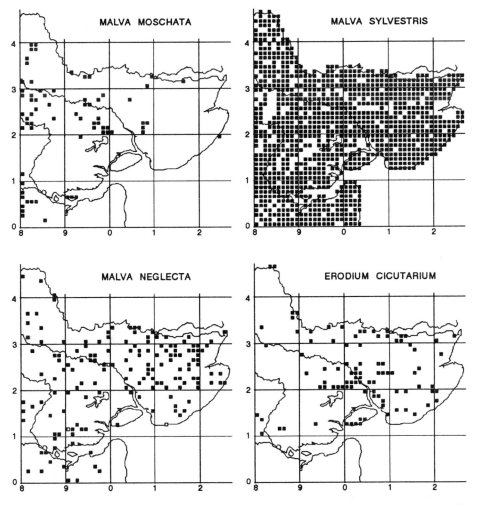

Long-stalked Cranesbill
Geranium columbinum

Gibson thought that this plant might be native in some parts of Essex but had evidently been introduced with seed at some localities. He gave four sites for north east Essex, one of which was "roadside between Halstead and Earls Colne". One of Jermyn's two records was in the same area, at Colne Engaine. We have not found it during our survey.

Cut-leaved Cranesbill
Geranium dissectum [925] M

Very common over the whole area. It shows no preference for any soil type and can occur in grassland as well as arable and bare soil habitats.

French Cranesbill
Geranium endressii [1]

A short-lived garden escape. Jermyn had recorded its occurrence at Colchester and Ardleigh (1927). We found one plant growing at the edge of a wood not far from houses in 1984, but it had disappeared by 1987.

Shining Cranesbill
Geranium lucidum [25] M

Scattered and infrequent but often persisting. The intensive coverage of the survey has revealed many more sites than given by Jermyn. Usually found in the grass at the bottom of a wall, or commonly growing against a gravestone in a churchyard, it also occurs on grassy ditchbanks, and, at one site, in the gravel at the edge of a road below a hedgerow. Generally it is not far from houses. Jermyn listed a record for Great Maplestead, where it had not been seen since 1964. It was found in 1988 in Great Maplestead churchyard.

Dovesfoot Cranesbill
Geranium molle [515] M

Very common and widespread in lawns, verges, tracksides and cultivated ground.

Dusky Cranesbill
Geranium phaeum

Introduced. Jermyn recorded it at Thorpe le Soken in 1970 where it was plentiful in a derelict garden. There are no additional records.

Meadow Cranesbill
Geranium pratense [7]

Although native elsewhere in Essex, it occurs in our area only as a garden escape.

Small-flowered Cranesbill
Geranium pusillum [81] M

Although under-recorded it is not infrequent but is usually found in small quantity. It avoids the heavier clays showing a preference for the free draining soils and gravelly valleys, where it occurs on grass verges, lawns, gardens, gateways and gravelly tracks.

Hedgerow Cranesbill
Geranium pyrenaicum [151] M

An introduced species which continues to increase. It is found on roadside verges, banks, hedgerows and churchyards.

Herb Robert
Geranium robertianum [529] M

Common in ditches, damp hedge bottoms and shady banks. Occasionally it can be found on walls, usually north-facing, as on the Roman Wall at Colchester.

Round-leaved Cranesbill
Geranium rotundifolium [1]

Not previously recorded in north east Essex, it was found on a grassy sea wall but within a year the site was over-grown with brambles. Its origin is unknown and although it did not look as though it was a result of tipping the fact that it was adjacent to a car park means this cannot be ruled out.

Bloody Cranesbill
Geranium sanguineum [1]

Another Cranesbill that had not previously been recorded for this area, it was found on a very wide grass verge which we understand had at one time been allotments.

Pencilled Cranesbill
Geranium versicolor [2]

A garden escape that can become naturalised. Jermyn's location of Hazeleigh, however, could not be refound.

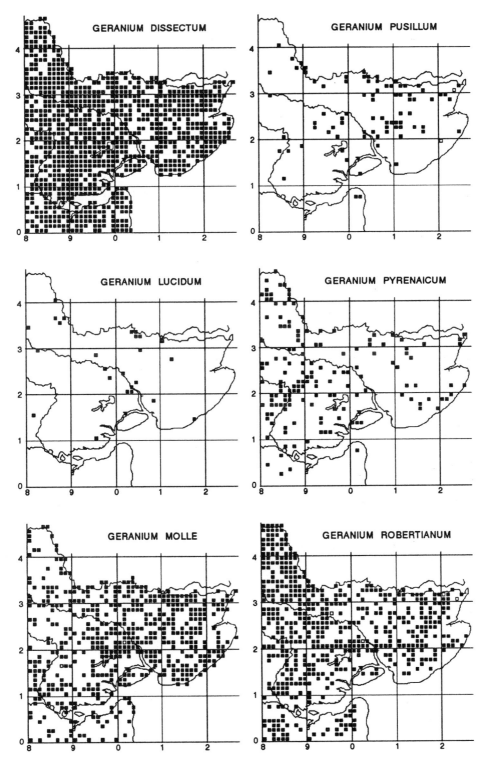

GERANIUM DISSECTUM

GERANIUM PUSILLUM

GERANIUM LUCIDUM

GERANIUM PYRENAICUM

GERANIUM MOLLE

GERANIUM ROBERTIANUM

WOOD SORREL FAMILY
OXALIDACEAE

Wood Sorrel
Oxalis acetosella [41] M
Restricted to ancient woodlands away from the clays. Generally found in small quantity on a streamside bank growing through the leaf litter and between fallen twigs and branches.

Oxalis articulata [8]
Oxalis corniculata [26]
Oxalis corymbosa [2]
Oxalis europaea [2]
Oxalis exilis [1]

All of the above Oxalis occur as garden escapes. *O corniculata* particularly likes brick paths where it grows in the cracks between the bricks. The tiny flowered *O exilis* also likes to grow between cracks in pavements but is also found in lawns. The other species tend to be found growing near to heaps of garden refuse which have been dumped in hedges and other unofficial tip sites.

BALSAM FAMILY
BALSAMINACEAE

Orange Balsam
Impatiens capensis [1]
An introduction that may well become established. To date it has only been found at Liston Pits.

Himalayan Balsam or
Policeman's Helmet
Impatiens glandulifera [35] M
An introduction that has become naturalised at many sites. It has increased considerably since Jermyn's time - he listed only two sites (Gibson did not list the plant at all). By rivers, streams, ponds, ditches and other damp places.

Small Balsam
Impatiens parviflora [13] M
A recent introduction to Gibson, that continued to increase for a number of years but had started to decline according to Jermyn. Of Jermyn's records, it can still be found around Halstead; at St Peter's churchyard and other sites in Colchester; it

was not refound in the vicinity of Heckfordbridge, Langham or St Osyth; and it appears to have moved from Little to Great Bentley where it occurs by the railway station. Other scattered records have been found, always near houses.

MAPLE FAMILY
ACERACEAE

Field Maple
Acer campestre [886] M
The native distribution of this tree is obscured by plantings that have gone on over the centuries. It has been recorded over much of the area but is missing from the acid soils and the coastal belt. In the west of our area, from Kelvedon northwards to Pentlow, it is very common on the calcareous boulder clays being a major component of every hedge along with **Dogwood**, **Spindle** and the wild **Clematis**. Although always present in woodland it is never the dominant tree, usually represented by a few individuals scattered throughout the wood. For so plentiful a tree it is uncommon to find a fine standard specimen as those in hedges are cut back by the hedge trimmer and the woodland trees are usually coppiced.

Norway Maple
Acer platanoides [28] M
Introduced and more commonly planted than before in large gardens, parks and the edges of plantations. There is some regeneration from seed.

Sycamore
Acer pseudoplatanus [704] M
Very common and widespread. Planted and self sown in a great variety of habitats; gardens, parks, woods, plantations and hedgerows. In some habitats the abundance of seedlings produced can prove disastrous for the native flora, as the dense canopy of a solid stand of **Sycamore** shades out the native plants. In order to protect some specialist plants and habitats there is no alternative but to 'weed' all **Sycamore** seedlings, although in the urban setting it provides a rich supply of insect food for birds.

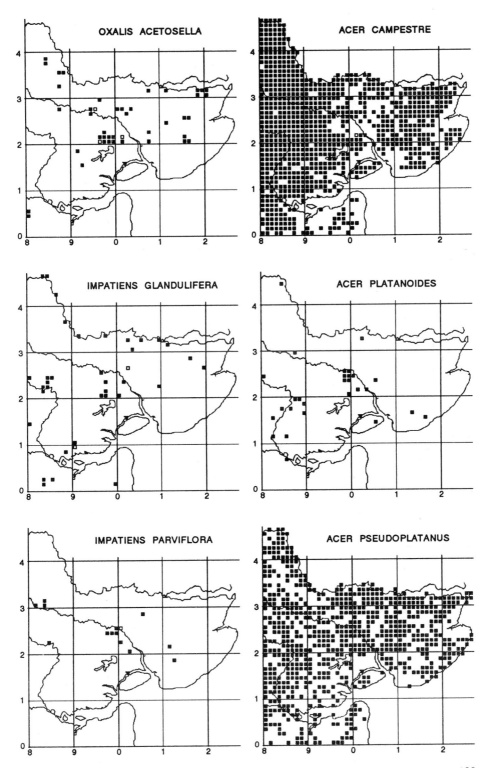

HORSE CHESTNUT FAMILY
HIPPOCASTANACEAE

Horse Chestnut
Aesculus hippocastanum [492] M
Commonly planted in large gardens, avenues and parks. The occasional tree can be found in hedgerows and woods.

HOLLY FAMILY
AQUIFOLIACEAE

Holly
Ilex aquifolium [732] M
A common tree of churchyards, hedgerows and woods. It avoids the coastal belt with its heavy London Clay, the scattered records coming from the sand and gravel outcrops. It does, however, occur on the chalky boulder clays between Halstead and Bures but is absent from the chalk itself in the Foxearth area. Along with the **Oak**, **Holly** is often left when hedgerows are cleared or cut, but despite this it is rare to see a well-shaped tree. It will readily regenerate when the seeds have passed through a bird's gut.

SPINDLE FAMILY
CELASTRACEAE

Spindle
Euonymus europaeus [285] M
A shrub or small tree that prefers an alkaline soil, it is now increasingly planted and occurring in areas where it was not previously found. On the chalky soils from Kelvedon north to Pentlow it forms a major component in many old hedges along with **Field Maple**, **Dogwood** and the wild **Clematis**. As one moves further from this area it gradually becomes less frequent with just an occasional shrub growing in the hedgerow.

BOX FAMILY
BUXACEAE

Box
Buxus sempervirens [11] M
Planted and occasionally becoming naturalised, never far from houses.

BUCKTHORN FAMILY
RHAMNACEAE

Alder Buckthorn
Frangula alnus [7] M
A rare tree of ancient woods and very old hedgerows; always as single specimens. Both Gibson and Jermyn give sites to the south of Colchester and it still occurs in the Roman River Valley. Gibson's site at Pods Wood was also refound. However, there are no recent records from Halstead, Chalkney Wood or Colne Park areas, all of which were mentioned by either Gibson or Jermyn. We did not find it around Dedham (per Gibson) but did locate three extra sites, at Nayland, Silver End and Woodham Ferrers.

Common Buckthorn
Rhamnus catharticus [22] M
A small tree or shrub that is commonest on the chalk soils and scattered elsewhere. It is usually found in very old large hedgerows or at woodland edges.

VINE FAMILY
VITACEAE

Common Virginia Creeper
Parthenocissus inserta
Recorded by Jermyn from Parkeston in 1964 and at Fingringhoe Wick Nature Reserve in 1979.

Parthenocissus quinquefolia [1]
This creeper was found twining its way up a tree in a small copse not far from some houses.

Grape Vine
Vitis vinifera [1]
A specimen was found growing at Harwich during the survey; it was possibly a relic of cultivation.

PEA FAMILY
LEGUMINOSAE

Kidney Vetch
Anthyllis vulneraria
A plant of dry banks on a chalky soil of the sort found in our area from Bulmer north to

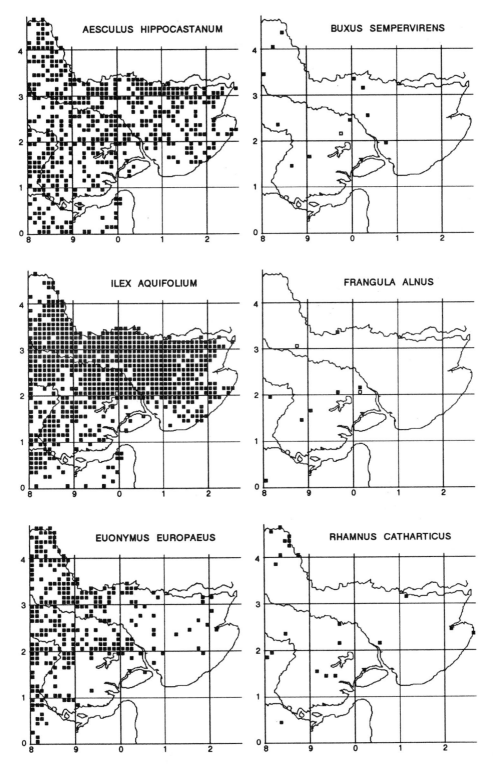

Pentlow. Gibson gave no records for north east Essex but Jermyn had found two sites on roadside banks around Bulmer, which despite extensive searches could not be refound.

Wild Liquorice
Astragalus glycyphyllos [2]
Wild Liquorice is another plant of chalky soils and could only occur in the same area as the previous species. For this plant, Jermyn had no records for north east Essex but Gibson did - Bulmer Hills, on the road to Sudbury. Four plants were found in this area at Pentlow in 1985 at intervals along a few hundred metres of road verge, but when the site was revisited in 1988 they were no longer in evidence.

Bladder Senna
Colutea arborescens [5] M
An introduced shrub planted in parks and large gardens that naturalises on waste ground used as unofficial tips.

Coronilla scorpioides
Once recorded from Hythe Quay, Colchester, 1927.

Broom
Cytisus scoparius
ssp scoparius [408] M
Common on sand and gravel soils, and reasonably so on the free draining brickearths, but avoiding both the clays and the chalk outcrop north of Bulmer. Most common on heaths and in sand and gravel pits, it is also found along railway tracks, in hedgerows and edges of woods, often on a bank. Gibson stated that it was common in the Colchester and Tendring districts, which still holds true today.

Goatsrue
Galega officinalis [14] M
Common in south Essex, it has not, as yet, really found its way to our part of the county. There is a cluster of records around Maldon and a few scattered records from elsewhere. It generally appears on waste areas used for tipping. It still occurs at Cook's Green and Brightlingsea where Jermyn found it but his other sites at Dovercourt and Little Maplestead were not refound.

Petty Whin
Genista anglica
Known to Gibson from Tiptree and Layer Breton Heaths. It was last seen on Tiptree Heath in the 1950s but it has not been seen at Layer Breton Heath this century.

Dyer's Greenweed
Genista tinctoria [13] M
Very local, commonest on the banks of the borrow dykes behind the sea walls around Hamford Water, otherwise a few scattered records. Jermyn's record along the coast between Frinton and Holland has been lost due to agricultural changes, but we have found plants in the vicinity of all his other sites. It is interesting to note that of the five records given by Gibson, four were inland, in pastures and thickets. In contrast, all of Jermyn's records were coastal, indicative of the almost total loss of inland ancient grassland.

Laburnum
Laburnum anagyroides [10] M
Not fully recorded during our survey, it is frequently planted in gardens and parks. It does regenerate from seed but often the seedlings are growing between pavement and fence where they will not reach maturity.

Yellow Vetchling
Lathyrus aphaca
A rare casual that Gibson recorded sparingly as an arable weed in several localities around Halstead. The only record since then was recorded by G C Brown in 1914 at the Hythe, Colchester.

Hairy Vetchling
Lathyrus hirsutus [2]
First discovered in 1666 in south Essex at Hadleigh Castle, it was subsequently found at a few other sites in the county. The only historical records for this part of the county come from the Dengie peninsula: Dale (1732) - in a field between the road and Mundon Church, likewise among bushes within the gate leading to Laydon Hall; T Benson (a contemporary of Gibson's who lived at North Fambridge) - Latchingdon; H Ibbotson - plentifully in a narrow grassy lane near T Benson's, 1851. Several plants were found in 1985 on a new verge created

during the construction of an emergency access road to an industrial estate in north Colchester. It can only have been introduced with the grass seed at this site.

Sea Pea
Lathyrus japonicus [2]
First discovered on The Naze, Walton in 1964, a small but well established patch was still there on the shingle in 1971. However, we have been unable to refind it during our survey. This area has been subject to coastal erosion and it may well be that the shingle that was present during Jermyn's lifetime has long since disappeared beneath the North Sea. We were also unable to locate Jermyn's site at Little

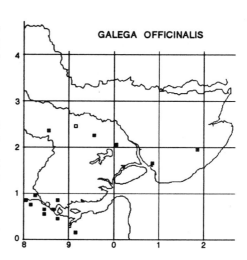

GALEGA OFFICINALIS

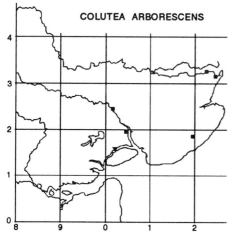

COLUTEA ARBORESCENS

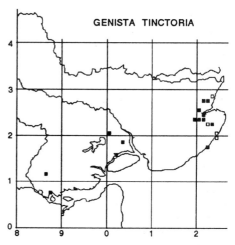

GENISTA TINCTORIA

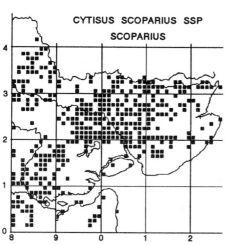

CYTISUS SCOPARIUS SSP SCOPARIUS

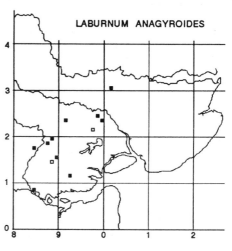

LABURNUM ANAGYROIDES

113

Oakley which was found in 1970, however, we did find good colonies a couple of kilometres north on the sand dunes just south of Dovercourt.

Broad-leaved Everlasting Pea
Lathyrus latifolius [31] M
Introduced, and often persisting in hedgerows and also on waste ground, where it originates from the tipping of garden refuse.

Bitter Vetch
Lathyrus montanus
A plant of woods, thickets and scrub now lost to north east Essex. Gibson had records for Kelvedon, Braxted, Rivenhall and Layer de la Haye, as well as Little Braxted and Totham for *var tenuifolius*. Jermyn's records were from Chalkney Wood, Pods Wood and Manwood Grove.

Grass Vetchling
Lathyrus nissolia [92] M
Under-recorded as it is almost impossible to see amongst grasses when not in flower or seed. It is commonest in the coastal grasslands around our sea walls but can occur in suitable rough grassy sites elsewhere. According to Gibson it was "on the cliffs between Walton and Frinton, plentifully" where it still occurs in abundance today; on some areas of the cliffs **Grass Vetchling** forms great patches several yards across.

Meadow Vetchling
Lathyrus pratensis [628] M
Very common throughout the area on grass verges and banks where it withstands mowing regimes that are unsympathetic to some of the more delicate wild flowers.

Narrow-leaved Everlasting Pea
Lathyrus sylvestris [1]
Jermyn had three records for this plant only one of which has been refound; on a chalky roadside bank on the road from Gestingthorpe to Bulmer. No additional sites were found.

Common Birdsfoot Trefoil
Lotus corniculatus [501] M
Common over the whole area in all types of grassland unless it is particularly wet when it is replaced by **Greater Birdsfoot Trefoil**.

Slender Birdsfoot Trefoil
Lotus tenuis [161] M
Common on the coastal grassland between the borrow dyke and sea wall, scattered elsewhere, usually on sandy waste ground. Our intensive coverage of the area has revealed a great many more sites than listed by Jermyn.

Greater Birdsfoot Trefoil STACE
Lotus uliginosus [254] M Pedunculatus
Not uncommon but scattered over the whole area, in ditches, pond margins, damp grassland and damp woodland rides.

Tree Lupin
Lupinus arboreus [25] M
An introduction which has increased since Jermyn's time, scattered on verges and waste areas. It is still common on the cliffs at Holland where it regenerates from seed, although it really needs disturbed sandy soil for it to naturalise in the abundance it has on the coast of Suffolk.

Garden Lupin
Lupinus polyphyllus [6]
Introduced, either as the result of the tipping of garden refuse, or with seed, as it was along stretches of the A12 and some gravel pits, in order to provide nitrogen fixing in the soil for newly sown grass.

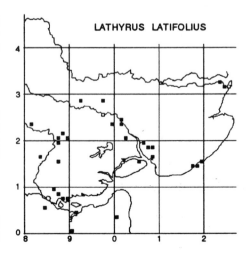
LATHYRUS LATIFOLIUS

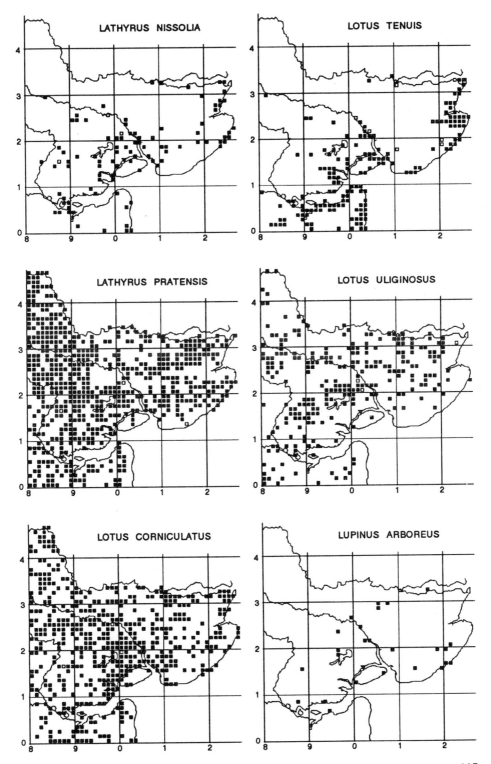

LATHYRUS NISSOLIA

LOTUS TENUIS

LATHYRUS PRATENSIS

LOTUS ULIGINOSUS

LOTUS CORNICULATUS

LUPINUS ARBOREUS

Spotted Medick
Medicago arabica [491] M
Common in urban areas, scattered elsewhere. It occurs in gardens, lawns, edges of car parks, building sites and disturbed ground in road verges.

Black Medick
Medicago lupulina [711] M
Very common over the whole area in grass verges, gardens, disturbed soils, waste places and reseeded grassland.

Bur Medick
Medicago minima
Recorded from a sandy shore at Harwich by Dale (1732), it has not been found since. However, it still occurs on the other side of the estuary at Felixstowe.

Toothed Medick
Medicago polymorpha [2]
Gibson had records from maritime pastures at West Mersea and Harwich and Jermyn recorded it from six sites, five of which were coastal. We only have two records; one from the Roman River Valley growing on a grassy bank by a corner of a stream where horses were watered. It was first recorded here in 1978 and was still present in 1980 but has not been seen since. The second site was found at Manningtree in 1987.

Sickle Medick
Medicago sativa ssp falcata [1]
Found once on a sea wall at Manningtree close to the premises of seed merchants, from which it presumably originated.

Medicago sativa
ssp falcata X ssp sativa
This hybrid occurs naturally in parts of Suffolk where both parents occur but this is not the case in our area. Jermyn had four records but considered that they had probably been introduced with impure seed when **Lucerne** was extensively grown. It has not been found during our survey.

Lucerne
Medicago sativa ssp sativa [132] M
Still grown as a crop on the Dengie peninsula which is reflected in the density of records. Scattered plants can be found over the rest of the area either as a relic of cultivation supplemented by the occasional inclusion of **Lucerne** in the crop rotation, or as part of the seed mix on new roadside verges.

White Melilot
Melilotus alba [18] M
Uncommon, although it can be found in good quantity where it does occur e.g. the interchange of the A12 and A120 to the north of Colchester. Almost invariably associated with car parks, roadworks and waste areas. It still occurs at Gibson's site on the banks of the Colne between Wivenhoe and Colchester.

Tall Melilot
Melilotus altissima [29] M
Rather local in Gibson's time, it had become common and well distributed according to Jermyn. From our findings it appears to be decreasing as we have found only scattered records in fourteen 10km squares (Jermyn had records from all nineteen). Found generally in disturbed waste areas, it also occurs on verges after major roadworks possibly introduced with the grass seed mix.

Small-flowered Melilot
Melilotus indica [7]
A casual introduction as a contaminant of seed and as a bird seed alien.

Ribbed Melilot
Melilotus officinalis [28] M
Found in grassy waste places, particularly on the coast, it occurs with the same frequency as **Tall Melilot**.

Sainfoin
Onobrychis viciifolia [1]
A plant associated with chalk soils, but which was often cultivated, Gibson had no records for the north east of the county. Jermyn had four, all in the area with a chalky influence although he considered it to be mainly a long established relic of cultivation. The only site found during our survey has been at West Mersea where it was introduced with the reseeding of grassland.

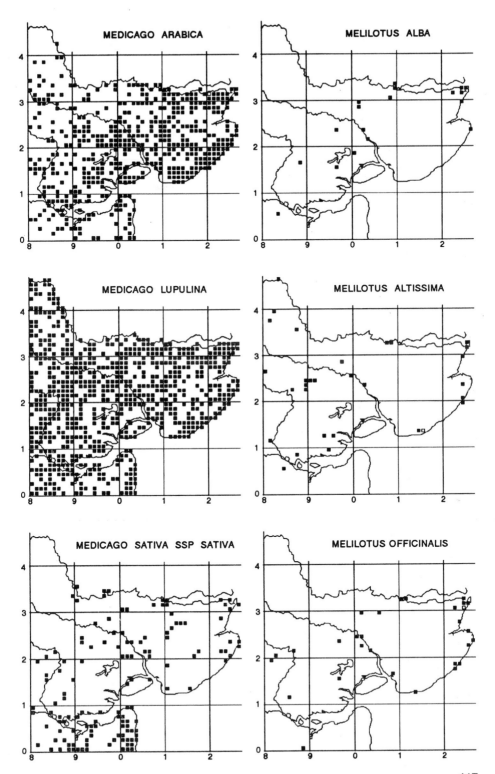

MEDICAGO ARABICA

MELILOTUS ALBA

MEDICAGO LUPULINA

MELILOTUS ALTISSIMA

MEDICAGO SATIVA SSP SATIVA

MELILOTUS OFFICINALIS

117

Ononis baetica [1]

A rare and unusual bird seed alien that occurred in 1985. This was the first time this species had been recorded for Essex.

Common Restharrow
Ononis repens [67] M

Reasonably frequent on grassy road verges and banks on the chalky boulder clay but very rare elsewhere. The two inland records east of Colchester were also on grassy verges; the plant at Bradwell-on-Sea was on a sandy beach (it is commonly found in this habitat on the Suffolk coast), and the record at Harwich was on waste ground. We have not seen this species in many of the coastal areas given by Jermyn (see also the following species).

Spiny Restharrow
Ononis spinosa [77] M

Frequent on the coast. With the loss of grazing marshes it is almost completely restricted to the grassland between the sea wall and the borrow dyke, usually growing beside the borrow dyke itself. In the few remaining grazing marshes it can be found growing along the sides of what were once the old saltmarsh creeks. Jermyn gives several inland records for this species (which we have not refound), and he mentioned that intermediate forms between this and the previous species are not infrequent. However, our findings have shown that each species is now restricted to its own habitat. It would appear that both species have contracted their range.

Birdsfoot
Ornithopus perpusillus [27] M

Uncommon, on light gravelly soils, occurring in gravel pits, tracks and bare patches in short grass on heathy areas. Commonest on the heathy parts of the Roman River Valley and Army lands at Middlewick. It has very much declined; we have found it in only eight 10 km squares, compared to Jermyn's fifteen.

False Acacia
Robinia pseudoacacia [49] M

Planted throughout the area for ornament.

Any seeds produced do not seem to germinate although it sometimes spreads by suckering.

Scorpiurus muricatus [1]

A rare bird seed alien.

Spanish Broom
Spartium junceum [4]

A garden escape that has naturalised along the coast from Jaywick to Frinton, particularly on the cliffs.

Mersea Pea or Dragon's Teeth
Tetragonolobus maritimus [1]

An introduction that has been established on Mersea Island since at least 1930. The classic site on the corner of Empress Avenue, a small piece of ancient grassland containing **Green Winged Orchids**, was destroyed by spraying. The species is now maintained in the gardens of several local botanists.

Haresfoot Clover
Trifolium arvense [42] M

A clover of sandy soils, occurring in old gravel pits, coastal sands and other places where the very light soil has been disturbed, often by rabbits. Despite our intensive coverage of the area, we were unable to find it in six of Jermyn's eighteen 10km squares, a decrease of 33%.

Hop Trefoil
Trifolium campestre [101] M

Considered common by both Gibson and Jermyn, we have found that its distribution is now scattered although still widespread. It is usually found amongst the shorter grasses in dry grassland and on dry grassy banks.

Lesser Yellow Trefoil
Trifolium dubium [802]

Very common, particularly as a garden weed where it can occur in both the flower bed and lawn. Otherwise it can be found on any patch of bare or waste ground, and many grassy places.

Trifolium foenum-graecum

Recorded on one occasion in Colchester, 1927.

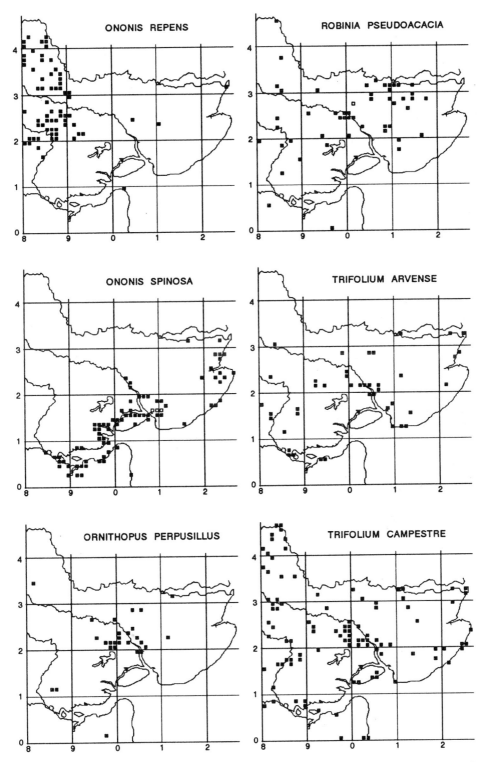

ONONIS REPENS · ROBINIA PSEUDOACACIA · ONONIS SPINOSA · TRIFOLIUM ARVENSE · ORNITHOPUS PERPUSILLUS · TRIFOLIUM CAMPESTRE

119

Strawberry Clover
Trifolium fragiferum [48] M
Reasonably frequent in the grassland on and behind our sea walls. Very little of Jermyn's habitat of drained estuarine marsh remains as these have been ploughed, but **Strawberry Clover** can be found on those left, growing in the grass along the banks of what were once the saltmarsh creeks. Many of Gibson's sites were inland and this distribution was confirmed by Jermyn who had records for several inland squares. Today, this clover is completely restricted to grazing marshes and sea walls - the latter being the only significant grassland habitat remaining in north east Essex. The one record from Colchester originates from imported turf.

Clustered Clover
Trifolium glomeratum [3]
Very much reduced since Jermyn; of his seven records there remains only Fingringhoe Wick Nature Reserve. The only other site is Great Holland Pits, another Essex Naturalists' Trust nature reserve.

Trifolium hybridum ssp elegans
A rare casual that, according to Gibson, "had maintained its position for some years about the sides of certain hilly fields of cornland at Great Braxted, but to the history of its introduction no clew can be obtained". There have been no subsequent records.

Alsike Clover
Trifolium hybridum
    ssp hybridum [41] M
Our findings are at variance with Gibson who said that "It has been cultivated as a seed crop, and is a striking instance of the complete naturalisation of a foreign plant" and Jermyn who recorded it as "Common, completely naturalised and spreading". We have found that it is introduced with seed on new verges and grassland, where it persists for a few years, but, as the grassland becomes more mature, it subsequently disappears.

Crimson Clover
Trifolium incarnatum
Jermyn had two records for this clover which occurred as a casual or, in his time,

as a relic of cultivation. Not found during our survey.

Zigzag Clover
Trifolium medium [11] M
Very much decreased since Jermyn when it was frequent but rather scattered. A good quantity still grows on the cliffs at Frinton, but otherwise it is just the odd plant that is found.

Slender Yellow Trefoil
Trifolium micranthum [100] M
Considered uncommon by Jermyn, we have found it reasonably frequent once you 'have your eye in for it'. It originally occurred in traditional grassland but nowadays it is found in lawns and parks which were laid down from turf many years ago. It is common in the grass around Colchester Castle and occasionally escapes into the flower beds. When the grass is treated with weed killer this Trefoil becomes abundant as it is resistant to the chemicals and fills the space where other plants have been eliminated. This was the case at Quietwaters Golf Course where it occurred on many of the fairways and greens.

Sulphur Clover
Trifolium ochroleucon [9] M
Declining and now uncommon on the chalky boulder clay, where it occurs on road verges and banks and at the edge of bridleways and grassy tracks. Usually less than five plants are found although at one site there were more than twenty.

Fenugreek
Trifolium ornithopodioides [24] M
Lost from Tiptree Heath, the only inland site, where it was also known to Gibson, but refound in many of Jermyn's other sites in coastal turf. We have additionally found it at Great Holland Pits and on gravel at a building site at Wivenhoe.

Red Clover
Trifolium pratense [642] M
Very common over the whole area, on verges, edges of fields, disturbed ground and rough grassy places. It is commonly introduced with reseeding of grassland and on verges after the completion of roadworks. **Red Clover** is still cultivated occa-

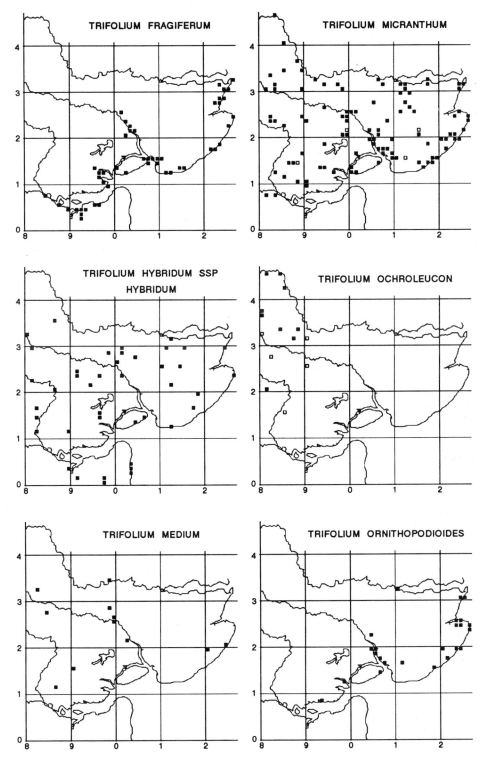

sionally, as, in common with all the Pea Family, it has the facility to fix nitrogen in the soil and is thus a useful addition to the crop rotation. It can sometimes be found being parasitised by **Common Broomrape**, whose roots attach themselves to those of the clover in order to draw nourishment for its own growth.

Trifolium pratense X squamosum
Jermyn found a few plants of this hybrid growing with their parents in 1970 at Little Oakley. We have not refound them during our survey but further searching may reveal their continued presence here, or at other sites around our coast where the two clovers grow in proximity.

White Clover
Trifolium repens [1152] M
Very common in any type of grassland and equally at home on bare soils. Phyllanthous forms where the flowers have mutated to leaves as a result of attack by a gall-causer have been noticed on two occasions.

Reversed Clover
Trifolium resupinatum
Recorded in malting refuse at Hythe Quay in 1927.

Rough Clover
Trifolium scabrum
Jermyn gave three sites; Colne Point, Crabknowe Spit (Walton) and the dunes in the Little Oakley area. The last sighting was in 1964.

Sea Clover
Trifolium squamosum [36] M
Restricted to sea walls and the grassland between the wall and the borrow dyke, it has decreased since Jermyn, having not been refound in four of his 10km squares. This is probably due to the conversion of grazing marsh to arable and also to development in coastal areas.

Starry Clover
Trifolium stellatum
Once recorded from Hythe Quay in 1927 when it was probably introduced with foreign seed.

Knotted Clover
Trifolium striatum [35] M
Infrequent and usually in small quantity on the lighter soils, occasionally found on sandy verges but more often in short turf. It also occurs in lawns and parklands where it continues to grow despite the mowing, only flowering if left uncut.

Subterranean Clover
Trifolium subterraneum [8] M
Very rare but difficult to detect in mown grassland where it has been found on a couple of occasions. Always in small quantity it still occurs at Jermyn's sites of Fingringhoe Wick Nature Reserve and Great Holland Pits on gravelly patches and rides, and at Walton in short turf. It could not be refound by the swimming baths at Dovercourt nor at any of his other sites, however, additional sites include Goldhanger and Howlands Marsh.

Trifolium tomentosum
Recorded from Hythe Quay, 1927, but not since.

Gorse
Ulex europaeus [419] M
Common on the sands and gravels and missing from the chalk and clays. Most abundant in old sand and gravel pits and on heaths, it also occurs on banks, in hedgerows and open woods on the appropriate soils.

Dwarf Gorse
Ulex minor [1]
Very rare for Essex with both Gibson and Jermyn giving no records for the north east although Jermyn does mention an early record at Witham which could not be refound in 1900. One plant was found in 1985 on the hill close by Manwood Bridge. It is unlikely that it is native as it was found where the road had been realigned and subsequently replanted. The plant has the more upright habit of those grown in nurseries.

Bithynian Vetch
Vicia bithynica [3]
Not recorded before in our part of the county, and previously only known from scrubby grassland on clay soil along the

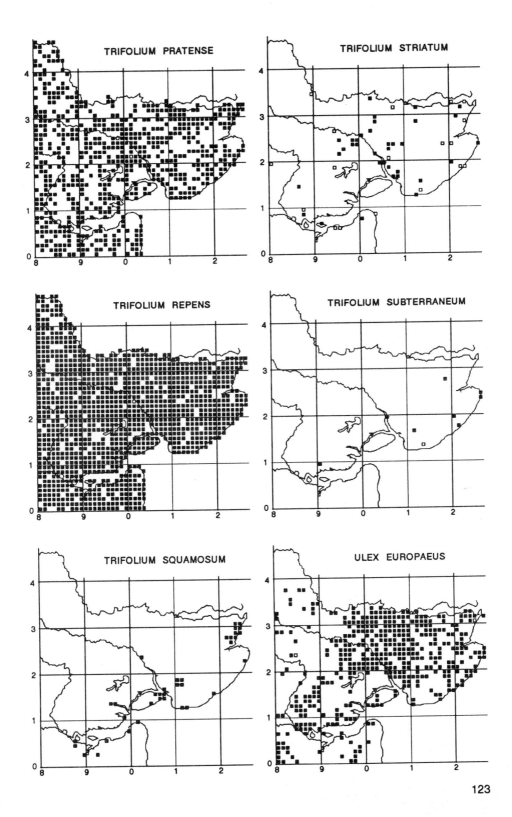

TRIFOLIUM PRATENSE

TRIFOLIUM STRIATUM

TRIFOLIUM REPENS

TRIFOLIUM SUBTERRANEUM

TRIFOLIUM SQUAMOSUM

ULEX EUROPAEUS

Thames foothills, it was found in 1985 on a south facing clay cliff at Frinton. There was just one patch but it was well established and covered quite an extensive area at the junction of four 1km squares. After much deliberation and measuring it was determined that it grew in three of them. It was still present in 1989.

Tufted Vetch
Vicia cracca [248] M
Reasonably common, but scattered throughout the area in verges, hedges and rough grassland.

Broad Bean
Vicia faba [2]
An occasional relic of cultivation that occurs on disturbed verges. Not fully recorded.

Hairy Tare
Vicia hirsuta [213] M
Reasonably common on rough grassland and verges on the free draining brick-earth and gravel soils.

Spring Vetch
Vicia lathyroides [3]
Jermyn had seven sites on open sandy habitats at Berechurch Common, Bradwell-on-Sea, Fingringhoe Wick Nature Reserve, Langham, St Osyth Beach, Colne Point and Lee-over-Sands. It has been refound at the latter two sites and, additionally, at Great Horkesley churchyard. A site at Abbey Fields, Colchester, has been reported but this has still to be confirmed. It is possible that it could still occur at the other sites listed, recording being limited by its short flowering season.

Yellow Vetch
Vicia lutea
This vetch occurs on the sandy beaches of Suffolk but is only a rare introduction in Essex. Jermyn had three records, two of which dated from the 1930s. The most recent was at Point Clear in 1965. We have not found this plant during our survey.

Common Vetch
Vicia sativa ssp nigra [688] M
There are many subspecies and varieties of the **Common Vetch** but we have only

separately recorded the cultivated plant *ssp sativa*, all other records are included here. Common in any grassland, including churchyards, verges, sea walls, etc. It is also a common component of seed mixtures for reseeding amenity grassland and wild flower meadows.

Vicia sativa ssp sativa [5]
Once grown as a crop, it is now only a casual introduction in reseeded verges and fields.

Bush Vetch
Vicia sepium [350] M
Very common on the chalky boulder clay, but scattered elsewhere. Road verges, hedgerows, churchyards, woodland rides and grassy waysides.

Slender Tare
Vicia tenuissima
Gibson had no records for our area and Jermyn only two, at Gestingthorpe and Belchamp Otten, neither of which have been refound.

Smooth Tare
Vicia tetrasperma [425] M
Common on the London Clay but scattered elsewhere in similar grassland habitat to that of the **Hairy Tare**.

Fodder Vetch
Vicia villosa ssp varia [2]
A short-lived casual introduced with seed mixtures.

ROSE FAMILY
ROSACEAE

Agrimony
Agrimonia eupatoria [612] M
Common and widespread on grass verges, banks, tops of ditches, woodland rides and borders and churchyards. Jermyn gives several records for **var sepium** but we have not recorded varieties separately.

Fragrant Agrimony
Agrimonia procera [2]
Jermyn gives just the one record for Berechurch Common 1962-63 which we were unable to refind although it has since been

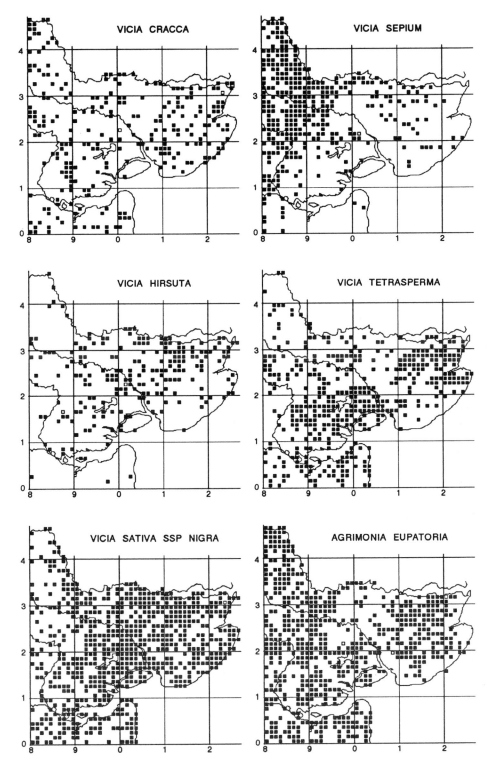

VICIA CRACCA

VICIA SEPIUM

VICIA HIRSUTA

VICIA TETRASPERMA

VICIA SATIVA SSP NIGRA

AGRIMONIA EUPATORIA

found at Bounstead Bridge about one kilometre away. It has also been found in a
field adjacent to Copperas Wood. In both
sites it was in old damp grassland.

Lady's Mantle
Alchemilla filicaulis ssp vestita
The only record is from Gibson, at Pattis-
wick.

Parsley Piert
Aphanes arvensis [393] M
A common arable and garden weed that
prefers the free draining soils. Although
normally a small plant, under suitable
conditions, it can be abundant and reach
several inches in height and width.

Slender Parsley Piert
Aphanes microcarpa [8] M
A few sites have been found, mainly in the
Roman River Valley. Many localities given
by Jermyn have not been refound but it is
such a small plant that it is very easily
overlooked and may well still occur. It is
found in sandy and gravelly areas and in
short turf on these soils. At a public garden
in Clacton it was frequent, growing between stone slabs and on the adjacent
grassy banks.

Cockspur Thorn
Crataegus crus-galli [1]
Planted. It is still present at Jermyn's site
at Fingringhoe, near the Roman River,
where several large trees grow in the
roadside hedge, but we have not found it
elsewhere.

Midland Hawthorn
Crataegus laevigata [136] M
Preferring the heavier, wetter soils, it is
reasonably frequent, although usually in
small quantity, in woods and older
hedgerows in the west of our area. Its
natural distribution is becoming somewhat
obscured by plantings and hybridisation
with the **Common Hawthorn**.

Crataegus laevigata
X monogyna [42]
Under-recorded, common at times in Victorian hedgerows. It is a very variable
hybrid with intermediates covering the
variations from one species to the other,
due to back-crossing with parents or other
hybrids.

Common Hawthorn
Crataegus monogyna [1238] M
Very common; occurring in hedges, thick-
ets and scrub.

Meadowsweet
Filipendula ulmaria [269] M
Common in wet flushes, by rivers, streams,
wet ditches and other wet and swampy
places.

Hautbois Strawberry
Fragaria moschata
Occasionally found as a garden escape but
we have not kept records for this species.

Wild Strawberry
Fragaria vesca [81] M
Infrequent and declining, occurring on dry
banks and sunny woodland rides. It is no
longer common along railway banks as the
management of this habitat has changed
allowing the banks to become scrubbed
over.

Garden Strawberry
Fragaria X ananassa
We have not kept records for this garden
escape but as most of Jermyn's sites were
from railway tracks and banks they are
likely to have suffered due to the habitat
changes mentioned above.

Water Avens
Geum rivale
Always very rare in our area. Gibson gives
a record for a bog in Essex about a mile
from Sudbury and it was found by Jermyn
at Stour Wood. Neither of these sites have
been refound.

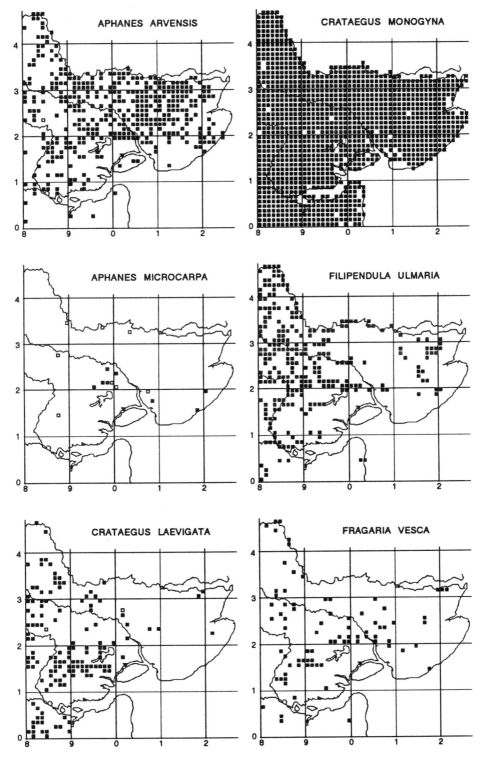

APHANES ARVENSIS

CRATAEGUS MONOGYNA

APHANES MICROCARPA

FILIPENDULA ULMARIA

CRATAEGUS LAEVIGATA

FRAGARIA VESCA

Wood Avens or Herb Bennet
Geum urbanum [456] M
Common on the chalky boulder clay and still reasonably frequent over much of the rest of the area. It is found in woodland rides and borders, older hedgerows and deep shady banks.

Apple
Malus domestica [127]
Scattered over the whole area as a result of discarded apple cores. Under-recorded.

Crab Apple
Malus sylvestris [172] M
Reasonably frequent in the west of our area and scattered elsewhere. It occurs in big old hedges and woods, both at the edge and deep within the wood. It is usually found in small quantity.

Trailing Tormentil
Potentilla anglica [5]
As with Jermyn, this is apparently rare. With the exception of the record for Fingringhoe Wick Nature Reserve all our sites are from rides or clearings in ancient woodland on heathy or gravelly soils. Jermyn's record for a clearing in Bungate Wood was not refound but it was present in a woodland ride in another of the Markshall complex of woods, 1986. Jermyn's record for Friday Wood was refound in 1980. Additionally it was found at two sites in Layer Wood, 1987.

Silverweed
Potentilla anserina [271] M
A plant of damp grassland, commoner on the water retaining clay soils. It is most prevalent on roadsides where the surface water run-off keeps the soil damp, particularly if the water lies in winter; also found in deep cart tracks which retain water. On the free draining soils it is usually restricted to streamsides and margins of ponds.

Hoary Cinquefoil
Potentilla argentea [19] M
Very occasional, and always in small quantity. It can vary from being a tiny prostrate plant to, in ideal conditions, plants a foot high. Dry light soils in heathy grassland, gravel pits and gravelly verges.

Tormentil
Potentilla erecta [19] M
This plant has decreased considerably in our area since Jermyn's time, we have recorded it sparingly in only nine 10km squares to his thirteen. However, on the acid heaths and woodland rides where it does occur it can be quite plentiful.

Potentilla erecta X reptans
Jermyn gave this as frequent where both parents grew together and had records for Tiptree Heath, Layer Breton Heath, Fordham Heath and Maldon Woods. We have not recorded this hybrid during our survey. This could be because it has been overlooked, but it could equally reflect the contracting range of **Tormentil**. With one of its parents retreating to its specialist habitats there is less chance for it to meet with **Creeping Cinquefoil**.

Potentilla intermedia
A casual that occurred in Berechurch Park in 1927.

Marsh Cinquefoil
Potentilla palustris
Gibson's records on the brink of the cliff at West Mersea and in marshy grounds by Bourne Pond, Colchester, had already been lost by Jermyn's time as he gives no records for our area. We have not found it during our survey.

Sulphur Cinquefoil
Potentilla recta [2]
Introduction. Found growing in the Roman River Valley at the site of a demolished cottage in 1980, it was still present in 1987. It also occurs at Chigborough Lakes.

Creeping Cinquefoil
Potentilla reptans [1042] M
Very common over the whole area, although thinning out through Tendring.

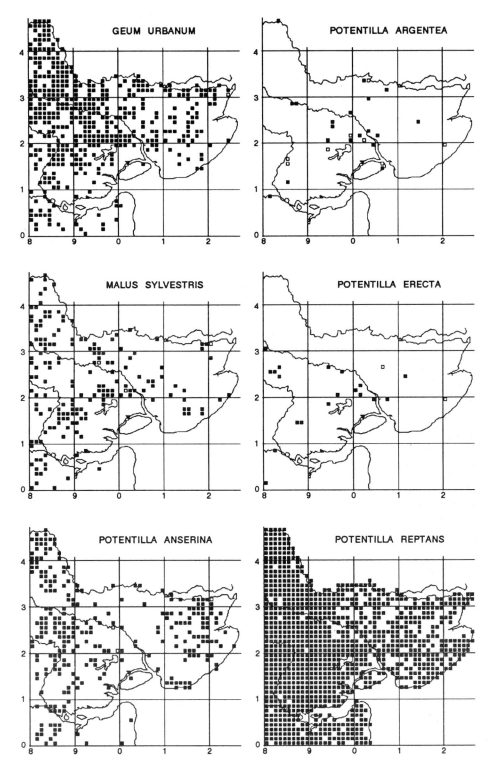

GEUM URBANUM

POTENTILLA ARGENTEA

MALUS SYLVESTRIS

POTENTILLA ERECTA

POTENTILLA ANSERINA

POTENTILLA REPTANS

Barren Strawberry
Potentilla sterilis [231] M
Reasonably frequent in woodland rides and margins, old hedgerows, grassy banks and churchyards away from the coast.

Wild Cherry
Prunus avium [168] M
Native and introduced. Usually found as a few trees along the woodland edges, particularly in the older woods. Gibson mentions it for the woods between Manningtree and Harwich, and, indeed, it appears to be quite common along the woodland margin by the river. Its native distribution has now been obscured by many years of planting.

Cherry Plum
Prunus cerasifera [113] M
Introduced; always planted. The density of records to the north and east of Colchester can be explained by the supply of this species from a nursery at Ardleigh to the local community. There are a few hedges of pure **Cherry Plum** (Great Bromley) but generally it is intermingled with **Blackthorn**. It is probably under-recorded as, whilst it is easy to identify in flower and fruit, it tends to merge into the hedge and be overlooked at other times. During the ten year survey it was noticed that fruit was only set in any quantity in 1988 and 1989, both of which had warm early springs, compared to the cold, late ones of the preceding few years.

Sour Cherry
Prunus cerasus
A cultivated species for which we did not keep records, but which can become naturalised.

Wild Plum, Bullace, Greengage
Prunus domestica [119] M
Prunus domestica ssp domestica
Prunus domestica ssp insititia
Prunus domestica
        ssp domestica X ssp insititia
The **Wild Plum** has proved difficult to record in detail in an area like ours with its history of fruit growing, so we have combined all our records into the map given here. In general the obvious 'domestic' forms are found in hedgerows near habitation but some obscure trees of mixed parentage are found along railway tracks and similar areas. The **Bullace** is found scattered mainly in the area from Maldon to Tiptree (the main fruit growing area) with odd records for elsewhere. The yellow fruited **'Shepherd's Bullace'** is found at a number of these sites.

Cherry Laurel
Prunus laurocerasus [26] M
Introduced to provide winter cover for game birds, it has become naturalised in places, e.g. Friday Wood. Not fully recorded.

Bird Cherry
Prunus padus [1]
A plant associated more with limestone in the north of England, it has always been very rare in our area. Gibson gave a record for Lexden, and Jermyn listed Mundon Furze and a copse near Felix Hall, Kelvedon. One bush was found in 1987 along a disused railway line near Sudbury where the soil is chalky. There are now introduced species of **Bird Cherry** which causes confusion over identification.

Blackthorn
Prunus spinosa [1156] M
Very common over the whole area as a native shrub and where it has been planted to provide stock-proof hedges. If left unmanaged it will sucker and spread out to form an impenetrable thicket.

Wild Pear
Pyrus pyraster [10]
Pear trees are very occasionally found but these are mainly escapes or relics of cultivation of the domestic Pear. We consider that only three records were of genuine **Wild Pears**; Bullock Wood, Colchester; Temple Lane, Silver End; and the most magnificent mature tree at Pear Tree Corner near Greenstead Green.

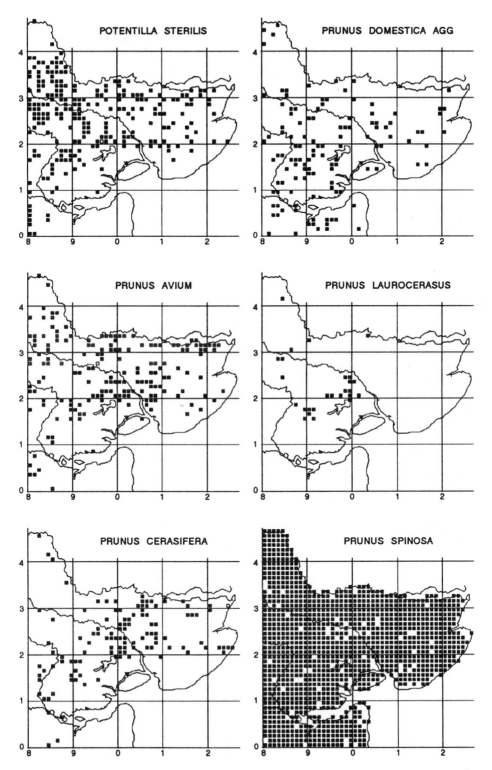

ROSES

Apart from the **Field** and **Dog Rose** we have only recently begun to record Roses in detail. We are indebted to Gordon Graham for help with identifications and advice.

Field Rose
Rosa arvensis [148] M
A widespread and distinctive species that sometimes forms large patches in hedgerows; most frequently found in the west of our area.

Dog Rose
Rosa canina [434] M
Under this name we have recorded all the '*canina*' type bushes (including *R dumetorum*). The considerable number of hybrids of this species with other Roses have added to the problem of its general variability which has always caused difficulties for botanists. Many of the 'Wild Roses' planted on new road verges have a very mixed parentage.

Rosa micrantha [1]
Known only from one site at Wrabness. Gibson's records for Mistley and Colchester have not been refound.

Rosa obtusifolia [1]
One bush was found in a hedgerow at Great Totham.

Sweetbriar
Rosa rubiginosa [5]
We have found a few scattered sites. With the availability of this species in local garden centres, its distribution could soon be obscured by garden throw-outs and deliberate plantings.

Japanese Rose
Rosa rugosa [7]
Always planted but becoming naturalised on some sandy coasts.

Rosa stylosa [12]
Rare except in the south west corner of our area. It is more often found as a hybrid with **Dog Rose.**

Downy Rose
Rosa tomentosa [21] M
This distinctive species has, in the main, a north west distribution in our area.

Dewberry
Rubus caesius [49] M
Not frequent, occurring on roadside banks and woodland rides on soils with a chalky influence. Probably over-recorded as it hybridises with other Brambles and our records may include some hybrid specimens.

BRAMBLES

Rubus fruticosus [1232]
There are many micro-species of **Bramble** which are difficult to determine, but in aggregate it is a widely distributed and common plant. Some of the micro-species are extremely local, indeed, one from Berechurch only occurs there and does not even have a name. We are grateful to Alec Bull for his help with this group, our study of which is still at a very early stage. The species identified to date include:

Rubus amplificatus
Rubus boudicae
Rubus cardiophyllus
Rubus confertiflorus
Rubus criniger
Rubus dasyphyllus
Rubus echinatoides
Rubus echinatus
Rubus flexuosus
Rubus laciniatus [10]
A garden species spread by birds. It is probably the only Bramble that is easy to identify due to its distinctive cut leaf.
Rubus lindleianus
Rubus londinensis
Rubus macrophyllus
Rubus nemoralis
Rubus nemorosus
Rubus norvicensis
Rubus pallidus
Rubus plicatus
Rubus polyanthemus
Rubus proceras [8]
This large leaved robust Bramble is widely cultivated in our area and escapes are more frequent than our limited records would indicate.

Rubus pruinosus
Rubus raduloides
Rubus rufescens
Rubus sciocharis
Rubus ulmifolius [182]
Widespread. It is fairly distinctive but our records may include a few hybrids.
Rubus vestitus

Raspberry
Rubus idaeus [48] M
Scattered records occur over much of our area. It is invariably bird sown, often in woods and rough scrubland close by 'pick your own' fruit farms, allotments and gardens.

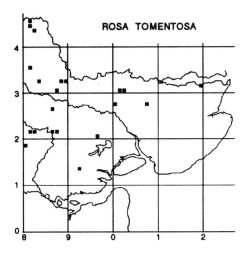

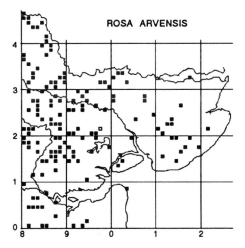

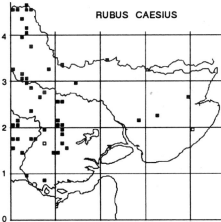

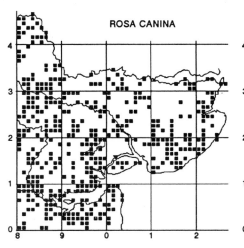

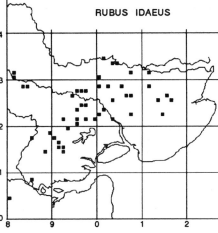

Salad Burnet
Sanguisorba minor ssp minor [4]
A plant of alkaline soils, it occurs in our area only on the chalk outcrop to the west of Sudbury. It grows along the Valley Walk at Borley and in Liston Pits.

Fodder Burnet
Sanguisorba minor ssp muricata [6] M
Occasionally introduced with seed on verges. It has persisted near Fingringhoe Mill for over 10 years.

Common Whitebeam
Sorbus aria [11]
Planted. Not fully recorded. There are many species and hybrids of Whitebeam that are now commonly planted. The **Swedish Whitebeam** (*S intermedia*) is one such which also regenerates freely from seed.

Rowan
Sorbus aucuparia [116] M
Planted and bird sown when it regenerates well in some woods. There are some large stools of **Rowan** in High Woods where it has been coppiced for several decades.

Wild Service Tree
Sorbus torminalis [65] M
The distribution map clearly shows this trees' preference for growing along the edges of clay soils where they emerge from beneath gravels. Found in woods and hedgerows, usually as a single tree except in the area south-west from Layer Wood where, in places, it occurs frequently in some hedgerows. Presumably, because it is not a common tree, it has been planted in the past as a 'marker' tree. Before the days of Ordnance Survey maps a distinctive tree could be a convenient landmark to denote the boundary of a property, often where a wood fell into more than one ownership.

PLANE FAMILY
PLATANACEAE

London Plane
Platanus hybrida [10]
Planted in parks and some large gardens. Not fully recorded.

STONECROP FAMILY
CRASSULACEAE

Crassula helmsii [8] M
An introduction from South Australia and Tasmania which had just reached west Essex by Jermyn's time. It has now arrived in north east Essex to the great detriment of the local flora and fauna. At Fingringhoe Wick Nature Reserve it invaded the large lake and smothered everything else, reducing the number of birds wintering on the lake by destroying their food supply. It is also abundant at Ardleigh Reservoir but was not found at Abberton Reservoir when the recording was carried out in 1988. It is still planted in garden ponds.

Biting Stonecrop
Sedum acre [70] M
Scattered. In our area it is probably a garden escape or introduction naturalising and appearing native at some sites. It grows on walls and roofs or on dry sandy and gravelly soils, where there is no competition. It can be seen on several roofs in Mistley and above Pizzaland in Colchester High Street. Other sites include old airfields, churchyards and the central reservation of the A133 Colchester-Elmstead Market road.

White Stonecrop
Sedum album [45] M
A garden escape that quickly becomes naturalised in similar situations to **Biting Stonecrop**. At Heckfordbridge it grows along the pavement from the Angel pub to the top of the hill.

English Stonecrop
Sedum anglicum
Jermyn had two records for the area which he thought were garden escapes; Berechurch Common, 1956, and on shingle at East Mersea, 1966. Our survey did not reveal any sites for this plant.

Thick-leaved Stonecrop
Sedum dasyphyllum
A contemporary of Gibson's had recorded this introduced Stonecrop from Halstead but it had already disappeared by 1862.

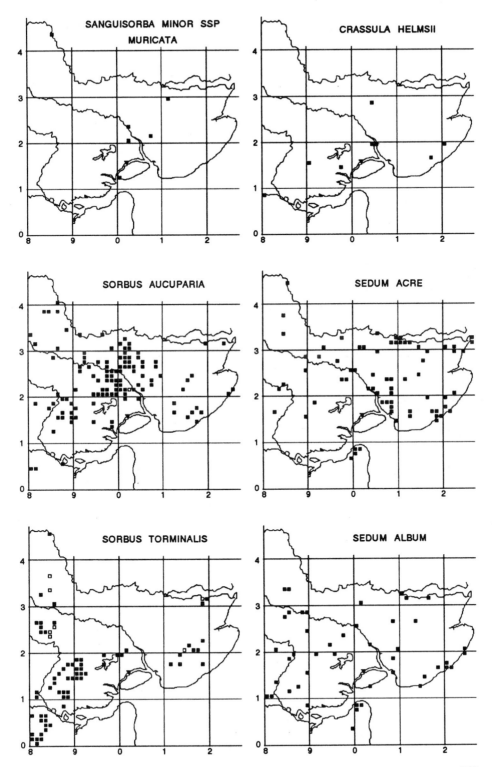

SANGUISORBA MINOR SSP MURICATA

CRASSULA HELMSII

SORBUS AUCUPARIA

SEDUM ACRE

SORBUS TORMINALIS

SEDUM ALBUM

Rock Stonecrop
Sedum forsteranum [1]
Introduced - it was found naturalised in a churchyard.

Reflexed Stonecrop STACE
Sedum reflexum [39] M Rupestre
A garden escape and introduction. It is commonly naturalised in churchyards and beside concrete paths.

Sedum spurium
A garden escape; Jermyn's site at Little Braxted was not refound during our survey.

Orpine
Sedum telephium [5]
As found by Jermyn, rare and in small quantity. Possibly native in the old woodland sites but an introduction elsewhere. The woods where it has been found are the Markshall complex and two woods north of Tiptree. There are two subspecies, and of those determined to that level, only *ssp telephium* has been found.

Houseleek
Sempervivum tectorum
Cultivated on roofs for centuries - Gibson gives it as frequent in this habitat at Dedham and Manningtree. By Jermyn's time it had decreased and the only record he gave was from the wall and roof of St Osyth Priory. We have not found it during our survey.

SAXIFRAGE FAMILY
SAXIFRAGACEAE

Bergenia crassifolia
An introduction occurring where garden rubbish is dumped, we have not kept records for this plant during our survey.

Alternate-leaved Golden Saxifrage
Chrysosplenium alternifolium [1]
Despite continued checking of all the Golden Saxifrage we have found, we have been unable to find any sites for this species. The only known site is a private wood at Mistley where it was deliberately introduced.

Opposite-leaved Golden Saxifrage
Chrysosplenium oppositifolium [27] M
Infrequent and scattered in the area, on permanently wet and boggy ground by shady woodland streams which often occur where the clay and gravel soils meet. At Jermyn's site in Pebmarsh, where it was dominant over an estimated area of more than an acre in 1966, it was still so in 1982.

Meadow Saxifrage
Saxifraga granulata [4]
Very rare; we are now reduced to just two areas. Jermyn's site at Mistley church remains and it also occurs in the nearby cricket field although not seen each year due to mowing. The second site was also a churchyard; Foxearth, 1985.

Rue-leaved Saxifrage
Saxifraga tridactylites [4]
In the Breckland part of Suffolk this delicate Saxifrage can be found as an arable weed on the very light sandy soils, otherwise it grows on walls and dry banks. In Gibson's time it was rather local but found in all districts of the county although only on walls and dry banks. It was rare during Jermyn's time and he commented on the great decline that this plant had suffered in the past century. Being an annual it is very reliant on old walls with suitable surfaces for its seed to germinate each year and unsympathetic maintenance to a wall could well destroy the population. There are only three sites in our area, St Osyth Priory, the wall of Belchamp Walter Hall and the Roman Wall, Colchester, where restoration work is currently taking place and its continued presence is in doubt.

CURRANT FAMILY
GROSSULARIACEAE

Black Currant
Ribes nigrum [12]
Infrequent, as it was with Jermyn. It generally originates from seeds in bird droppings near gardens, allotments or fields where **Black Currants** are grown.

Red Currant
Ribes rubrum [76] M

Originating in the same way as the previous species it establishes itself in woods, hedgerows and waste places far more frequently.

Flowering Currant
Ribes sanguineum [1]

Frequently planted in gardens, it can occasionally be found growing in waste places. Not fully recorded.

Gooseberry
Ribes uva-crispa [28] M

Another bird sown species that can be found in hedges and woodland edges.

SUNDEW FAMILY
DROSERACEAE

Round-leaved Sundew
Drosera rotundifolia

In Gibson's time there were records for this insectivorous plant from Tiptree Heath, Pods Wood and West Bergholt Heath but they have long since disappeared.

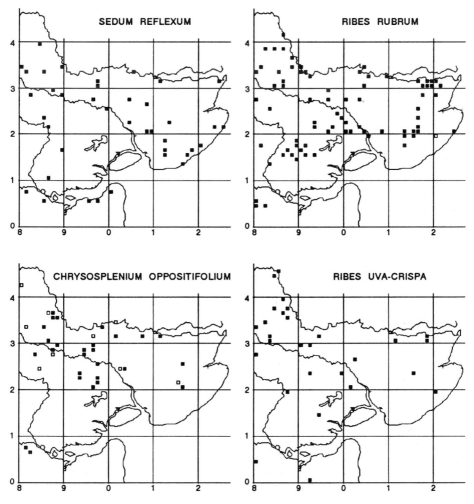

LOOSESTRIFE FAMILY
LYTHRACEAE

Water Purslane
Lythrum portula [10] M
Rare, but it can be overlooked. Usually found on heathy soils, in damp hollows in tracks, woodland rides and pond margins. It seems to have decreased since Jermyn's day.

Purple Loosestrife
Lythrum salicaria [92] M
Common along the banks of the major rivers and larger streams of our area, and occasionally it spreads out across a wet meadow or marsh, for example, Feering and at Bull Meadow, Colchester.

DAPHNE FAMILY
THYMELAEACEAE

Spurge Laurel
Daphne laureola [42] M
Scattered and infrequent but more common on the chalky boulder clays. Usually found at woodland edges, copses and in thick old hedges.

Mezereon
Daphne mezereum
According to Gibson this used to grow in a small wood on a farm at Feering. The labourers were in the habit of transplanting the young shrubs into their cottage gardens and these shrubs were still in existence at the time he wrote his Flora, although the wood had been stubbed up 20 years before. It has not been found since.

OLEASTER FAMILY
ELAEAGNACEAE

Sea Buckthorn
Hippophae rhamnoides [6]
Planted at several coastal sites, it then spreads as the thrushes devour its berries and deposit the seeds elsewhere.

EUCALYPTUS FAMILY
MYRTACEAE

Eucalyptus gunnii [5]
Introduced and not fully recorded. Jermyn gives an interesting account of the trees at Lodge Farm, Brightlingsea - "This native of Tasmania was introduced to Great Britain soon after its discovery in 1840. It is stated by Elwes & Henry, Trees and Shrubs of Great Britain and Ireland, 1912 "The most remarkable plantation that is known in England was made by the late John Bateman Esq of Brightlingsea Hall Farm, from seed he received in 1887". Some of these trees are now of very great size and they have survived the rigours of our English winters, in this rather bleak spot near the east coast for 85 years, including the arctic conditions of 1962-3". We understand that at one time nurserymen from other parts of England used to come to Brightlingsea to collect seed. Many of the trees were lost in the storms of October 1987 but some still remain.

WILLOWHERB FAMILY
ONAGRACEAE

Rosebay
Chamerion angustifolium [682] M
Common and locally plentiful along wood margins, in clearings and on heathlands, where, after a fire, it can quickly spread over a large area. It is also found in hedgebanks, grassy areas and waste places.

Enchanter's Nightshade
Circaea lutetiana [121] M
Reasonably frequent in damp shady places in the older woods. Its seeds are readily transported on clothing.

American Willowherb
Epilobium ciliatum [644] M
Common as a weed of ditchsides, gardens, disturbed soils, edges of car parks and similar sites.

Great Hairy Willowherb
Epilobium hirsutum [1147] M
Very common over the whole area in any non-saline damp situation. It tolerates pol-

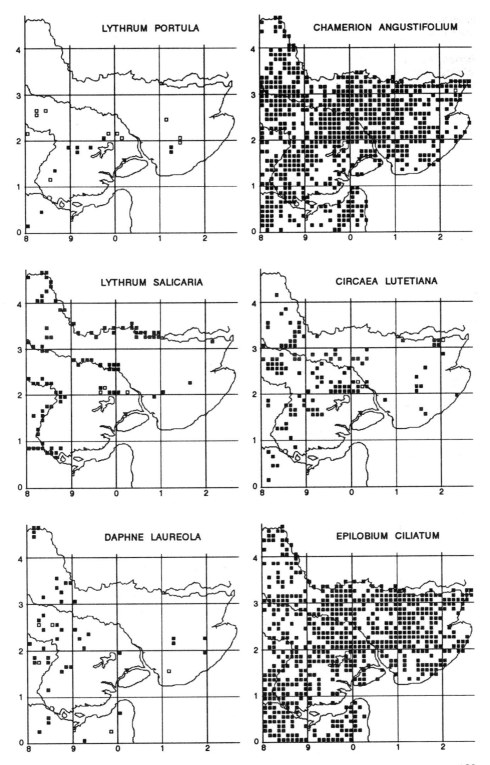

LYTHRUM PORTULA

CHAMERION ANGUSTIFOLIUM

LYTHRUM SALICARIA

CIRCAEA LUTETIANA

DAPHNE LAUREOLA

EPILOBIUM CILIATUM

luted water and is often the only remaining plant in a ditch.

Broad-leaved Willowherb
Epilobium montanum [42] M
Infrequent and scattered. It can be found in a variety of habitats from gardens to woodland rides and margins.

Short-fruited Willowherb
Epilobium obscurum [4]
Very rare. All our records are from damp areas close to farm buildings, in one case where a water tank was overflowing. This willowherb appears to have declined dramatically since Jermyn, who had records for eighteen 10km squares; our four records fall into only three 10km squares.

Marsh Willowherb
Epilobium palustre [1]
Very rare. Gibson gave Tiptree Heath and Thorpe, whilst Jermyn, who considered it to be decreasing through drainage of the wetlands, had a record for Layer de la Haye. Our only record is from Chigborough Lakes.

Hoary Willowherb
Epilobium parviflorum [36] M
Decreasing - Gibson considered it common, Jermyn quite common, and we have found it scattered and infrequent. One would expect to find it in similar situations as the **Great Hairy Willowherb** but our observations indicate that it occurs only where the water is 'clean'. If its decline is due to pollution this is an indictment on the condition of the majority of our ditches and small watercourses.

Pale Willowherb
Epilobium roseum [39] M
Scattered and infrequent. Generally in ditches and other damp places but occasionally in dry conditions.

Square-stemmed Willowherb
Epilobium tetragonum [183] M
Reasonably common as an arable or garden weed, or along ditchsides. The *ssp lamyi* has been found on two occasions in a waste area and as an arable weed but is probably under-recorded.

Lesser Evening Primrose
Oenothera biennis [12]
Both this and the **Large Evening Primrose** are garden escapes which can become established on waste ground.

Large Evening Primrose
Oenothera erythrosepala [31]
More common than its smaller counterpart, found in similar situations.

Oenothera fallax [4]
Where the above two species occur together it is possible for this hybrid to occur, although this is not essential as *O fallax* comes true from seed and can be found away from both parents. It has been found at The Moors (Colchester), Rowhedge Pits, Langford and Maldon.

WATER MILFOIL FAMILY
HALORAGIDACEAE

Gunnera tinctoria
Planted for ornament; usually by lakes in large gardens or parks. At Birch Hall where Jermyn recorded it as naturalised by the lake it was not refound, the lake bank is now much overgrown by **Willow** scrub. We have no records of this plant from our survey.

Alternate Water Milfoil
Myriophyllum alterniflorum
Recorded in Gibson's time from ponds at Tiptree Heath, but not found since.

Myriophyllum aquaticum [3]
This Water Milfoil is used in aquaria and we have recently started to find it well-naturalised in ponds.

Spiked Water Milfoil
Myriophyllum spicatum [29] M
Decreased since Jermyn, and although still common in the Chelmer-Blackwater Canal and on Old Hall Marshes it is scattered elsewhere in ponds, farm reservoirs, flooded gravel pits and borrow dykes.

Whorled Water Milfoil
Myriophyllum verticillatum
Despite all the pond-dipping during the survey we have been unable to find this

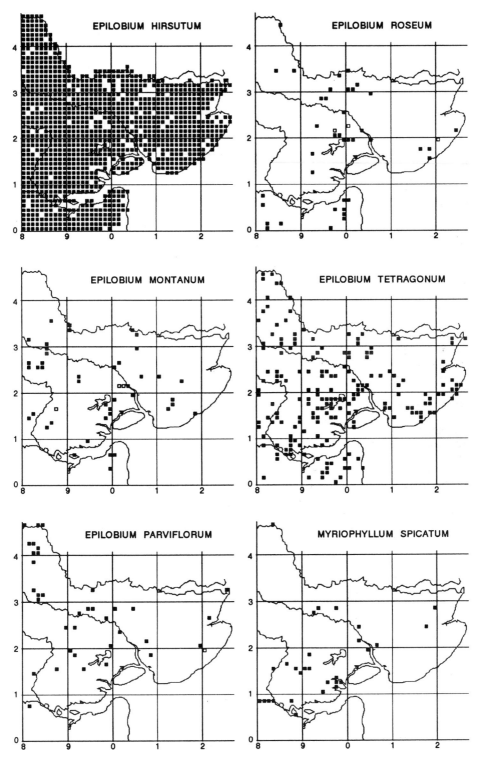

EPILOBIUM HIRSUTUM

EPILOBIUM ROSEUM

EPILOBIUM MONTANUM

EPILOBIUM TETRAGONUM

EPILOBIUM PARVIFLORUM

MYRIOPHYLLUM SPICATUM

species. Gibson had two records - Halstead and in a ditch at Salcott, and Jermyn one - Foxearth, gravel pits (now referred to as Liston Pits).

MARESTAIL FAMILY
HIPPURIDACEAE

Marestail
Hippuris vulgaris [2]
Now very rare, only one site remains in our area. In Gibson's time it was on the Colne at Halstead and the Stour near Bures bridge. Jermyn recorded it in the Rivenhall-Kelvedon area, on the Stour at Henny Street and several places between Bures and Dedham, as well as Tollesbury, and Liston Pits. It is this latter site where it is still present.

WATER STARWORT FAMILY
CALLITRICHACEAE

Water Starwort
Callitriche agg [198] M
The difficulties in the identification of this group have lead us to record it as an aggregate species; most is probably *C stagnalis* (for which we have eight definite records). *C obtusangula* has also been definitely identified twice, with records from Fingringhoe and Mayland. Both Gibson and Jermyn had also found *C hamulata* and *C platycarpa* in our area. Further work is needed on this group.

MISTLETOE FAMILY
LORANTHACEAE

Mistletoe
Viscum album [13]
Native and introduced, infrequent, parasitic on a variety of trees and shrubs, including fruit trees (**Apple** and **Plum**), **Lime**, **Poplar** and **Ash**. Jermyn's record on **Ash** at Braxted was refound and, as Gibson mentions that it grew on thorns in Braxted Park, **Mistletoe** has been in this area for well over a century.

DOGWOOD FAMILY
CORNACEAE

Dogwood
Cornus sanguinea [398] M
Common in hedgerows and woodland edges on the chalky boulder clay but scattered elsewhere. Jermyn had recorded it over the whole of north east Essex but this is no longer the case. With the loss of its hedgerow habitat, **Dogwood** has disappeared from the areas with unsuitable soils where it was already rare.

IVY FAMILY
ARALIACEAE

Ivy
Hedera helix [1092] M
Very common over the whole area, in hedges, woods, banks, buildings, walls and trees. It is often assumed, incorrectly, that **Ivy** kills the trees up which it climbs.

CARROT FAMILY
UMBELLIFERAE

Ground Elder
Aegopodium podagraria [448] M
Common and widespread. It was also known as **Goutweed** as it was used in treating gout, and as such is commonly found in old gardens and on road verges close to habitations. It is almost impossible to eradicate.

Fool's Parsley
Aethusa cynapium [255] M
A common arable and garden weed. There are two subspecies - the majority of our records refer to *ssp cynapium*, but *ssp agrestis* is found occasionally.

Ammi majus [1]
An uncommon bird seed alien; several plants occurred in 1986.

Wild Angelica
Angelica sylvestris [184] M
Still reasonably common where suitable habitat remains, but it has decreased since

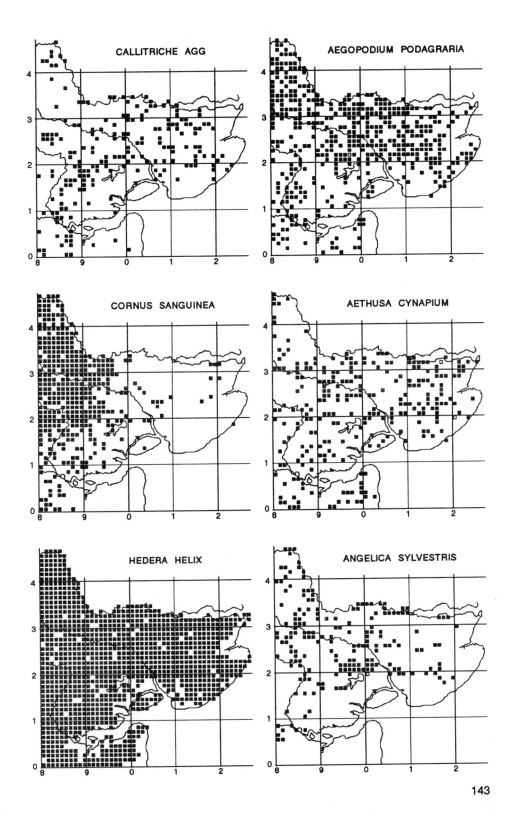

CALLITRICHE AGG

AEGOPODIUM PODAGRARIA

CORNUS SANGUINEA

AETHUSA CYNAPIUM

HEDERA HELIX

ANGELICA SYLVESTRIS

143

Jermyn due to the drainage of many of the marshy places in our area. Damp wooded and shady areas by streams and marshy places.

Bur Chervil
Anthriscus caucalis [107] M
Scattered inland on the lighter soils where it occurs on rough ground, around warehouses, industrial estates and railway stations. It is also found around the coast along the well-drained tops of the sea walls.

Garden Chervil
Anthriscus cerefolium
Gibson gives a record for this plant from a hedge bank at Kelvedon - "perhaps originally a straggler from cultivation, though the plant has occupied its present position for many years". There have been no other records.

Cow Parsley
Anthriscus sylvestris [1226] M
Very common over the whole area although it is absent from the old grazing marshes of Langenhoe and Old Hall.

Wild Celery
Apium graveolens [41] M
Now infrequent in its traditional sites in the borrow dykes along our coast. Neither Gibson nor Jermyn give any inland records but our intensive coverage of the area has revealed a few, although none are very far from the coast.

Marshwort
Apium inundatum [1]
Very rare. Gibson had a record for Tiptree Heath which Jermyn was unable to refind. However, in the late 1980s, a new management regime was instituted for the Heath and it appeared in a cleared pond in 1987. This is the only record for our area. Jermyn's other sites at Abberton Reservoir and Fordham Heath were not refound.

Fool's Watercress
Apium nodiflorum [368] M
Common in damp ditches and ponds. It can often be abundant in nutrient enriched ditches.

Lesser Water Parsnip
Berula erecta [9] M
This plant has severely declined - common to Gibson, local to Jermyn, it is now rare. We were unable to refind any of Jermyn's sites although we did find a few new ones. These were at pond edges, or, in ditches which were fed by seepage from the sand and gravel soils above clay.

Sickle Hare's Ear
Bupleurum falcatum
Jermyn gives a detailed review of the history of this plant. It was known outside our area from a damp roadside verge and ditchbank, adjacent hedgerows and field borders at Norton Heath (between Chelmsford and Chipping Ongar) from 1831-c1962, but due to hedge clearance and road realignment was lost at its only site in the county. However, he had grown some plants in his garden from seed collected previously and from this stock it was introduced into Fingringhoe Wick Nature Reserve. It has now, unfortunately, died out here too. The Nature Conservancy Council have since reintroduced it to the original site.

Shrubby Hare's Ear
Bupleurum fruticosum
An introduced species that was naturalised on the Naze Cliffs between 1959 and 1964, but which we were unable to refind.

Thorow Wax
Bupleurum rotundifolium
For a time there was confusion between this species and the next and Jermyn had a report for **Thorow Wax** from a garden at Colchester, c1920, which he considered was probably *B subovatum*. In consequence, it appears that this plant has never occurred in the north east of the county.

Bupleurum subovatum [3]
A bird seed alien that occurs occasionally.

Slender Hare's Ear
Bupleurum tenuissimum [64] M
Locally common on sea walls especially by the Blackwater Estuary and Hamford Water. It is found on mature sea walls where the soil is poor and the grass rather

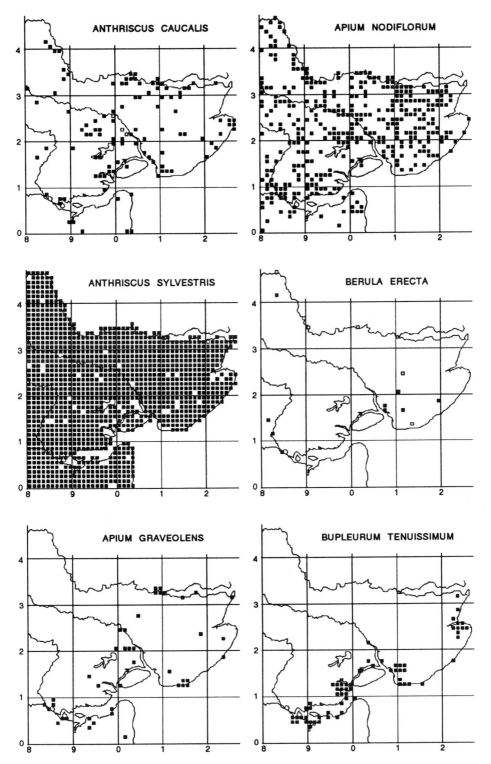

ANTHRISCUS CAUCALIS

APIUM NODIFLORUM

ANTHRISCUS SYLVESTRIS

BERULA ERECTA

APIUM GRAVEOLENS

BUPLEURUM TENUISSIMUM

sparse. **Slender Hare's Ear** blends into the background and, as it has also been found by chance in long grass on a coastal grazing marsh, it is possible that it grows in a wider range of coastal grassland than the habitat mentioned above.

Caraway
Carum carvi [2]
Introduced. Occasionally found as an escape from cultivation on road verges.

Rough Chervil
Chaerophyllum temulentum [328] M
Common in shady lanes, hedgerows and wood borders, usually on the lighter gravel soils.

Hemlock
Conium maculatum [504] M
Common over the whole area in both wet and dry situations. Usually associated with damp ditchsides, streams and rivers, it also occurs on road verges, including the central reservation of the A12. There is a particularly fine stand between Easthorpe and Kelvedon.

Pignut
Conopodium majus [72] M
Decreasing with the loss of old grassland. It occurs on the gravel soils, either in woods - it is common in Stour Wood - or in old grassland, particularly if it was once wooded. It is often found in churchyards as these can be the only places where old grassland still occurs.

Coriander
Coriandrum sativum [1]
An escape from cultivation, our only record was a seedling growing by the roadside close to houses.

Rock Samphire
Crithmum maritimum [5]
Very rare. It had not been found in the county in Gibson's time, and appears to have first been discovered in 1887 at Great Oakley, where it still occurs (1989). Jermyn had found it at Colne Point in 1971, where it was still present in 1988. His Walton site (1969-70) could not be refound, but in 1988 we did discover a further site on the coastal cliffs.

Wild Carrot
Daucus carota ssp carota [268] M
Common on the coastal grasslands along the sea walls where it generally grows on the upper half of the wall where the drainage is better. It also occurs in sandy areas on the coast. Once away from the coastal influence its distribution becomes scattered occurring on rough grassy verges and banks on the lighter soils, until the chalky outcrop is reached in the very north west of our area. Here it becomes common again.

Sea Holly
Eryngium maritimum [11] M
Very local on sandy beaches. It occurs in much the same sites as Jermyn gave, except that coastal erosion has reduced the dunes in the Crabknowe Spit area. A candy was once made from the roots of this plant. It was first mentioned in 1597 in Gerard's Herbal. Ray, quoted in Camden's **Britannia,** stated that : "This plant being common enough on sandy shores I should not have mentioned, but Colchester is noted for first inventing or practising the candying or conditing of its roots, the manner whereof may be seen in Gerard's Herbal". Jermyn was able to add further information "This candy was apparently a great speciality that was served at Mayorial banquets at Colchester as far back as the fifteenth century and up to comparatively recent times. It has been reported that this candy was still made from the original recipe and sold in the town during the first quarter of the present century". Please remember, times have changed, and it is now illegal to uproot wild plants.

Longleaf
Falcaria vulgaris [1]
Not previously recorded for our part of Essex, it occurred for the first time in 1989. It is introduced and possibly arrives as a seed contaminant.

Fennel
Foeniculum vulgare [75] M
Fennel has been grown in many gardens over the years, from which it has subsequently escaped, obscuring the native

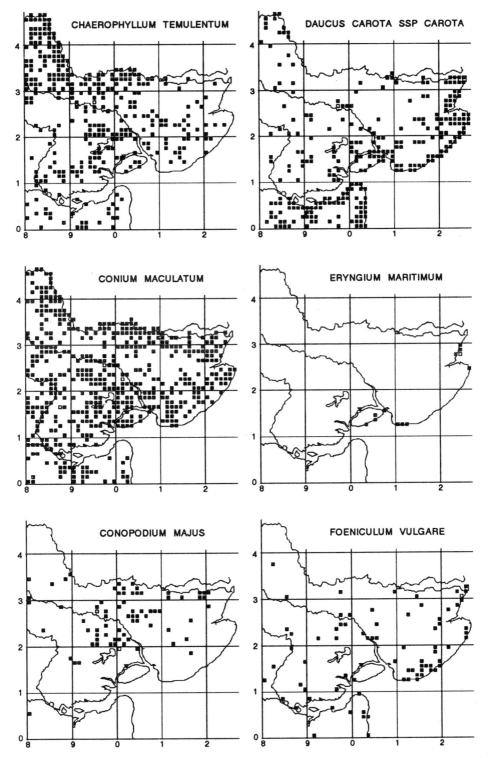

CHAEROPHYLLUM TEMULENTUM

DAUCUS CAROTA SSP CAROTA

CONIUM MACULATUM

ERYNGIUM MARITIMUM

CONOPODIUM MAJUS

FOENICULUM VULGARE

distribution. At many of the localities in coastal and estuarine grassland it is probably native.

Giant Hogweed
Heracleum mantegazzianum [29] M
Introduced and still spreading in damp places by rivers and streams and occasionally roadside verges. It is inadvisable to touch this plant as there are hairs on the stem which contain an irritating chemical. This reacts with sunlight to cause a skin rash, which will reoccur each time the skin is exposed to sunlight. It is now illegal to plant **Giant Hogweed**.

Hogweed
Heracleum sphondylium [1045] M
Very common except on the low lying coastal areas which remain as grazing, or have only recently been converted into arable.

Marsh Pennywort
Hydrocotyle vulgaris [1]
Known from Tiptree Heath by both Gibson and Jermyn, it was still present in 1981. They also both knew it from West Bergholt Heath but this is now farmland. Neither of Jermyn's other sites at Weeley or Fordham Heath could be refound, the latter heath having deteriorated over the years through scrub encroachment.

Sweet Cicely
Myrrhis odorata
This fragrant plant, which partially takes the place of **Cow Parsley** in the north of England, was found as a garden escape at Lawford in 1958 but it did not persist.

Fine-leaved Water Dropwort
Oenanthe aquatica [16] M
Jermyn commented that it was decreasing with the infilling of ponds, its main habitat, and we have found this trend has continued; it now has only an infrequent and scattered distribution, although it fills some ponds almost to the exclusion of other vegetation.

Hemlock Water Dropwort
Oenanthe crocata [5] M
Not known to Gibson from our area, Jermyn found it sporadically on the Stour

between Wormingford and Bures but we were unable to refind it here. However, it does occur on the Colne in Colchester and at Fingringhoe Wick Nature Reserve.

Tubular Water Dropwort
Oenanthe fistulosa [2]
Very rare. The only remaining site is at Great Holland Pits Nature Reserve and adjacent area. It was found in a drainage ditch close to Colchester Bypass in 1979 but this could not be refound during our survey. It must once have been reasonably widespread in wet meadows and ponds as Gibson gives records for Halstead, Kelvedon, Inworth, Easthorpe and Wivenhoe.

River Water Dropwort
Oenanthe fluviatilis [3] M
According to Gibson this was once common in most of the rivers of Essex and also in the ditches and streams connected with them. Jermyn considered that it was not as widespread but still had records for the upper reaches of the Blackwater and Stour, although he had been unable to find it on the Colne. However, we have found it at three sites on the Colne but none at all on the Blackwater and Stour. At all of our sites there were just a few plants. It grows where the river bed has a gravelly bottom and if removed during dredging does not seem to be able to recolonise.

Parsley Water Dropwort
Oenanthe lachenalii [18] M
Infrequent in the grass beside the borrow dykes around our coast, usually only in small quantity. However, at one site in the Hamford Water area, there was a population of over twenty plants, and at Holland Haven, many tens if not hundreds of plants were found, in both wet and dry ditches, in 1989.

Corky-fruited Water Dropwort
Oenanthe pimpinelloides [1]
E G Varenne, a contemporary of Gibson's, wrote "Roadsides, fields and pasture land at Wigborough and Virley plentifully; not in the saltings which bound the meadows. The tubers are well known to the rustic population of the locality by the name of pig nuts". He also found it at Mersea. It is common in a field at Epping but Jermyn

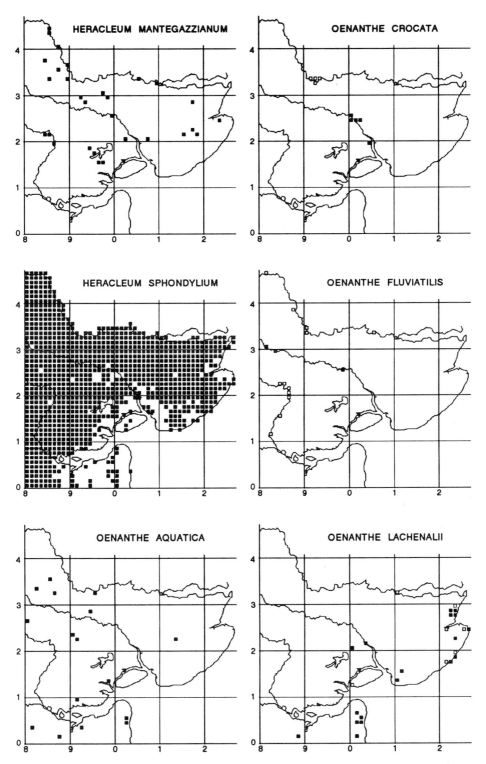

was unaware of this as he considered it lost to the county. In 1988 we found two plants growing on a damp verge on the main road into Clacton. They were in danger of being mown but that must have been their fate for many years.

Narrow-leaved Water Dropwort
Oenanthe silaifolia
In 1966 a small number of plants were found in a water meadow by the River Stour at Henny Street. Two years later a large colony was found nearer the river but the site was due to be destroyed by river widening and deepening operations. As this was the only known Essex station Jermyn made arrangements for transferring a number of the plants to a safer place in the immediate vicinity. We were unable to refind this plant in the area.

Garden Parsnip
Pastinaca sativa ssp sativa [33] M
This occurs as a relic of cultivation or garden escape on road verges and waste places. However, in some parts of Suffolk, on the light alkaline soils, the **Garden Parsnip** maintains itself in the wild and it is possible that some of our records refer to similar plants where there is a chalky influence in the soil.

Wild Parsnip
Pastinaca sativa ssp sylvestris [300] M
Common on grassy verges and rough grassland on the sands and gravels and where there is an acidic influence in the soil. It differs from the previous subspecies being a taller, thinner plant with a greyish look to it compared with the shorter, wider and greener appearance of *ssp sativa*.

Garden Parsley
Petroselinum crispum [4]
Occasionally found as a garden escape - it can become naturalised given a suitable site.

Corn Parsley
Petroselinum segetum [11] M
Now rare and still decreasing - all Jermyn's inland sites have been lost and many of his coastal records too. **Corn Parsley** once not only grew in coastal grassland but also inland in cornfields and waste places. On

examining the habitat and sites where it used to occur, it appears that it has been eradicated as a cornfield weed by today's chemicals and from former coastal grazing marshes by their conversion to arable cultivation. It is now mainly found in the grassland between the borrow dykes and sea wall.

Sea Hog's Fennel
Peucedanum officinale [24]
Nationally this plant only occurs in our part of Essex and at Faversham in Kent. It was first discovered in the Walton area by Gerard in 1597: "It groweth very plentifully on the south side of a wood belonging to Walton on the Naze by the highway side". It has subsequently been found at many places around Hamford Water, although it no longer occurs at the Naze. Our survey has shown that it is still widespread around Hamford Water and it can be abundant on sites with restricted access. We have also found two out-lying stations in the area but whether these are native or introductions is not known. The caterpillar of the **Fisher's Estuarine Moth**, (*Gortyna borelii* Pierr) initially feeds inside the stem of **Sea Hog's Fennel** and then finishes its life cycle amongst the roots. The only area in Britain where this moth occurs is around Hamford Water. During the survey we noticed that some of the more accessible sites for this plant had been destroyed by irresponsible individuals interested only in collecting this rare moth. Please remember, it is illegal to uproot any wild flower and it isn't very pleasant for the moth either!

Burnet Saxifrage
Pimpinella saxifraga [123] M
Widespread on the chalky boulder clay in old grassland, particularly in churchyards and on some verges. Its range has greatly contracted since Jermyn, and even in its stronghold it is now nowhere "locally abundant".

Sanicle
Sanicula europaea [6]
Very rare due to lack of suitable habitat. It requires old woodlands on a chalky soil. It has declined dramatically since Jermyn - to him it was frequent and locally common

and occurred in nine 10km squares. We have just six sites.

Shepherd's Needle
Scandix pecten-veneris [12]
Very rare. Scattered plants are infrequently found, usually just one or two in a corner of a field where the spray has missed, but on one occasion it was found to be abundant along the edge of a **Sugar Beet** field.

Pepper Saxifrage
Silaum silaus [34] M
Another of the Umbellifers which has decreased through loss of mature grassland habitat. Jermyn considered this to be "frequent and well distributed"; our

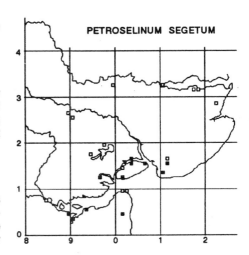

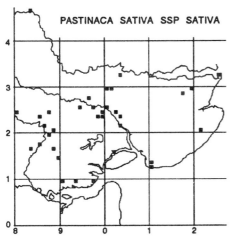

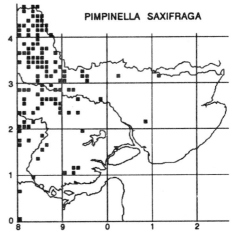

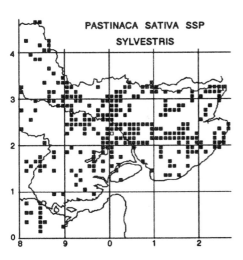

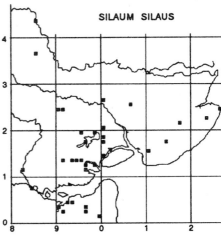

description now is infrequent and uncommon. A few plants have been found on mature verges and a golf course, but it occurs mainly in churchyards, again indicating the importance of this habitat as a relic of ancient grassland. The two sites where it can be found in any quantity are, however, rough grassland behind the sea wall on the Howlands Marsh Nature Reserve (about 20-30 plants), and our largest colony, in a damp meadow at High Woods Country Park where over 100 plants were found.

Stone Parsley
Sison amomum [355] M
Common on the heavy clay soils but scattered elsewhere, it is found on road verges, rough grassland and ditchsides. This plant has a most amazing aroma - smell the crushed seeds and it is guaranteed that all cobwebs will be cleared from your head, instantly!

Alexanders
Smyrnium olusatrum [118] M
Commonest in hedgerows, verges and waste ground near the coast, it seems to be increasingly found inland. Gibson gives a record for near Fordham and we have found it growing along the A604 in this vicinity.

Spreading Hedge Parsley
Torilis arvensis [2]
Very rare; just two sites (Ardleigh, 1982, and Elmstead, 1984) have been found during our survey. On both occasions there were just two or three plants in a field edge.

Upright Hedge Parsley
Torilis japonica [228] M
Reasonably common with a widespread distribution in woodland rides and edges, scrub, rough grassland and verges.

Knotted Hedge Parsley
Torilis nodosa [27] M
Still locally common on the dry parts of some sea walls but its range has contracted as many of its inland localities have been lost. Inland it used to occur on dry banks, and, on the lighter soils, as an arable weed.

MELON FAMILY
CUCURBITACEAE

White Bryony
Bryonia dioica [775] M
Very common over most of the area but singularly absent from areas which were, in the past, traditionally grazing lands. Whether this is because the stock grazed it out or because it needs disturbed soils to gain a foothold is not known. Usually found scrambling over hedgerows, scrub, woodland borders, fences and telegraph poles; however, if these are not present it will inter-twine with itself forming a tangled mass.

Water Melon
Citrullus lanatus [1]
In 1989 a plant occurred growing from cracks in a concrete garden path where it flowered throughout the summer until it was killed by the autumn frosts. It did not, however, produce any fruit.

BIRTHWORT FAMILY
ARISTOLOCHIACEAE

Birthwort
Aristolochia clematitis [1]
It was introduced into the churchyard at Colchester Natural History Museum in 1958 where it continues to flourish.

SPURGE FAMILY
EUPHORBIACEAE

Wood Spurge
Euphorbia amygdaloides [84] M
In our area this plant has had to adapt - Gibson gives its habitat as "woods and thickets", Jermyn "damp woods and scrub, very occasionally hedgerows". It still occurs in the old woodland but the majority of our records now come from ditchsides, presumably those which would once have had hedgerows or woodland adjacent, but which have now been grubbed out. Its overall distribution, however, seems to have remained fairly constant.

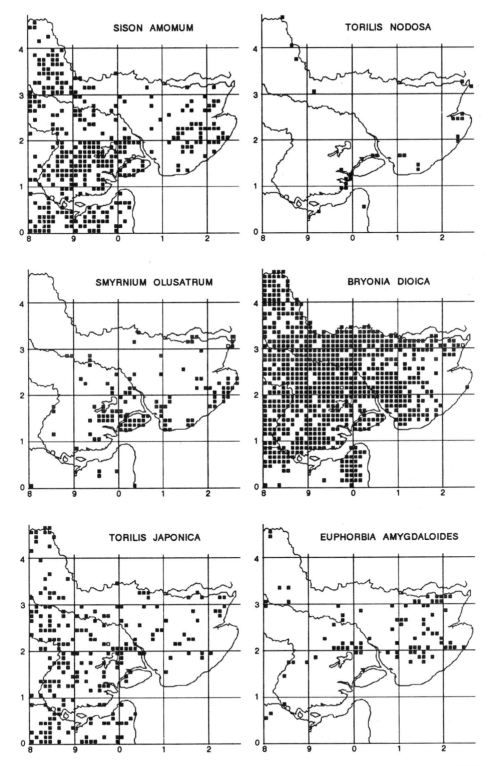

SISON AMOMUM

TORILIS NODOSA

SMYRNIUM OLUSATRUM

BRYONIA DIOICA

TORILIS JAPONICA

EUPHORBIA AMYGDALOIDES

Twiggy Spurge
Euphorbia esula [3]
An introduced species that is decreasing. Only Jermyn's site by the canal at Ulting was refound but two new sites were discovered.

Dwarf Spurge
Euphorbia exigua [73] M
An arable weed that has decreased in frequency although it still maintains a widespread but scattered distribution. Only where there is a chalky influence in the soil can it be found both more frequently and in greater quantity.

Sun Spurge
Euphorbia helioscopia [339] M
Common as an arable and garden weed and on waste areas. Less common on the chalk soils.

Caper Spurge
Euphorbia lathyrus [19]
An introduced plant that becomes naturalised.

Sea Spurge
Euphorbia paralias [4]
As with Jermyn this is very rare on coastal shingly sand. Gibson's record for Dovercourt and Jermyn's for Little Oakley relate to the same general area where it was still present in 1988 and 1989. We were unable to refind Jermyn's records for Colne Point and Walton but found two other sites at West Mersea, 1986, and Bradwell-on-Sea, 1987.

Petty Spurge
Euphorbia peplus [468] M
Very common and widely distributed as a garden weed and on any disturbed waste and tipped soils.

Broad-leaved Spurge
Euphorbia platyphyllos
Gibson had several records from cultivated fields at Halstead, Rivenhall, Inworth and Layer Marney, but there have been no sightings since.

Annual Mercury
Mercurialis annua [151] M
Locally plentiful as a weed of gardens,

allotments and tipped soil heaps.

Dog's Mercury
Mercurialis perennis [356] M
Common in woods, bridleways and hedgerows on the chalky boulder clays but scattered elsewhere, usually only in the older woods and hedges.

DOCK FAMILY
POLYGONACEAE

Buckwheat
Fagopyrum esculentum [3]
Introduced. Now mostly as a bird seed alien but it may become temporarily established in woods where the seed has been fed to pheasants.

Russian Vine
Fallopia aubertii [24] M
Always planted, in some old cottage gardens it survives long after the dwelling has been pulled down.

Black Bindweed
Fallopia convolvulus [725] M
Very common over the whole area, as an arable and garden weed as well as occurring on any area of disturbed bare soil.

Amphibious Bistort
Polygonum amphibium [187] M
Jermyn found the aquatic form to be

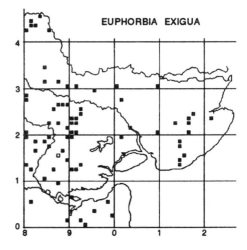

EUPHORBIA EXIGUA

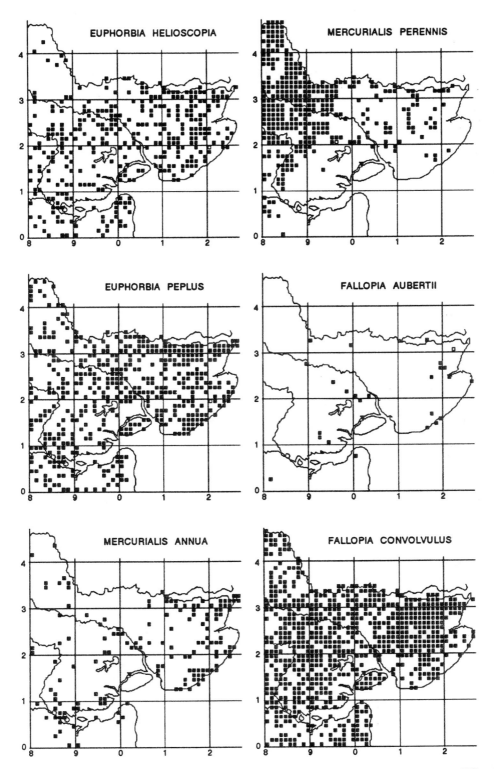

EUPHORBIA HELIOSCOPIA

MERCURIALIS PERENNIS

EUPHORBIA PEPLUS

FALLOPIA AUBERTII

MERCURIALIS ANNUA

FALLOPIA CONVOLVULUS

common in large areas of open water, but during our survey we have rarely met with this form. Our records almost invariably refer to the terrestrial form in damp situations near rivers, ponds, ditches and even occasionally as an arable weed. We have often found it growing on river banks amongst the soil and vegetation dredged out of the river; presumably this would once have been the aquatic form. The terrestrial form has only been seen in flower occasionally, most notably at Bull Meadow Nature Reserve in Colchester.

Equal-leaved Knotgrass
Polygonum arenastrum [256] M
Avoiding the clay soils it is frequent on tracks, paths, cracks in concrete and pavements.

Common Knotgrass
Polygonum aviculare [1114] M
Very common on all soils, as a weed in arable fields and gardens, or on tracks, paths and any bare patches of disturbed ground.

Bistort PERSICARIA
Polygonum bistorta [2]
Only one of Jermyn's sites has survived - the marshy plantation near the sewage works at Great Maplestead. Our only other locality is at Inworth churchyard.

Polygonum cognatum
An introduction at Hythe Quay, Colchester, it persisted over thirty years (1925-1955) but has now vanished.

Water Pepper
Polygonum hydropiper [138] M
Reasonably frequent in wet woodland rides and cart tracks, particularly where water stands in winter.

Pale Persicaria
Persicaria *Polygonum lapathifolium* [467] M
Common on arable land, particularly sugar beet fields, as well as gardens, tipped soil heaps and other disturbed ground.

Small Water Pepper
Polygonum minus
Gibson had a record for the lane near Dedham workhouse but it has long since

been lost to the county.

Ray's Knotgrass
Polygonum oxyspermum ssp raii [2]
Not previously found in Essex although in 1862 Gibson wrote that he thought this was a plant not unlikely to be found in the county. It took 124 years to prove him right, but in 1986 we found a few plants on a sandy beach on Mersea Island. Two years later another site was found, at Dovercourt, where again several plants were located.

Persicaria or Redleg Space-Persicaria
Polygonum persicaria [623] M Maculosa
Very common as an arable and garden weed and on any bare disturbed ground.

Cornfield Knotgrass
Polygonum rurivagum [4]
Very rare. This knotgrass is a weed of arable fields which sets seed very late in the year. Fields are now harvested, burnt, ploughed and sown almost within a few days, a regime that is unsympathetic to the survival of this knotgrass.

Japanese Knotweed
Reynoutria japonica [69] M
This species was a popular garden plant in Victorian times but it is so persistent and virtually impossible to eradicate that it has long since lost favour. It is now reasonably frequent by road and streamsides and in waste places although usually near houses. Because of its spread and diffi-

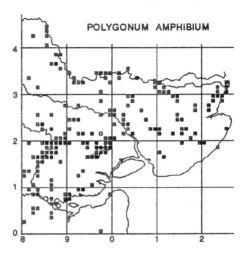

POLYGONUM AMPHIBIUM

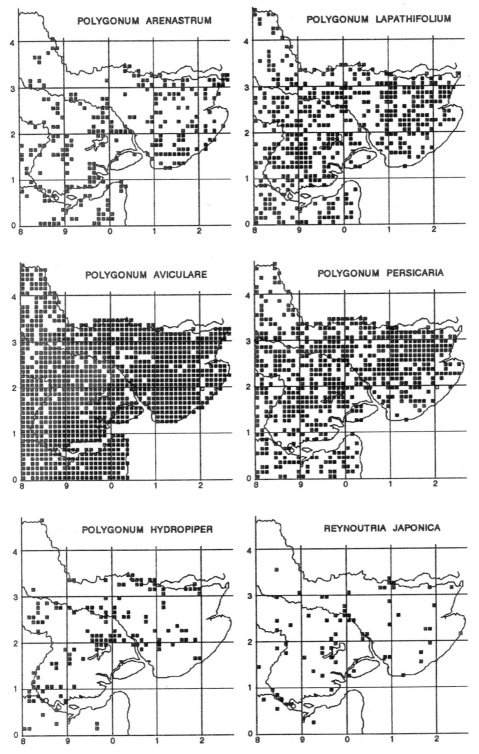

POLYGONUM ARENASTRUM

POLYGONUM LAPATHIFOLIUM

POLYGONUM AVICULARE

POLYGONUM PERSICARIA

POLYGONUM HYDROPIPER

REYNOUTRIA JAPONICA

culty of control it has been placed on the list of species which it is illegal to plant in Britain.

Giant Knotweed
Reynoutria sachalinensis [4]
Like the last species, this is a garden escape which has naturalised in a few places, however, it is much less frequent. A patch has been known from the Hythe, Colchester, for many years.

Rheum palmatum
Introduced. We have not kept records for this species but Jermyn mentions that two large plants had naturalised in a roadside ditch at Liston.

Common Sorrel
Rumex acetosa [559] M
Common on most types of grassland including verges, churchyards and old lawns, but not sea walls.

Sheep's Sorrel
Rumex acetosella [496] M
Common on the lighter soils, particularly acid heaths, sand and gravel pits and dry banks as well as other dry areas where there is little competition from more vigorous plants.

Rumex altissimus
This casual occurred at Hythe Quay, Colchester in 1941-2.

Clustered Dock
Rumex conglomeratus [478] M
Common and widely distributed throughout the area, in ditches and hedges and by streams.

Curled Dock
Rumex crispus [1162] M
Very common throughout the area on any grassland and as a weed of gardens and bare disturbed soils. **Curled Dock** also hybridises with other Docks, the two most likely to occur being *crispus X obtusifolius* and *crispus X sanguineus*.

Great Water Dock
Rumex hydrolapathum [46] M
It is now infrequent along the fresh water

rivers where both Gibson and Jermyn found it to be common. However, we have found large stands on the brackish dykes in Howlands and Brightlingsea Marshes and generally around the Flag Creek area, as well as the upper reaches of the estuarine Blackwater at Maldon. Recorded from Manningtree Station in 1983 this site has since been lost due to the expansion of the station car park.

Golden Dock
Rumex maritimus [31] M
Very common around Abberton Reservoir and also at Ardleigh Reservoir. Otherwise a few very scattered localities have been found, some of these are at farm reservoirs where it has probably arrived with the waterfowl. An unusual site was in a horse paddock where it was growing in hoofprints in soggy ground at the edge of a pond.

Rumex obovatus
A casual that was found at Hythe Quay in 1927 but has not been seen since.

Broad-leaved Dock
Rumex obtusifolius [1174] M
Very common over the whole area. As with so many of the plants that are this common, it can live in many different habitats. **Broad-leaved Dock** is absent only from the old grazing marshes of Langenhoe and Old Hall.

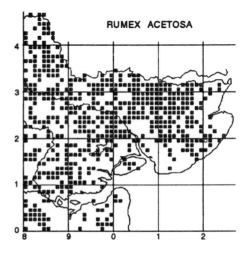
RUMEX ACETOSA

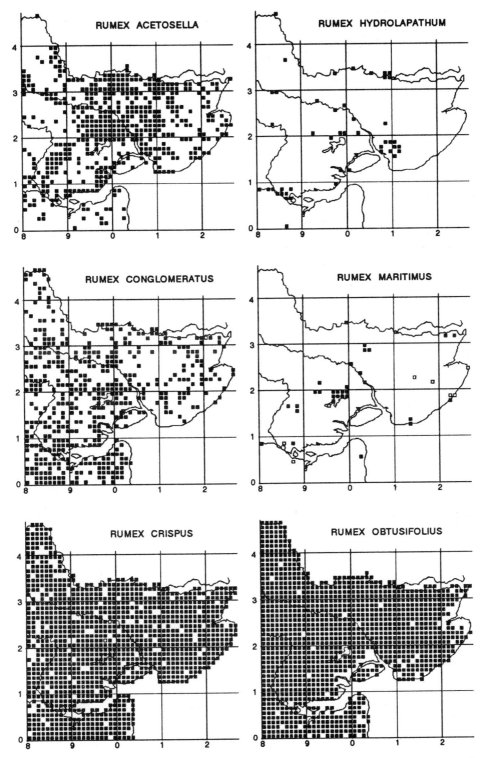

Marsh Dock
Rumex palustris
Until the seed of this Dock is reasonably mature it is difficult to identify positively. We have no confirmed records.

Western Dock
Rumex patientia ssp orientalis
A rare alien Dock that was recorded from Salcott-cum-Virley, 1909-1921, and again in 1927. It has not been recorded since.

Fiddle Dock
Rumex pulcher [7] M
This Dock has decreased and is now quite rare whereas it was described by Gibson as common. Found on grassy verges and banks at Maldon, Colchester and at Frinton Golf Course.

Wood Dock
Rumex sanguineus var viridis [378] M
Common and well distributed although generally avoiding the immediate coastal strip. It is found in woods and wood borders, as well as shady hedgerows and scrub.

Linear-leaved Sheep's Sorrel
Rumex tenuifolius [1]
Changes in the identification criteria of this species were published during our survey and we have been unable to confirm our record for this species due to destruction of the site.

Willow-leaved Dock
Rumex triangulivalvis
A casual that occurred at Hythe Quay in 1927.

NETTLE FAMILY
URTICACEAE

Pellitory of the Wall
Parietaria judaica [29] M
Rather local on the shady side of old walls, churches and tombstones. Mainly in urban areas.

Mind Your Own Business
Soleirolia soleirolii [6]
A garden escape that has become naturalised in a few places. It is invariably found in damp lawns in the shade of the north side of a wall or building.

Stinging Nettle
Urtica dioica [1252] M
Universally very common, especially in areas enriched with nitrates or phosphates; as such, it is often an indicator of old habitation sites.

Roman Nettle
Urtica pilulifera
A casual that used to occur, probably as a contaminant of seed, and which was last seen in the area at Hythe Quay between 1915-1927. Earlier records include "the north side of Harwich church and in a meadow on the west side of the gate, plentifully" (Dale, 1732), Copford (Babington, 1856) and the railway station at Kelvedon in 1845.

Annual Nettle
Urtica urens [320] M
Common as an arable and garden weed in the Tendring area but scattered elsewhere.

HEMP FAMILY
CANNABACEAE

Hemp
Cannabis sativa [2]
Better known by its scientific name of **Cannabis** it is illegal to grow this plant in Britain but it does occur occasionally as a bird seed alien or as a casual of rubbish tips. We found it once growing along the high tide line where its seed had been washed ashore and germinated. Our intensive coverage did reveal other sites, usually the bottom of derelict gardens and orchards! Not fully recorded.

Hop
Humulus lupulus [346] M
Common on the gravel soils, particularly when associated with a river or stream system, but scattered elsewhere. It occurs in hedges, wood borders, copses and is often seen climbing up the stay wires of telegraph poles. Jermyn's comment that the female plants bearing 'cones' were most commonly found is still valid as only a few male plants were recorded.

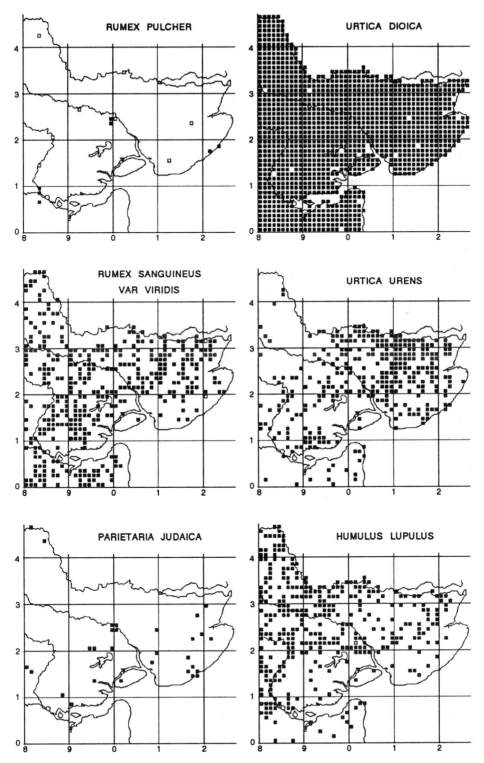

161

ELM FAMILY
ULMACEAE

According to Richens (Forestry 40, 1967, p184) "the Elm flora of Essex is probably the richest in its range of forms of any county in England". Fourteen of his sixteen groups are found in our area but their identification is a specialist task, about which specialists disagree. We have chosen, therefore, to follow Clapham Tutin & Moore and divide our records into *U glabra*, the **Wych Elm**, and *U minor*, the **Smooth-leaved Elm**.

The spread of Dutch Elm disease in our area has made it difficult in many places to find mature trees from which to collect the type of leaves needed for identification. It is only in the Dengie peninsula, where a distinct group of Elms is found, that there are many mature trees left. The gall mite *Eriophyes campestricola* Frauenfeld (*E ulmi* Nalepa) is widespread in our area and does not appear to be restricted to any particular 'group' of Elms.

Wych Elm
Ulmus glabra [98] M
Scattered in small quantity in hedgerows, becoming more frequent inland. *Ulmus glabra cv 'Pendula'* was previously known from some churchyards in Colchester but those at St James and All Saints have had to be cut down due to the ravages of Dutch Elm disease and it is not known if any other specimens of this variety now survive.

Smooth-leaved Elm
Ulmus minor [419] M
An Elm that is common on the clay soils, particularly on the Dengie peninsula. We follow **Flora of the British Isles**, 1987, in including all Elms other than **Wych Elm** under this heading. Should Dutch Elm disease die out and mature trees again become a common sight in our countryside, it might be possible to undertake further work on this group.

WALNUT FAMILY
JUGLANDACEAE

Juglans nigra
An ornamental tree recorded from Wivenhoe in 1977 but it was not rerecorded during our survey.

Walnut
Juglans regia [37] M
Infrequent and scattered over most of the area. It is planted in hedgerows, gardens, parks, and avenues. Not included in the records is the Walnut orchard at Boxtedhall, which we understand was planted during the 1920s.

BIRCH FAMILY
BETULACEAE

Italian Alder
Alnus cordata [9]
Becoming increasingly popular as a planted tree, particularly in shelter belts around orchards. Not fully recorded.

Alder
Alnus glutinosa [263] M
The native distribution has become obscured by plantings as it is one of the recommended trees for wet ground. It is associated with damp areas and river valleys, often growing beside the river with its roots stabilising the bank. Occasionally on the chalky boulder clays small pockets of Alder carr can still be found.

Silver Birch
Betula pendula [275] M
Originally a tree of light, heathy soils, it has become widespread due to planting although it is still either rare or absent on the heavy clay soils.

Downy Birch
Betula pubescens [100] M
The **Downy Birch**, unlike the previous species, is a tree of damp places in woods.

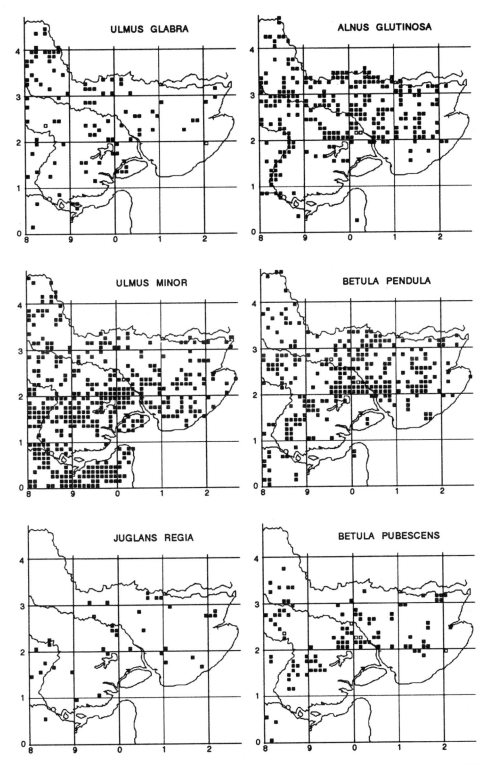

It is usually found in small quantity in the older woodlands of our area.

HAZEL FAMILY
CORYLACEAE

Hornbeam
Carpinus betulus [172] M
A native tree of old hedges and ancient woods, where it is often coppiced; most frequent on the mixed gravel soils around Tiptree and south west through Maldon. It is becoming increasingly planted in the creation of new hedgerows on farm planting schemes. Many of our **Sweet Chestnut** woods were probably originally of this species, they were replanted because of the more rapid coppice regrowth of the Chestnut.

Hazel
Corylus avellana [706] M
Very common in woods and hedges away from the low lying coastal areas.

BEECH FAMILY
FAGACEAE

Sweet Chestnut
Castanea sativa [268] M
Thought to be introduced to Britain by the Romans it is now a widely distributed tree. In Chalkney Woods the size of the stools indicate that it has been regularly coppiced for hundreds of years. Parts of Stour Wood where the species was first recorded about 1789 are almost pure **Sweet Chestnut**. It is also planted for ornament in parks and along roadsides, for example, the Avenue of Remembrance, Colchester. It is one of the trees being used to replant woods damaged in the storm of October, 1987.

Beech
Fagus sylvatica [162] M
Never native in our area, it is now widely planted. There is a small plantation of **Beech** in Friday Wood but this is unusual.

Roble Beech
Nothofagus obliqua [1]
Many foreign trees can now be found in our parks and gardens, the **Roble Beech** being just one example. Not fully recorded.

Turkey Oak
Quercus cerris [73] M
Originally planted, it has become naturalised in the hedgerows in some parts of our area, e.g. around Tiptree and south of Maldon.

Holm Oak
Quercus ilex [88] M
Planted in parks and gardens for ornament. There is a particularly fine specimen opposite the gates to Hyderabad Barracks in Colchester.

Sessile Oak
Quercus petraea [51] M
The Oak with stalks to its leaves but none to its acorns, it is usually found in damp situations on acid clays, but is also planted in other situations.

Quercus petraea X robur [1]
A variable hybrid between the **Sessile** and **Pedunculate Oaks** which must occur more frequently than our recording indicates.

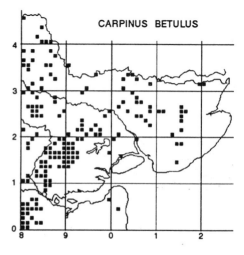

CARPINUS BETULUS

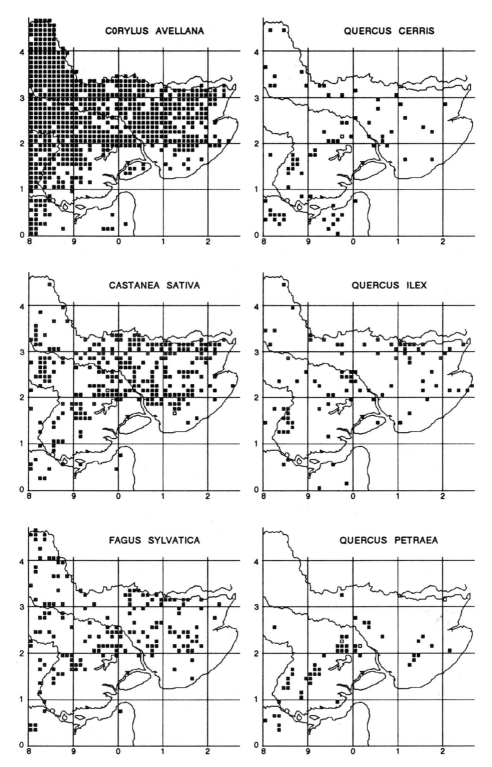

Pedunculate Oak
Quercus robur [1115] M
Very common in all woods and hedgerows throughout the area. Where a hedge is flailed or completely grubbed out, the **Oak** trees are often allowed to remain untouched.

WILLOW FAMILY
SALICACEAE

Poplars
The majority of the Poplars seen in north east Essex have been planted by man. Some are distinctive and easily recognised, like the **Lombardy Poplar**, others are less so, being cultivated varieties of mixed parentage for which full records have not been kept.

White Poplar
Populus alba [44] M
Most often found planted around farms, but also occasionally in churchyards and parks.

Black Italian Poplar
Populus X canadensis [16] M
Frequently planted especially round orchards to provide a windbreak and on damp valley soils. The following cultivated varieties have been noted, but full records have not been kept : *cv 'eugenii', cv 'robusta', var regenerata . Var serotina* was not definitely recorded during our survey, but only a few samples were critically examined and it could easily have been overlooked.

Balsam Poplar
Populus candicans [1]
As they suffer from canker, **Balsam Poplars** are not planted now and have consequently decreased in our area. We have only one record from Bullock Wood, Earls Colne. Not fully recorded.

Grey Poplar
Populus X canescens [18]
Scattered plantings, sometimes in hedgerows and semi-natural sites.

Black Poplar
Populus nigra [13] M
The Stour valley is probably a natural site for this rare native tree which has since been introduced to other localities by man. Male trees are commonly planted as they do not cause the problem that females do with large quantities of fluffy seeds. Of the 23 trees in our area only two female trees are known, one of which was lost in 1988. The Dedham Vale Project has recently planted several new trees but these are not as yet established.

Lombardy Poplar
Populus nigra var italica [35] M
A distinctive tree with its tall columnar shape; often planted by roadsides and parks.

Aspen
Populus tremula [182] M
A native species found in ancient woodlands on winter-wet soils. It is common in only a few woods, most records being of small groups of trees. Single trees are occasionally found in hedgerows and on one restricted area of Tiptree Heath it is unusually abundant.

Willows
With this group, many types are planted for ornamental purposes, these can be species from America or Asia as well as cultivated varieties of native species. We have not kept full records for these, having mainly confined ourselves to recording the native species and, where possible, their hybrids. **Willows**, like **Poplars**, have the male and female flowers on separate plants and many single-sex groups of trees can be found, indicating planting by man. We have received considerable help from Desmond Meikle who has corrected our identifications and given training and guidance to our work. Specimens of all the species mentioned can be found in the Colchester Natural History Museum herbarium.

Violet Willow
Salix acutifolia [2]
An introduced Willow, recorded from Colchester and Coggeshall; at the latter site

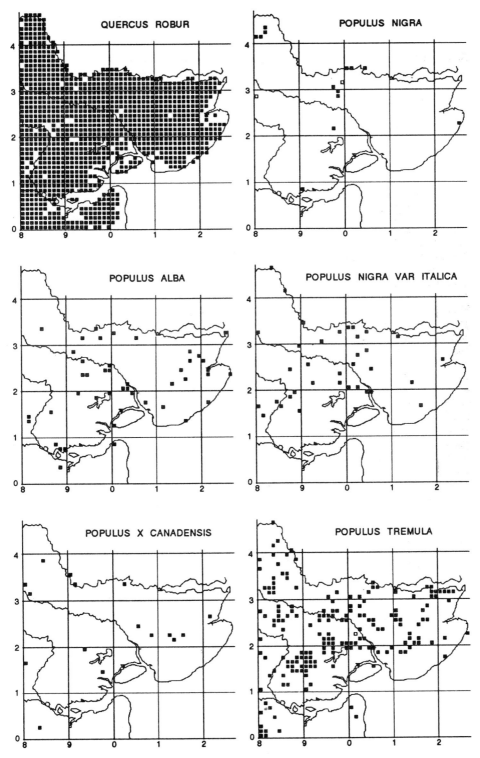

QUERCUS ROBUR

POPULUS NIGRA

POPULUS ALBA

POPULUS NIGRA VAR ITALICA

POPULUS X CANADENSIS

POPULUS TREMULA

167

planted into natural riverside vegetation.

White Willow
Salix alba
Widespread and common, often planted.
var alba [439] M
Widely distributed.
var caerulea
(Cricket-bat Willow) [92] M
This variety has a more westerly distribution and is always planted. As its English name suggests this is the Willow from which cricket bats are made. The highest grade wood comes from trees grown in Essex, however, the population is beginning to be affected by watermark disease which makes the timber unusable.
var vitellina (Golden Osier) [2]
Sometimes planted, generally for ornament, as its twigs are a marvellous orange-red colour in winter.
forma argentea (Silver Willow) [4]
Planted by road verges and in parks and gardens, we have only one apparently naturalised record from an old gravel pit at Eight Ash Green.

Salix alba X fragilis (X rubens) [8]
A possibly naturally occurring hybrid at Eight Ash Green and the Hythe but it is also sometimes included in plantings. The following *S alba X fragilis* hybrids have been recorded: *X rubens nothovar basfordiana* and *X rubens nothovar basfordiana forma basfordiana*. They have generally been found planted around caravan sites, flats, road verges and similar places.

Salix alba X pentandra [1]
One solitary tree in the middle of a wet meadow, adjacent to the old by-pass, Colchester, is our only record; it is probably of planted origin.

Eared Willow
Salix aurita [4]
Very much over-recorded in the past, this is a rare species in our area. It is found on sandy acid soils in the Roman River Valley and at one other site near Tiptree.

Goat Willow
Salix caprea [320] M
Widespread and common in some wet

woodlands it is also found growing beside ditches and ponds.

Salix caprea X cinerea [54]
Fairly common and probably under-recorded.

Salix caprea X viminalis [6]
Occurs as a native in the upper Stour valley and has been found planted at Bradwell-on-Sea and Brightlingsea.

Grey Willow
Salix cinerea agg [429]
Salix cinerea ssp cinerea [90] M
Salix cinerea ssp oleifolia [49] M
A widely distributed and often abundant species especially in disused gravel workings. Many of the Essex plants are not easily placed in the recognised subspecies, being somewhat intermediate in character in general. *Ssp cinerea* is rare in the Dengie peninsula being replaced by *ssp oleifolia* which is more frequent there (it is the dominant subspecies in south Essex).

Salix cinerea X viminalis [7]
A natural hybrid found in a few localities, usually not far from the parent species.

Salix daphnoides [4]
Always introduced, usually into municipal plantings. At Clacton it has been planted on a good area of natural wet grassland.

Salix elaeagnos [2]
Introduced at two sites; several fine plants grow by the old by-pass in Colchester and it has recently been planted into natural vegetation by the river at Coggeshall.

Crack Willow
Salix fragilis [368] M
A common and widespread tree, many of which are probably planted. Pollarded trees are frequent along river banks, for example, along the Roman River downstream from Bounstead Bridge. All our records are of *var russelliana* except for one of *var furcata*, the form with divided catkins, from Great Tey, which seems to be the first record for north Essex.

Salix fragilis X pentandra [1]
One record only, planted by a farm reser-

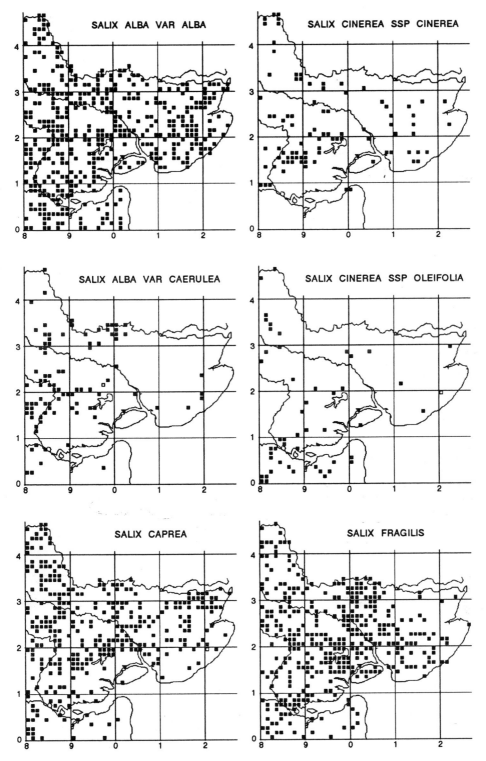

voir at Tillingham.

Bay Willow
Salix pentandra [1]
Introduced to one site in Colchester.

Purple Willow
Salix purpurea [7]
A planted willow, only male clones have been found in north east Essex; it is always in small quantity on damp ground.

Creeping Willow
Salix repens [1]
No longer found naturally in our area, it has been recently introduced to Fingringhoe Wick Nature Reserve.

Almond Willow
Salix triandra [10] M
Probably planted in the past as a basket-makers willow, it is now found naturalised in a few places, such as Liston Pits and Chigborough Lakes, or as a relic of **Osier** beds in the Roman River Valley and Colchester.
Salix X mollisima var undulata [3]
Jermyn thought that this hybrid was extinct in the county but during our survey we found three sites: Borley, Blue Mills Bridge at Witham and Colchester.

Osier
Salix viminalis [72] M
Scattered and usually in small quantity except for the restored **Osier** bed in the Roman River Valley. It is very variable in leaf width. Its hybrids with *S caprea*, *cinerea* and *triandra* are dealt with under those species.

HEATHER FAMILY
ERICACEAE

Ling Heather
Calluna vulgaris [16] M
Very local on light heathy soils. It is still plentiful at Tiptree Heath where it was known to Gibson, but his sites at Halstead and Maldon no longer exist. He also had records from Colchester and Jermyn, too, knew it from Berechurch Common, Dony-land and Layer de la Haye - it is still present in several spots in the Roman River Valley. The heather field at Layer de la Haye was planted many years ago with conifers and by 1979 the **Ling** was having to achieve a height of 6ft in places in order to compete. However, recent opening up of the area has resulted in the germination of seeds left in the soil and a healthy population of plants is now present. Jermyn's other sites have not fared as well - it continues at Fordham Heath; a single plant was last seen in 1984 in Maldon Wood where it has since been shaded out; and both West Bergholt Heath and Spratt's Marsh no longer exist, having been brought into cultivation. We have found a few extra sites, namely Great Totham Pits, Pods Wood and a few plants at Alresford and Crockleford. It has been introduced to Fingringhoe Wick Nature Reserve.

Bell Heather
Erica cinerea [3]
Always rare in our area, Gibson knew it from Tiptree and West Bergholt Heaths. By Jermyn's time it remained only at Tiptree Heath where it is still present today. In 1978 a few plants were found in scrub encroached grassland on Army lands in the Roman River Valley. With permission from the Ministry of Defence a CNHS work party cleared back the scrub to preserve this small patch. This heather has also been introduced to Fingringhoe Wick Nature Reserve.

Cross-leaved Heath
Erica tetralix [2]
As with the previous species, this heather was known to Gibson from Tiptree and West Bergholt Heaths but only Tiptree remained for Jermyn. It is still present at Tiptree but was also found at Great Totham Pits in 1984.

Rhododendron
Rhododendron ponticum [12] M
Often planted in woods where it becomes naturalised, particularly if the soil is acid. In some parts of Britain it has become so invasive it is likely to destroy acres of upland moorland. Not fully recorded.

WINTERGREEN FAMILY
PYROLACEAE

Round-leaved Wintergreen
***Pyrola rotundifolia* [1]**
Never native in our area it has been
introduced at Fingringhoe Wick Nature
Reserve.

SEA LAVENDER FAMILY
PLUMBAGINACEAE

Thrift
***Armeria maritima* [94] M**
A saltmarsh plant that requires stabilised
gravelly mud covered with short vegetation

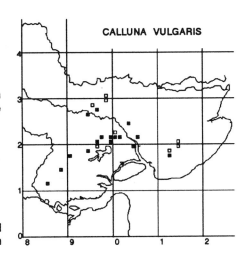

CALLUNA VULGARIS

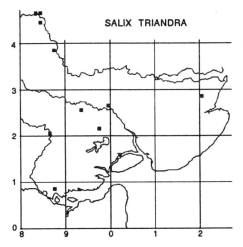

SALIX TRIANDRA

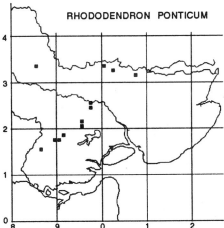

RHODODENDRON PONTICUM

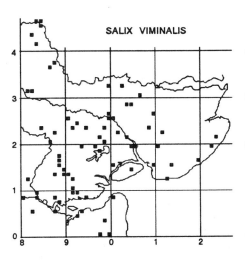

SALIX VIMINALIS

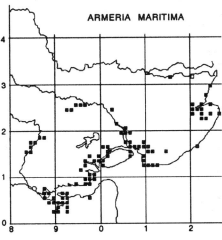

ARMERIA MARITIMA

171

in the high zone of the marsh. This habitat is not present on all our saltmarshes, for instance, around the tip of the Dengie peninsular, as the high zone has been reclaimed and is now arable fields behind the sea wall. On the Stour, where it was known both to Gibson and Jermyn from Harwich to Manningtree, there has been much erosion of the marshes in the last decade and the only site left on that estuary which has the required habitat is at Wrabness. Otherwise it can still be found at many of its former sites. Modern transport has provided a further habitat, it can now be found growing on the central reservation of the A12. This phenomenon was discussed in detail under **Danish Scurvy Grass**.

Rock Sea Lavender
Limonium binervosum [6]
First discovered by Ray in 1696 at Harwich but Gibson added that it was "probably now lost". In 1930 it was found at St Osyth Beach and then at Colne Point and Lee-over-Sands in 1964, where it still occurs in good quantity in areas of stabilised shingle. A further site at Little Oakley was discovered in 1969 on fixed shingly dunes and a few plants were still present in 1985. An additional site, found in 1988, contained only two plants growing on the sea cliffs.

Lax Sea Lavender
Limonium humile [55] M
Records for this Sea Lavender at Walton date back to 1700, and Gibson also gives it for the Maldon, Heybridge and Goldhanger area of the Blackwater. It still occurs in both these areas as well as other sites mentioned by Jermyn except it appears to have been lost from TM 11 (Colne Point to Clacton). The best site is around Old Hall Marshes. It is usually found in small quantity interspersed with **Common Sea Lavender**, and, although there are no confirmed records, our observations indicate that the hybrid between the two might occur, as possible intermediate forms were seen during our survey.

Limonium latifolium [4]
Introduced and now naturalised on the cliffs at Clacton.

Common Sea Lavender
Limonium vulgare [182] M
Common on the saltmarshes round the coast and often abundant in patches. It appears to be able to grow over a wide span of the marsh and not be restricted to one particular niche. It still retains much the same distribution as given both by Gibson and Jermyn.

PRIMROSE FAMILY
PRIMULACEAE

Scarlet Pimpernel
Anagallis arvensis
ssp arvensis [750] M
Very common over the whole area as a weed of arable, gardens and any bare disturbed soils. Occasionally colour forms other than the traditional scarlet are met with - they can be of differing shades of mauve through to a blue, which can be mistaken for the **Blue Pimpernel**.

Blue Pimpernel
Anagallis arvensis ssp foemina
In view of the comment made above concerning the varying colour forms of the **Scarlet Pimpernel** it is not possible to be certain that the early records are accurate. Gibson gives several records from cornfields and disturbed soils scattered over the area but Jermyn's single record was for Hythe Quay, 1954. The only record discovered by our survey was in Colchester Museum herbarium, a specimen collected by G C Brown in 1914, from the Hythe area of Colchester.

Chaffweed
Anagallis minima [1]
Recorded in Gibson's time from Tiptree Heath where the turf had been removed, there were no further reports of this tiny plant from this site until it was refound in 1985. Jermyn had a report of it growing in a wood clearing at Wrabness, 1952, where it was possible that it may have been introduced with grain for feeding the pheasants.

Bog Pimpernel
Anagallis tenella
Gibson gave a record from a bog near Kelvedon but it was lost through drainage even in his time.

Cyclamen
Cyclamen hederifolium
This introduction had become well naturalised in a plantation at Inworth in 1927 but whether it still exists is unknown.

Sea Milkwort
Glaux maritima [58] M
Fairly common in most of our saltmarshes, it is usually found amongst the grass at the very back where marsh and land vegetation meets. It seems to have maintained its distribution over much of the range mentioned by Jermyn.

Water Violet
Hottonia palustris [3]
Rare and decreasing. Gibson had several records, generally from ponds and ditches in soils with a chalky influence. This was reduced to three sites in similar areas in Jermyn's time, none of which have been refound. However, we have found three new locations; a fenced ditch in the middle of a grazing paddock at Henny, a pond in Pods Wood and a pond in Thrift Wood.

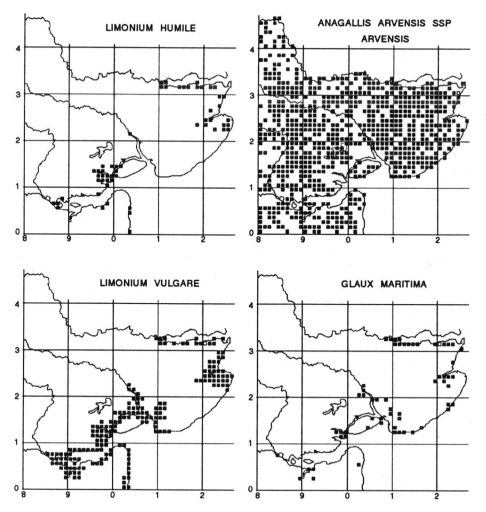

Yellow Pimpernel
Lysimachia nemorum [41] M

Infrequent in damp rides in our older woods. It appears to have declined since Jermyn when it was "common and well distributed". It was known by Gibson from Chalkney Wood and the Markshall complex where it still occurs indicating the stability of these woods over more than a century.

Creeping Jenny
Lysimachia nummularia [43] M

Commoner on the boulder clays but still infrequent. It is usually found around the margins of woodland ponds and on shady damp verges. Again it has declined and contracted its distribution since Jermyn's time.

Dotted Loosestrife
Lysimachia punctata [10]

A garden throw-out that can become naturalised. Usually near houses.

Yellow Loosestrife
Lysimachia vulgaris

Not found during our survey, it must now be considered lost to north east Essex. Gibson gave it as common near Colchester and also noted it from the Blackwater at Langford. Jermyn found it in the vicinity of the latter, by the canal at Ulting.

Oxlip
Primula elatior

A speciality of woods of north west Essex and adjoining parts of Suffolk, it may never have occurred in our area. However, Gibson does record it "sparingly in a meadow near Grinstead Green [Greenstead Green?]".

Cowslip
Primula veris [79] M

Reasonably common on the chalky boulder clays but scattered elsewhere. It is now mainly confined to churchyards, road verges, banks and ditches, its main habitat of meadowland having been lost because of 'improvement' or ploughing. With the availability of seed and pot-grown plants from nurseries we can expect an increase in records from garden escapes and deliberate introductions some of which have already been noted.

False Oxlip
Primula veris X vulgaris [5]

Uncommon, this hybrid may be found wherever the two parents occur together. Although usually occurring in small quantity one site was discovered, a ditch at Little Tey, which was full of both parents and the hybrid.

Primrose
Primula vulgaris [320] M

Again reasonably common on the chalky boulder clay but tolerant of a more varied soil type than **Cowslip** and therefore occurring over a much wider area. In shady places in churchyards, woods, hedge bottoms, banks, and very frequently on ditchsides.

Brookweed
Samolus valerandi

Jermyn considered **Brookweed** possibly extinct in the county and we have not found it during our survey. Gibson had several records; ditchside between Maldon and Heybridge, Langford, river ditches at Kelvedon, by the River Stour at Dedham and Dovercourt. It has not been seen since c1930 at G C Brown's site at East Donyland on the Roman River. Jermyn had found it on the Stour at Great Henny in 1961 but this site was lost during river widening operations carried out in the early 1960s; it was known from Fingringhoe Wick Nature Reserve (last seen 1962).

BUDDLEIA FAMILY
BUDDLEJACEAE

Buddleia
Buddleja davidii [45] M

Introduced and becoming naturalised in many waste places, car parks, railway lines and industrial sites. It appears to have increased substantially since Jermyn's time.

OLIVE FAMILY
OLEACEAE

Ash
Fraxinus excelsior [1020] M

Very common over the whole area although thinning out close to the coast. It

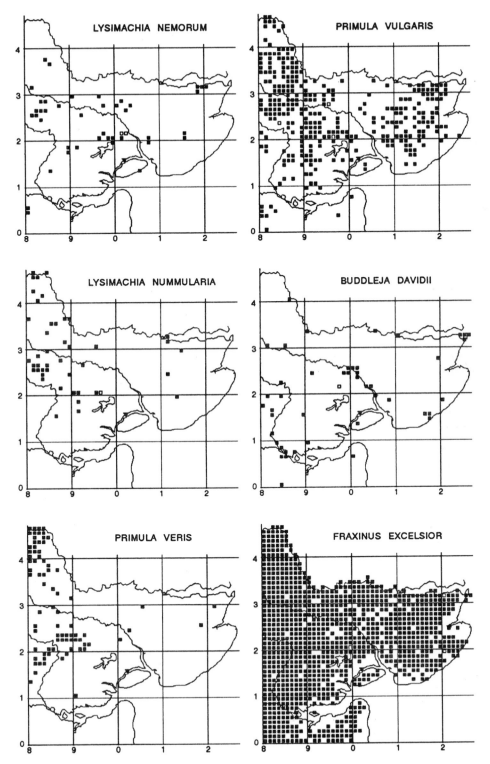

never seems to be present in any great quantity but a few trees can always be found in wood or hedgerow. In both Chalkney and High Wood it often occurs as a coppice. *Fraxinus excelsior var pendula* is a weeping variety that can be seen very occasionally in a park or large garden, not fully recorded.

Garden Privet
Ligustrum ovalifolium [26]
Commonly planted to form a garden hedge, it is occasionally found away from houses. This could be where the cottage in whose garden it originally grew has long since been demolished. Although not fully recorded all our records are for sites where it was growing away from habitation.

Wild Privet
Ligustrum vulgare [214] M
Reasonably frequent but scattered over much of the area, although commoner south from Kelvedon and through the Dengie peninsula. It is commonly found in hedges to cottages where it was originally introduced from nearby woodlands.

Lilac
Syringa vulgaris [19]
Planted in hedges around houses, it can appear away from habitation, probably for the same reason as that given for the **Garden Privet.** Our records again are only for those growing away from habitation.

PERIWINKLE FAMILY
APOCYNACEAE

Greater Periwinkle
Vinca major [68] M
A garden plant that had already escaped into the countryside by Gibson's time. It has become naturalised in hedges, ditches and woodland edges over the years but it is still usually close to houses. Scattered over the whole area.

Lesser Periwinkle
Vinca minor [30] M
A garden escape that has become well naturalised and appearing native in some woods. It is less frequent than its larger

relation.

GENTIAN FAMILY
GENTIANACEAE

Yellow-wort
Blackstonia perfoliata [2]
A plant that occurs on two distinct soil types, either calcareous grassland or sandy places. All Gibson's records were from the former. He had a record for Pattiswick and it was still present over a century later, but we have been unable to refind either Gibson's or Jermyn's sites in this vicinity (Pattiswick, Moat and Chalkney Woods). However, in 1986, a colony of 28 healthy plants was found growing by the A12 at Witham which is in the general area of Gibson's sites of Kelvedon, Rivenhall and Braxted. It is possible that these plants have been there since the bypass was built, the seed being uncovered during construction, and only the discipline of our survey leading the botanist to walk where no-one was foolhardy enough to have walked before! In 1988 another site was found, on the chalk outcrop at Pentlow where two rather scrappy plants were growing by a ditch along a bridleway. Jermyn's remaining records were from gravel pits (Rowhedge, Fingringhoe Wick Nature Reserve) or sandy places (Berechurch Common) but it has not been refound at any of these sites. It occurred on an old railway line at Alresford in 1967 but has not been found there since.

Common Centaury
Centaurium erythraea [108] M
In Gibson's time this plant was common and frequent over the whole county, so much so, that he did not give any specific sites. It was still common and widespread in Jermyn's time but is now declining. It continues to be widely distributed but has become rather infrequent, usually found on poor soils along woodland rides, on heathlands and in gravel pits.

Felwort
Gentianella amarella
A plant of chalk grassland, it was once recorded (before 1732) by Dale from Belchamp St Paul, a tiny part of which parish

falls into our area.

BOGBEAN FAMILY
MENYANTHACEAE

Bogbean
Menyanthes trifoliata [3]
Once native in our ponds and boggy meadows it is now only found planted in village ponds which have been subject to a restoration project. Gibson gives several sites - Markshall, Henny Street, Rivenhall, Totham, East Mersea and Berechurch - all lost by Jermyn's time.

Fringed Water Lily
Nymphoides peltata [1]
Never before recorded for north east Essex, it was found in a pond by Great Henny church in 1984 where it had doubtless been introduced.

HYDROPHYLLACEAE

Phacelia ciliata
Phacelia tanacetifolia [1]
Both the above species are casual introductions. *P ciliata* was found in 1934 on waste ground by the maltings at Hythe

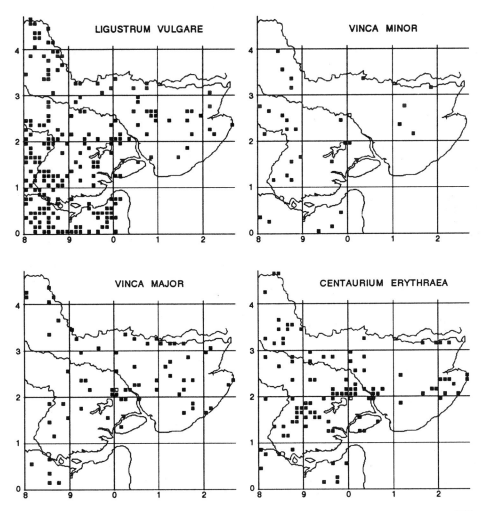

Quay, Colchester, but *P tanacetifolia* is of more recent origin. It is now sometimes planted as a food plant for bees. It was found growing near a barn in 1986.

BORAGE FAMILY
BORAGINACEAE

Amsinckia micrantha [17] M
An introduced species which can now be found as an arable weed on the lighter soils or imported with soil from Suffolk where it is more common. It is not very widespread and is most frequent in the Dedham area.

Bugloss
Anchusa arvensis [66] M
Decreasing as an arable weed on the lighter soils. It is found now only in small quantity in corners of fields where the sprays have missed, or, if the crop grown is such that the chemicals used do not harm broad leaved plants, as in the case of market garden fields growing potatoes, cabbages, etc.

Borage
Borago officinalis [33] M
Increasingly grown as a crop with the resultant increase in casual records on verges and waysides; however, it never persists.

Green Houndstongue
Cynoglossum germanicum
A plant long since lost to the county but it was known to Gerard (1597) on the "London road between Witham and Esterford", and later to Ray (1724) "between Kelvedon and Witham and more plentifully about Braxted by the wayside". In Gibson's time it still occurred in shady places at Braxted and Salcott.

Houndstongue
Cynoglossum officinale [2]
Gibson gave several records scattered over our area but these had decreased by Jermyn's time, he had just three records. We were unable to refind it either on Osea Island or at Mill Hill, Lawford and his site at an old gravel pit at St Osyth no longer exists as it became the local rubbish tip

until filled and grassed over. Our survey has revealed two other sites, in both cases just one or two plants were present. They were in contrasting habitats; a green lane at Old Hall Marshes, and on the chalk outcrop near Sudbury along a disused railway track.

Viper's Bugloss
Echium vulgare
Now lost to our area. **Viper's Bugloss** requires very well-drained soils as is found on dry chalk, sand dunes or gravel pits. Gibson had a few records for our area, one of which was St Osyth. It remained in this area for over a century as Jermyn recorded it from old gravel pits north of St Osyth, however, it was lost when the pit became a local rubbish tip (it was the same site as that for **Houndstongue**). Jermyn's other site for a railway bank at Great Tey could not be refound.

Lappula squarrosa [1]
A bird seed alien that has been recorded only once.

Corn Gromwell
Lithospermum arvense [36] M
Once a common cornfield weed it is now infrequent. It occurs in small quantity and always at the edges or corners of fields where it has been missed by the chemical sprays.

Common Gromwell
Lithospermum officinale
Gibson gave records from dry stony places in the Kelvedon, Rivenhall and Easthorpe area as well as from Kirby and near Walton. Jermyn was unable to refind it in either of these vicinities but did have a record from waste ground at Gestingthorpe. We have not found **Common Gromwell** during our survey.

Common Forgetmenot
Myosotis arvensis [466] M
Common along the edges of cultivated fields and in gardens and vegetable patches in country areas.

Changing Forgetmenot
Myosotis discolor [28] M
An early flowering Forgetmenot of dry open

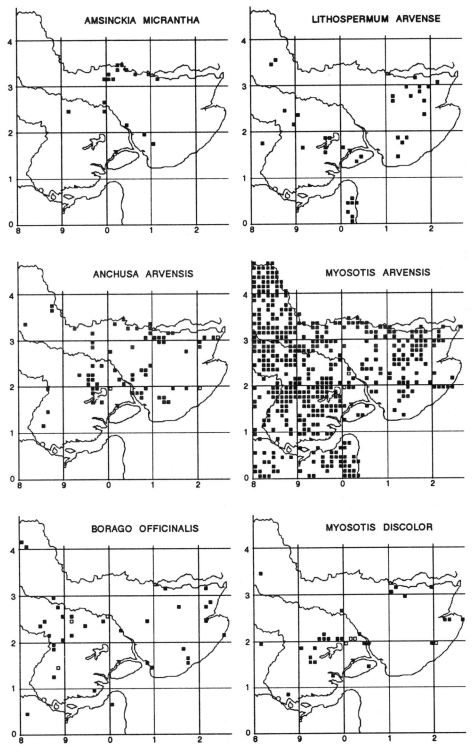

AMSINCKIA MICRANTHA

LITHOSPERMUM ARVENSE

ANCHUSA ARVENSIS

MYOSOTIS ARVENSIS

BORAGO OFFICINALIS

MYOSOTIS DISCOLOR

situations on light soils. It has decreased since Jermyn's time. It is often found growing in the scratched soil around rabbit burrows, on sandy banks and in old sand and gravel pits. It can also be found in grassland in dry situations such as the tops of large anthills on the coastal grazing marshes.

Tufted Forgetmenot
Myosotis laxa ssp caespitosa [24] M
Described by Gibson as "frequent in all districts", it is now infrequent due to loss of its habitat - marshy places by rivers, streams, ditches and ponds. It occurs occasionally in the creeks of old grazing marshes.

Early Forgetmenot
Myosotis ramosissima [17] M
This species occurs in similar situations to that of the **Changing Forgetmenot** but we have also found it, rarely, as an arable weed. Many of Jermyn's sites could not be refound due to changes in the habitat - railway banks becoming scrubbed over, and gravel pits either being infilled or the vegetation maturing to another stage in its recolonisation. Other sites where it was not refound but could still occur are Tiptree Heath, St Osyth Beach, Great Holland Pits and Abberton Reservoir (crevices in concrete wall).

Water Forgetmenot
Myosotis scorpioides [105] M
Very much a plant of moving water - the distribution shows its reliance on the major river systems as well as the smaller streams such as Roman River, Holland and Bentley Brooks. It is occasionally also found in ponds. As with so many once common water plants, its range has contracted.

Wood Forgetmenot
Myosotis sylvatica [12]
The following comment made by Jermyn still applies: "It is difficult to assess the status of the native plant owing to the persistence of the cultivated form which occurs as a garden escape or outcast and readily establishes itself". Our records have been restricted to those that appear to be native.

Blue-eyed Mary
Omphalodes verna
A garden escape that Jermyn recorded on a roadside near a church at Witham but this species was not found during our survey.

Green Alkanet
Pentaglottis sempervirens [89] M
A garden escape that is increasing and spreading through the area, in hedges and verges; usually near houses.

Common Lungwort
Pulmonaria officinalis [1]
A garden throw-out that can become naturalised. Jermyn's site at Pattiswick, 1965, was not refound but two plants were found growing on a verge at Elmstead, 1986.

Rough Comfrey
Symphytum asperum
Introduced. Jermyn had recorded this plant in 1964 on a roadside near houses on the Naze at Walton but it has not been recorded since.

Common Comfrey
Symphytum officinale [62] M
Scattered, but often in good quantity where it does occur. River and streamsides as well as damp and boggy areas.

White Comfrey
Symphytum orientale [55] M
A naturalised escape that has spread considerably since Jermyn. Usually found in hedges and verges near houses as well as churchyards and waste ground. Jermyn gave it as plentiful at Mistley Park and it still abounds in the churchyard and at Mistley Towers.

Tuberous Comfrey
Symphytum tuberosum
Gibson gives the only records for our area - Water Lane, Dedham, between the ford and the footbridge, and a queried record for Kelvedon. Whether these were native or introductions is not indicated.

Russian Comfrey
Symphytum X uplandicum [91] M
The commonest Comfrey of our area, it is

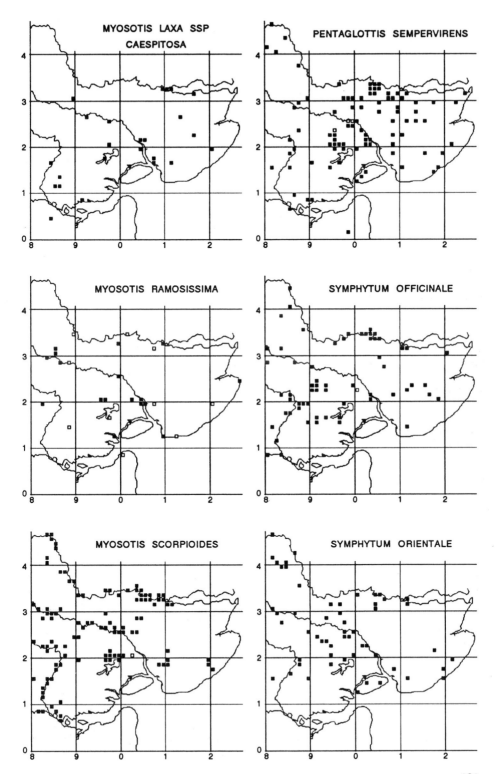

MYOSOTIS LAXA SSP
CAESPITOSA

PENTAGLOTTIS SEMPERVIRENS

MYOSOTIS RAMOSISSIMA

SYMPHYTUM OFFICINALE

MYOSOTIS SCORPIOIDES

SYMPHYTUM ORIENTALE

often plentiful along river and streamsides as well as being found on damp verges and waste places. Jermyn notes that it was first introduced to this country c1827 as a green fodder plant and is most probably a relic of cultivation. Doubleday, a seedsman at Coggeshall, imported it from Russia in 1870, which could explain the high density of records along the Blackwater both up and downstream from Coggeshall.

Abraham, Isaac & Jacob
Trachystemon orientalis
An introduction that we have not found during our survey, although Jermyn had two sites where it had naturalised, both at Thorpe le Soken.

BINDWEED FAMILY
CONVOLVULACEAE

Pink Bindweed
Calystegia sepium ssp pulchra [3]
An introduction found in hedges near houses.

Hedge Bindweed
Calystegia sepium ssp sepium [640] M
Very common over the whole area in hedges, ditches, scrub and damp waste places. Many intermediates between this and the next species were noted during our survey, indicating hybridisation, but no detailed work was conducted to confirm this.

Large Bindweed
Calystegia sepium
ssp silvatica [274] M
Common, occurring in many of the same habitats as the previous species, but it is more often met with near houses, builders yards, industrial sites and waste ground.

Sea Bindweed
Calystegia soldanella [10]
Requiring coastal sands Sea Bindweed was found during our survey on Mersea and Osea Islands, St Osyth Beach and surrounding area, and Dovercourt. This means that it has been known from Mersea Island for c380 years as it was first recorded from there by Gerard. It was known by both Gibson and Jermyn from

Stone Point, Walton, but we were unable to refind it here as there has been much erosion of the coast and this site, as well as Jermyn's at Crabknowe Spit, has been lost to the sea. It has been recorded in the past from Bradwell-on-Sea (Jermyn), and Great Clacton, Little Holland and Harwich (Gibson).

Field Bindweed
Convolvulus arvensis [1162] M
Very common in all types of grassland and disturbed soil. It has several different patterns of marking, from pure white, through stripes of pink to a beautiful deep red ring. This latter colour form often occurs by the coast.

Convolvulus siculus
A casual that Jermyn recorded from Brooks Seed Trial Grounds at Mistley in 1967.

Cuscuta campestris [1]
This unusual Dodder was found growing on seedlings of the herb Basil in a greenhouse at Wivenhoe in 1986. It probably arose as a seed contaminant.

Common Dodder
Cuscuta epithymum
Gibson gave a record for its parasitising Lady's Bedstraw near Colchester, but no further reference can be found for this plant in north east Essex.

Great Dodder
Cuscuta europaea [8]
A parasite on Stinging Nettle it twines round the stem of a nettle and then winds its way onto another forming a 'knitted tangle' through the bed of nettles. Gibson gave a record for Halstead although he noted that it was rare. Jermyn was unable to find any and considered it lost to the county; however, it was found in 1984 growing on the Suffolk side of the Stour at Wormingford. A resultant search on the Essex bank revealed its presence. It grows in nettle beds that occur on or very close to the river bank. Following this find, many nettle beds were (painfully) searched along the Stour revealing in total eight sites, all between Wormingford and Dedham, (2,1984; 2,1986; 3,1988; 1,1989).

Lucerne Dodder
Cuscuta hassiaca
Recorded by a contemporary of Gibson's from a field of **Lucerne** near Witham. There have been no records since.

Cuscuta trifolii
First discovered in this country by Gibson in 1842, he submitted specimens to C C Babington, a leading British botanist of the day. Gibson says that "It appears to have reached Britain almost exclusively with foreign clover seed, but has excited little attention abroad, being confused with a variety of the **Common Dodder**. It is most destructive, especially to the second crop of clover, spreading itself in circles and twining tightly and closely round its victims; in these respects differing from **Common Dodder**, which spreads itself vaguely, and does not kill the plants on which it grows." It was known in Gibson's time from Kelvedon, Inworth, Messing and Rivenhall. Changes in agricultural practices, even in Victorian times, resulted in Dodders on crops generally becoming rarer, and there have been no records for this species since.

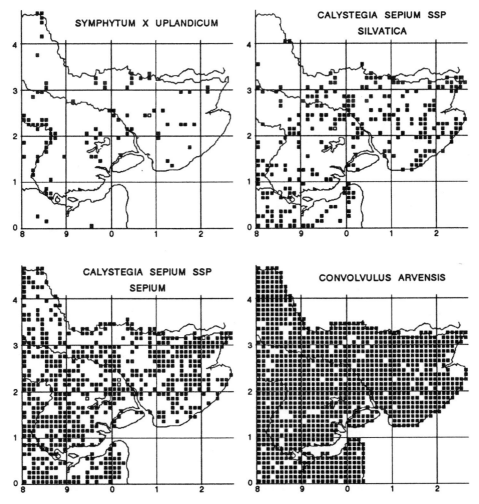

NIGHTSHADE FAMILY
SOLANACEAE

Deadly Nightshade
Atropa bella-donna [4]
Now very rare and persecuted as the berries are poisonous, hence its name. It is more common as a native plant on the chalk in the north west of Essex and would always have been rare in our area, usually as an introduction. However, several plants were found in 1987 growing, apparently native, on a grassy track by a field on the chalk outcrop which occurs west of Sudbury. It occurs in two Colchester churchyards, one where it has been known for many years and another where it was originally introduced and has since become naturalised. Other records are casual occurrences.

Datura metel
A casual from Hythe Quay, Colchester, in 1938. There have been no further records for this species.

Thorn Apple
Datura stramonium [12]
The following comment by Jermyn still applies: "sporadic in occurrence, plentiful and widespread in some years, scarce in others". An impression gained during the survey is that it occurs more frequently in years with hot summers, such as 1989, but we have carried out no detailed analysis to confirm this. Its sporadic appearance also indicates that its seed is long-lived, awaiting suitable conditions in which to germinate. It usually occurs in fields of vegetables, e.g. cabbages, or on waste areas.

Henbane
Hyoscyamus niger [11]
Henbane was more widespread in both Gibson and Jermyn's time and is now infrequent. It occurs in two distinct habitats in our area; on sandy shores and as an arable weed. One of Gibson's sites is St Osyth and Jermyn gives it for both a roadside at St Osyth and from Colne Point showing it had been in the area for over a century (it is still present at Colne Point). This is also the case with another of Gibson's localities; he records it from Rivenhall and it was found a short distance

away in a cabbage field at Witham and in a blackcurrant field at Kelvedon. We have found it growing with other crops such as strawberries.

Duke of Argyll's Tea Plant
Lycium barbarum [152] M
Lycium chinense
These two species have now been merged as it has been concluded they are different variants of the same species. We have only found *L barbarum*. It was originally introduced as a garden hedging plant, and it has now become naturalised in many places, particularly near the sea.

Apple of Peru
Nicandra physalodes [2]
This can be found occasionally not only as a garden escape but also as a contaminant of seed.

Woody Nightshade or Bittersweet
Solanum dulcamara [1030]
Very common over the whole area in a variety of habitats, often near shallow water. It scrambles through shrubs and over other vegetation at the edges of woods, and in hedges, and can be found in most ditches and ponds.

Black Nightshade
Solanum nigrum [582] M
Common as a garden weed, in vegetable plots and allotments. It also occurs on any waste and tipped area as well as in arable when a crop other than a cereal is being grown. A form with greenish-yellow berries occurs occasionally.

Several other species of *Solanum* occur as a bird seed alien or seed contaminant from time to time, and the following have been recorded during our survey: *S capsicoides* [1], *S nitidibaccatum* [1], *S rostratum* [4], *S sarrachoides* [4]. *S cornutum* was not found during our survey but had been recorded in 1974.

FIGWORT FAMILY
SCROPHULARIACEAE

Snapdragon
Antirrhinum majus [8]
Found occasionally on roadsides and

waste areas where it has been discarded with garden refuse. However, it can also become naturalised on old walls, for example, the Roman Wall in Colchester where it has occurred for many years.

Small Toadflax
Chaenorhinum minus [10]
This species has suffered a drastic decline; Gibson: "frequent in all districts"; Jermyn: "frequent and locally common". We have just ten records, mainly from arable fields where one or sometimes two plants have been found.

Ivy-leaved Toadflax
Cymbalaria muralis [64] M
Reasonably frequent as a garden escape

onto old walls, particularly when built of stone and mortar, rather than of brick. It is common on parts of the Roman Wall in Colchester. It was originally introduced by William Coys to his garden in North Ockendon c1602 and from there it gradually spread and had reached Halstead and Dedham by the Gibson era.

Foxglove
Digitalis purpurea [276] M
Common on the free draining acid soils in woodland rides and hedgerows. It also occurs now as a garden throw-out and its native distribution is becoming obscured.

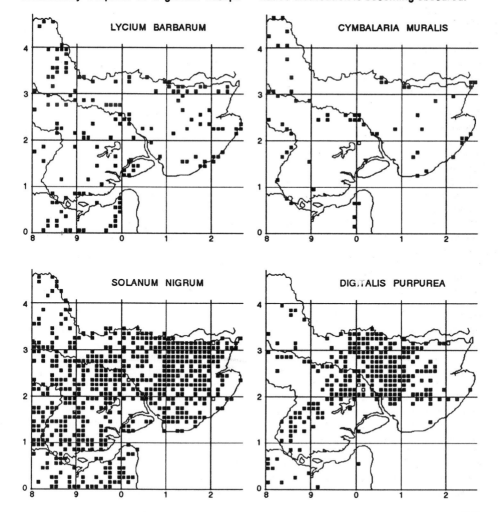

LYCIUM BARBARUM

CYMBALARIA MURALIS

SOLANUM NIGRUM

DIGITALIS PURPUREA

Eyebright
Euphrasia nemorosa [1]
Euphrasia pseudokerneri
During the course of our survey we have found only one site where a species of **Eyebright** still occurs. This is Alphamstone gravel pits where Jermyn records *E nemorosa*. **Eyebrights** were common in Gibson's day, so much so that he did not consider it worth giving specific locations. A major decline had already occurred by Jermyn's time as he considered them uncommon but did list nine locations in our area. All have been searched thoroughly but, other than the site already mentioned, with no success. His sites were: *E nemorosa* - Ulting, gravelly waste ground near canal; Tiptree Heath (the new conservation measures being instituted may result in its being refound here); Great Tey, railway bank; clearing near Bungate Wood; Liston Park (now arable fields - it was meadowland in Jermyn's time); Layer Breton Heath (much encroached by birch and scrub); Fordham Heath (very much covered by scrub); Bath Side, Harwich. *E pseudokerneri* - White Colne and Twinstead, c1931; Fordham Heath, 1931 (not refound at a later date by Jermyn). Specimens from White Colne are in the British Museum (Natural History) and have been reidentified as *E nemorosa* by P F Yeo, so it is best to regard the other two records as unconfirmed.

Sharp-leaved Fluellen
Kickxia elatine [137] M
Reasonably frequent as an arable weed, especially in cornfields where it is more noticeable in the stubble.

Round-leaved Fluellen
Kickxia spuria [115] M
Not quite as frequent as the **Sharp-leaved Fluellen**, this species shows a more marked preference for the lighter soils, however, the two species are often found together in many fields. It is interesting to note that Gibson had not found **Round-leaved Fluellen** in the Tendring area, and our coverage confirms its scarcity there.

Purple Toadflax
Linaria purpurea [26] M
Scattered over much of the area. It is a garden plant that has escaped into the nearby hedgerows either by its own means or with the help of man.

Pale Toadflax
Linaria repens [1]
Not previously recorded in our area, it was found in 1989, at Parkeston railway sidings. There were several large patches of more than 100 plants.

Common Toadflax
Linaria vulgaris [523] M
Common over much of the area, its distribution plots the better drained soils, even to the extent of picking out the gravels in the valleys. Dry grassy banks and verges.

Field Cowwheat
Melampyrum arvense
A very full account of this extremely rare but beautiful plant is given by Jermyn. Its main localities do not fall within our recording area but Jermyn does mention that it was recorded from Wickham Bishops and Witham sometime after Gibson but prior to his 'contemporary recording' (1930?). No further details are given.

Crested Cowwheat
Melampyrum cristatum
Another very rare and beautiful **Cowwheat** native to Essex. It appears that the only record for our area was in woods near Gestingthorpe, 1724.

Common Cowwheat
Melampyrum pratense [10] M
Decreasing. Jermyn had recorded **Common Cowwheat** from ten sites scattered over our area, and we have only been able to refind two of his localities. Its stronghold is now the woods of the Roman River Valley Conservation Zone. These include Donyland Wood (a Jermyn locality), Friday Wood and Chest Wood. We refound his site at Maldon Wood, Little Clacton, as well as a new record at nearby Hartley Wood. Other sites include High Woods, Colchester, small wood at Alresford and two small woods near Cock Clarks, Maldon.

Monkey Flower
Mimulus guttatus [2]
Mimulus guttatus X luteus [1]
These plants are introductions or garden escapes naturalising in wet places, by streams and marshy areas. Because of the number of garden varieties there is difficulty in identifying the actual species, or hybrid, involved.

Musk
Mimulus moschatus [1]
A garden escape that was found on tipped soil at Manningtree in 1981.

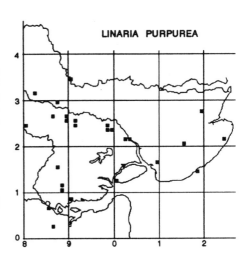

LINARIA PURPUREA

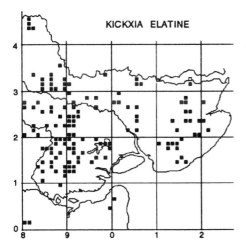

KICKXIA ELATINE

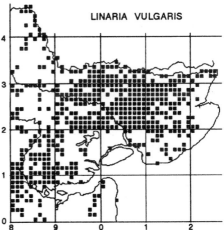

LINARIA VULGARIS

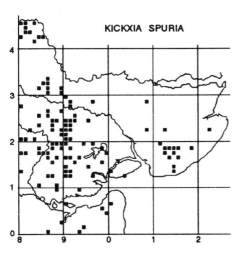

KICKXIA SPURIA

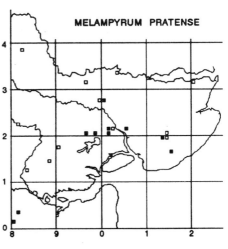

MELAMPYRUM PRATENSE

187

Lesser Snapdragon
Misopates orontium [5]
This charming little **Snapdragon** has always been uncommon, although Gibson does state that it was frequent in fields at Dedham. Its habitat originally included cornfields but we have found it only on cultivated ground such as allotments. At each site there were only one or two plants present.

Red Bartsia
Odontites verna [153] M
Semi-parasitic on grasses and other plants, this species is found in grassy cart tracks, woodland rides, and areas of rough grassland. Although still frequent over much of our area it appears to have declined. Previously two subspecies, *ssp serotina* and *ssp verna*, had been recorded in north east Essex but we did not distinguish these in our recording. During the course of our survey these subspecies were raised to the rank of species with *ssp serotina* becoming *O vulgaris* and *ssp verna* becoming *O verna*. Of the specimens held in Colchester Natural History Museum and specifically determined all have been identified as *O vulgaris* except one. This one specimen of *O verna* was collected in 1977 and therefore predates our survey.

Marsh Lousewort or Red Rattle
Pedicularis palustris
Marsh Lousewort had been lost to the county by Jermyn's time. Gibson had records from marshy meadows by the Colne at Halstead, near Henny and from Bergholt Heath.

Lousewort
Pedicularis sylvatica
Gibson gives several records for this semi-parasitic plant of wet heathy places, including Tiptree Heath. It was still present here according to Jermyn but we have been unable to refind it during our survey. Nor could we relocate Jermyn's other sites at Liston Park (now arable), Fordham Heath (now much scrubbed over) and Langham-Boxted area. With no additional sites it seems that this plant is lost to our area.

Yellow Rattle
Rhinanthus minor [1]
According to Gibson **Yellow Rattle** was common in the moist meadows and pastures at Halstead, Maldon, Kelvedon, Colchester and Dedham, but it then suffered a decline due to loss of habitat. Jermyn had only three records; gravel workings at Ulting, Rivenhall-Kelvedon area and a water meadow at Henny Street. We do not think that the latter site is the same as ours, although adjacent, as our little patch was growing in a grassy **Poplar** plantation. We understand that the patch has since spread due to the poplars being brought down in the storm of October 1987, allowing more light to reach the ground flora.

Water Figwort
Scrophularia auriculata [226] M
Still common in streams, wet ditches, ponds and riversides in the west of our area, it has declined in the Tendring and Dengie peninsulas and is now either very scarce or absent altogether over large areas of north east Essex. Jermyn describes it as "very common in wet habitats".

Common Figwort
Scrophularia nodosa [317] M
By contrast to the previous species, the **Common Figwort** appears to be holding its own, its distribution remaining much as given by Jermyn. It occurs in woodland rides, grassy verges and ditchbanks.

Balm-leaved Figwort
Scrophularia scorodonia [1]
An introduction that, according to Jermyn, was plentiful around the Martello Tower at Point Clear c1957. It has since found its way into the gardens of a private estate where it was still present in 1986.

Green Figwort
Scrophularia umbrosa [1]
Not previously recorded for north east Essex, it was found for the first time in 1984 at the edge of the lake in the grounds of the University of Essex. Unfortunately it has not been seen since.

Yellow Figwort
Scrophularia vernalis [2]

An introduced plant that was known to Gibson from several sites around Lawford: "Near Dedham Heath. Kennel Lane and towards Lawford Mill wood. Near a railway bridge at Ardleigh. Local, but occurring in some profusion and very fine, on the turnpike road between Colchester and Harwich, near the 58th milestone from London, in the parishes of Ardleigh and Lawford. Also in a lane at Dedham." Jermyn found that it was still present at Humberlands Lane and Bargate Farm, Ardleigh, c1950, and our survey has revealed that a sprinkling still occurs in the hedges around Lawford. It appears in different places in different years. However, it has not been refound at the 58th milestone, which itself does still exist. In 1980 it occurred as a casual in a garden at Witham.

Moth Mullein
Verbascum blattaria

Not known since Gibson's records from a clover field at Kelvedon and on gravel at Tiptree Heath, 1849.

Verbascum densiflorum

A casual that does not persist which Jermyn recorded on roadsides and waste ground.

Dark Mullein
Verbascum nigrum [7]

Known from Stanway since 1834, it still occurs on the wide grassy verges of the Maldon Road between Colchester and the Zoo. It prefers a light dry soil, as can be found on chalk, and our survey also recorded it from the chalk outcrop to the west of Sudbury, again on wide grassy verges.

Orange Mullein
Verbascum phlomoides [3]

A short-lived casual that escapes from gardens occasionally.

Hoary Mullein
Verbascum pulverulentum [2]

Not known at all to Gibson, it was first found in the Colchester district in 1907. Jermyn subsequently found it at three sites near Colchester - railway, just east of River Colne crossing, 1945-51; Lexden, 1952;

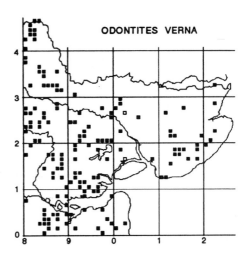

ODONTITES VERNA

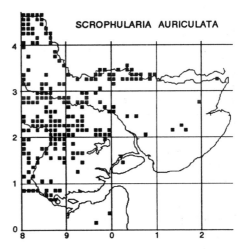

SCROPHULARIA AURICULATA

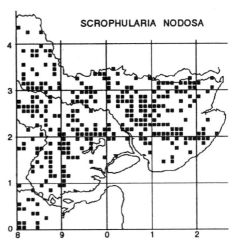

SCROPHULARIA NODOSA

189

and railway near West Bergholt Road, 1958. A few plants still exist at this latter site (1989), and a single plant was found at Parkeston sidings in the same year.

Great Mullein
Verbascum thapsus [109] M
Scattered over the whole region, usually growing on dry bare ground. It has been seen since the storm of October 1987 growing on several occasions in the bare hollows left by uprooted trees. Whether this is as a result of germination of long buried seed, or an opportunist colonisation of the bare ground is unknown.

Twiggy Mullein
Verbascum virgatum
A casual recorded from waste ground at Colchester by Jermyn. There have been no further records.

Green Field Speedwell
Veronica agrestis [4]
Apparently decreased and now rare, but it is possible that it has been under-recorded as it is rather inconspicuous. Arable land and gardens.

Blue Water Speedwell
Veronica anagallis-aquatica [14] M
Gibson considered the **Blue Water Speedwell** "common and apparently frequent in all districts" but as he did not list the **Pink Water Speedwell** it is possible that, in his day, it was not realised that there were, in fact, two species. However, Jermyn found it to be frequent and locally common in the shallow water of rivers, streams and ditches over most of the area, except the maritime localities. Our findings have shown that it is now rare, occurring mainly on the river systems and, occasionally, along a major stream.

Wall Speedwell
Veronica arvensis [607] M
Common as an arable and garden weed and on dry banks and walls.

Brooklime
Veronica beccabunga [244] M
No longer common, but still frequent, and often plentiful, in the shallow water of rivers, streams, ditches and ponds as well as flooded ruts in woodland rides.

Pink Water Speedwell
Veronica catenata [26] M
Scattered and infrequent, it is commonest on the River Stour, particularly at Cattawade where it occurs in large quantity. It is not so dependent upon the main river systems as the **Blue Water Speedwell** as it also occurs in ponds and reservoirs.

Germander Speedwell
Veronica chamaedrys [678] M
Common in most grassland, including churchyards and verges. It is often spotted by the distinctive furry gall that may form on its buds; this is particularly noticeable in mown grass. Our major remaining grassland habitat is round our coast along the sea walls, but here, this otherwise common Speedwell is absent.

Slender Speedwell
Veronica filiformis [82] M
A relatively recent introduction that is continuing to spread throughout the area; Jermyn had over 60 sites for the whole county, compared now to 82 for just the north east. It is most often found in garden lawns and churchyards but is increasingly colonising other habitats.

Ivy-leaved Speedwell
Veronica hederifolia [458] M
Common on arable land, and as a weed in gardens, also hedgebanks and disturbed

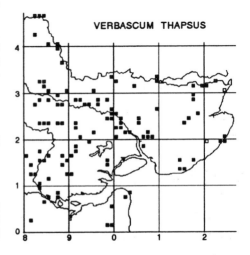

VERBASCUM THAPSUS

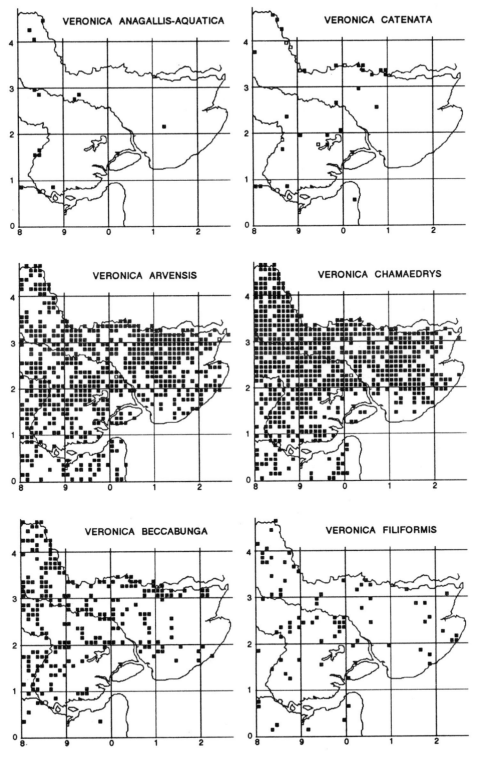

VERONICA ANAGALLIS-AQUATICA

VERONICA CATENATA

VERONICA ARVENSIS

VERONICA CHAMAEDRYS

VERONICA BECCABUNGA

VERONICA FILIFORMIS

patches of soil on verges. The species has now been split into two subspecies (*ssp hederifolia* and *ssp lucorum*). Our recording has shown that both are common in our area but *ssp lucorum* is slightly more frequent. Identification of the subspecies is not always possible as specimens are found which have some characters of both subspecies and our map, therefore, shows all our records.

Wood Speedwell
Veronica montana [69] M
Decreasing and becoming uncommon. Restricted to old woodlands, it occurs, usually in small quantity, along the rides and ditchbanks at the woodland edge where it can receive some light. When the wood has been recently coppiced it can occur in greater quantity.

Heath Speedwell
Veronica officinalis [40] M
Still frequent on the sand and gravel soils of the Roman River Valley and around Tiptree, but very uncommon elsewhere. At Iron Latch Meadow, an Essex Naturalists' Trust reserve, **Heath Speedwell** became abundant in the grass as the scrub was cleared and the site gradually returned to meadowland.

Common Field Speedwell
Veronica persica [1035] M
Very common; it can be found on any bare soil and is one of the few arable weeds which seems to be able to withstand any chemical thrown at it.

Grey Field Speedwell
Veronica polita [5]
Now apparently rare, but it is possible that it has been overlooked as the flower closes up when there is no sunshine, making the plant very inconspicuous. At one site, it was abundant, growing in great patches where the soil on an area of waste ground had recently been disturbed in preparation for development.

Marsh Speedwell
Veronica scutellata
Probably now extinct in the area. Gibson described it as "rather rare, though widely distributed" and, of the sites he gave, only

Chalkney Wood remains, the others being lost to farmland or urban development. Jermyn's only record for our area is from a boggy area by a pond at Gallows Green where it has not been refound.

Thyme-leaved Speedwell
Veronica serpyllifolia
    ssp serpyllifolia [210] M
Frequent but scattered over the whole area in damp short grass on damp heaths, woodland rides, churchyards and lawns.

Fingered Speedwell
Veronica triphyllos
Gibson gives a rather vague record of this delicate little Speedwell, known as a speciality of the Brecklands of Suffolk, "is said to grow in a field on the right of the road from Sudbury towards Braintree".

BROOMRAPE FAMILY
OROBANCHACEAE

Purple Toothwort
Lathraea clandestina [2]
First found in the Roman River Valley (Chest Wood) in April 1974, it continues to flourish on **Poplar** and **Willow** trees. The plant arrived in this locality from a garden further upstream where it was introduced from continental stock.

Toothwort
Lathraea squamaria [2]
This plant which is a parasite on the roots of trees has always been rare, and all sightings have been around Halstead. Gibson records it "in a meadow near Halstead, but very rare". Jermyn gives further records from this area : "1887 - in a meadow at Marks Hall, near Halstead, its only locality in Essex; 1894, again in a meadow near Halstead; 1958 beside Bourne Brook, Greenstead Green, near Halstead, mostly on elms, plentiful 1970-71; 1969-70, Markshall, by lake, several small and sizeable colonies, on Sycamore, Holly and a number of other planted trees and shrubs." Although we have not been able to refind it at Markshall it could well still occur there. Jermyn's site at Greenstead Green was refound in 1988 - about 20 flowering spikes but apparently growing

on Willow rather than Elm as mentioned by Jermyn. A further record was found, again in this locality, with one flowering spike growing in an old pollarded Willow. However, it was not parasitising the roots, but growing in a cavity in the pollard itself, 10ft above the ground!

Knapweed Broomrape
Orobanche elatior [1]

By Jermyn's time this parasite of **Greater Knapweed** which is a chalk loving plant, had already contracted its range to the traditional chalk soils of Essex, the outlying stations given by Gibson of Pattiswick and Rivenhall having been lost. However, Gibson also gave a record for the chalk

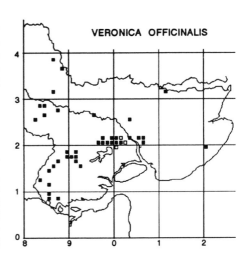

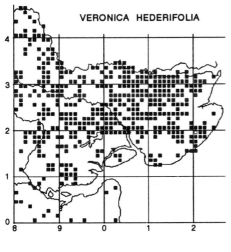

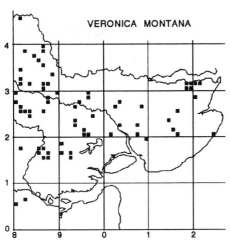

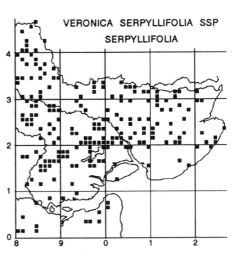

outcrop to the west of Sudbury, at Middleton. Jermyn subsequently found it on this same chalk outcrop, at Belchamp Otten (his only record for our area). Our survey also found it in this area, at Belchamp Walter, 1km east of Jermyn's site.

Common Broomrape
Orobanche minor [15] M
Infrequent and scattered, usually parasitising **Red Clover** but also on **Smooth Hawksbeard**. Clover is still grown as a crop occasionally and if the Broomrape is found in the field, then the whole crop is blighted, as, even with modern seed cleaning, it is difficult to separate the dust-like Broomrape seed from the larger Clover seed.

Great Broomrape
Orobanche rapum-genistae
Considering that its host is **Broom**, which is common in our area, it is surprising that this Broomrape has not been found in north east Essex since Gibson's time. He gave several records for it from Halstead, roadside between Colne and Colchester, Little Maplestead, Inworth, Langham, and a grove near Colchester.

BUTTERWORT FAMILY
LENTIBULARIACEAE

Greater Bladderwort
Utricularia vulgaris
There have been no records for north east Essex since Gibson's time when it was found in some ponds at Kelvedon.

ACANTHUS FAMILY
ACANTHACEAE

Bear's Breech
Acanthus mollis [2]
A garden plant that occasionally escapes into neighbouring verges.

VERBENA FAMILY
VERBENACEAE

Vervain
Verbena officinalis [6]
According to Gibson this plant was common on roadsides and waste ground, generally near houses. However, it is now quite rare. It was still present in 1983 at Jermyn's only site, the canal bank at Heybridge, and it was subsequently found on the railway track by Copperas Wood, 1985; on a gravel track at Liston Pits, 1986; by a footpath at Tenpenny Heath, 1986; and near a pond at St Osyth, 1989.

THYME FAMILY
LABIATAE

Bugle
Ajuga reptans [129] M
No longer common, but still reasonably frequent in damp places in woods and copses, especially on grassy woodland rides or close by woodland streams.

Black Horehound
Ballota nigra [1088] M
Very common on any scruffy roadside, waste ground, bottom of fences and hedges. The only areas that it does not appear to occupy are saltings and the old grazing marshes at Langenhoe and Old Hall.

Lesser Calamint   *Clinopodium*
Calamintha nepeta [96] M
Nationally a notable plant, its stronghold in Britain is north east Essex and neighbouring parts of Suffolk. It is widespread on light sandy soils, declining in some areas due to mowing of the road verges which are its main habitat. Other sites include grassy banks and churchyards. Although normally preferring a sunny aspect **Lesser Calamint** occurs on the north face of the Roman Wall, Colchester.

Clinopodium
Common Calamint
(Calamintha sylvatica) ssp ascendens
Although both Gibson and Jermyn gave
records for north east Essex for this spe-
cies, which is very similar to **Lesser
Calamint**, our intensive coverage has
revealed no sites for this plant. All her-
barium material held at Colchester Natural
History Museum has been confirmed as
Lesser Calamint by Dr R M Harley - there
are, therefore, no reliable records for
Common Calamint for north east Essex.

Wild Basil
Clinopodium vulgare [49] M
Wild Basil requires a chalk soil, and, as a
consequence, is commonest on the chalk

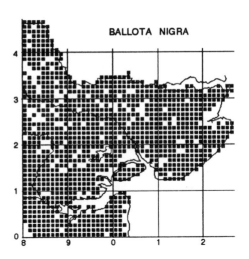

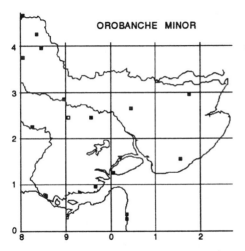

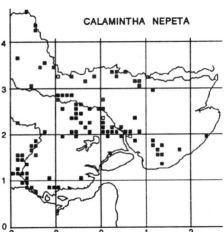

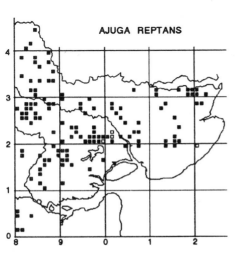

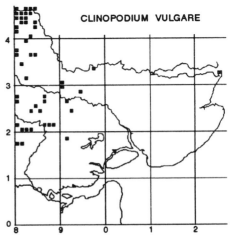

195

outcrop around Pentlow. The plant was more widespread in Jermyn's time and it appears that its range is now contracting as there are fewer records from other areas. It is usually found on grassy banks, beside bridleways and in hedge bottoms.

Narrow-leaved Hemp Nettle
Galeopsis angustifolia
This plant was common in the Gibson era - he gave records for Halstead, frequent; Kelvedon; Berechurch and, common near Colchester. Jermyn regarded it as rare and only found it in a stubble field at Wormingford and a hedgerow at Lawford. It was not found at all during our survey.

Galeopsis bifida [3]
Some things don't change; there was confusion in Jermyn's time concerning the classification of this species, on which he commented at length, and this is still the case today. Reference to several wild flower books will show that it is treated as an aggregate with, or a variety of, *G tetrahit*, or, as here, as a distinct species. Whatever the case, its distribution remains imperfectly known. Jermyn had found it at Tiptree Heath, a roadside at Halstead, Layer Wood and Berechurch Common. We have not refound any of these records, but have found it in a large hedgerow at High Woods, at the edge of thick scrub at Fordham Heath and in a damp grassy open area of a wood south of Maldon.

Downy Hemp Nettle
Galeopsis segetum
Gibson gave records for Berechurch and Villa Ponds, Elmstead, but there have been none since.

Large-flowered Hemp Nettle
Galeopsis speciosa [1]
Although Jermyn had no records for the north east of the county he described it as a colonist of cultivated ground and waste places. In 1986 two plants were found on waste ground adjacent to Great Totham recreation ground. Gibson, however, considered it as rare on "damp peaty ground" showing that his records for Kelvedon, 1845, and an oat field at Birch, 1860, were probably of native origin, whereas now it occurs only as a casual.

Common Hemp Nettle
Galeopsis tetrahit [214] M
Reasonably frequent on the drier, lighter soils, where it occurs at the top of ditch-banks, hedge bottoms, and also as an occasional arable weed. Although it usually has mauve flowers, white forms are not infrequent.

Ground Ivy
Glechoma hederacea [966] M
Very common in hedges, ditchbanks, woodlands, copses, thickets and road verges, it generally avoids the coastal strip.

Yellow Archangel   SS? Montanum
Lamiastrum galeobdolon [69] M
Scattered over the area, in damp woods and occasionally in large hedgerows and on roadsides. It often occurs where seepage gives damp conditions, or, by roadsides where surface water run-off keeps the soil moist.

White Dead Nettle
Lamium album [994] M
Very common on roadside verges, rough grassland, hedgerows and waste places.

Henbit
Lamium amplexicaule [88] M
Scattered and infrequent, on the lighter soils. Generally just a few plants are found, as an arable weed or more often in allotments and market garden fields.

Cut-leaved Dead Nettle
Lamium hybridum [166] M
Found on similar soils and in similar places as the previous species but over a much wider area. It was possibly under-recorded in the past as Jermyn only had a few records, although Gibson gave records covering much of the area.

Spotted Dead Nettle
Lamium maculatum [2]
A garden plant that becomes naturalised when discarded in ditches and hedgerows. Not fully recorded.

Red Dead Nettle
Lamium purpureum [928] M
Very common as a weed of arable fields,

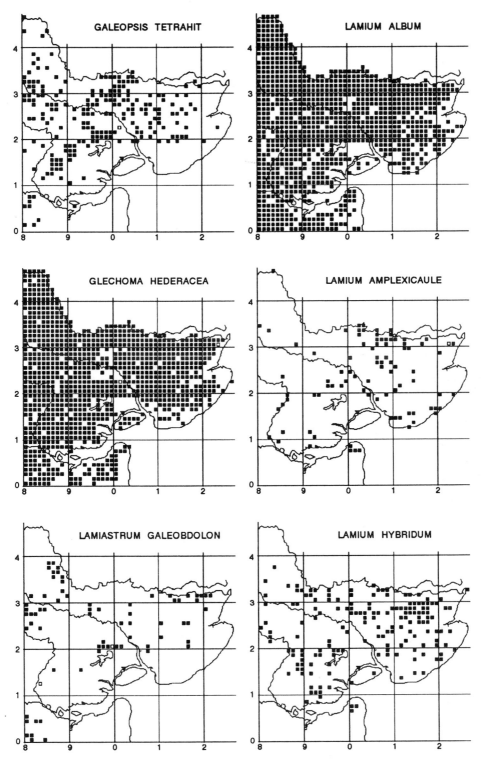

GALEOPSIS TETRAHIT

LAMIUM ALBUM

GLECHOMA HEDERACEA

LAMIUM AMPLEXICAULE

LAMIASTRUM GALEOBDOLON

LAMIUM HYBRIDUM

gardens, allotments and any bare disturbed soils.

Gipsywort
Lycopus europaeus [212] M
No longer common, but still reasonably frequent in still-water conditions such as wet ditches, ponds and farm reservoirs.

White Horehound
Marrubium vulgare
White Horehound was a rare plant of waste places in Gibson's time; he gave records for Tiptree Heath and a pit near Dedham. There have been no records since.

Balm
Melissa officinalis [10]
A garden plant that occasionally naturalises in verges where it has been discarded, or in churchyards where it has been introduced. Its lemon-scented foliage is distinctive.

Water Mint
Mentha aquatica [276] M
Although still common it is probably not as widespread as previously. Wet ditches, marshy places, by ponds, streams and rivers.

Corn Mint
Mentha arvensis [89] M
No longer common, it is, however, still reasonably frequent, although usually in small quantity. Whilst still found occasionally amongst the stubble, it is more often met with in a field that has been taken out of production, perhaps in an awkward corner or where the land is awaiting building development.

Pennyroyal
Mentha pulegium
Gibson gave several records from wet commons; Tiptree Heath, Langford Moor, Ardleigh and elsewhere near Dedham, Bergholt Heath and roadside between Walton and Thorpe. However, Jermyn considered that it was probably extinct in the county and we have no records.

Garden Mints and Hybrids
A selection of these are recorded in both the previous Floras of Essex, but due to changes in identification criteria in recent years it is not possible to know definitely to which species they refer. The following have been identified by Dr R M Harley for us from specimens collected on road verges, waste places and tip sites.

Spear Mint
Mentha spicata [24]
Scattered records from discarded garden plants.
Mentha X villosa var alopecuroides [5]
Records from Colchester, Boxted, Wivenhoe, Little Bentley and Thorpe le Soken.
Mentha X villoso-nervata [1]
Recorded from Booses Green in 1982, this is the first record for the county for this species.

Wild Catmint
Nepeta cataria
This plant has not been found during our survey and must be considered lost. Jermyn considered it to be very rare, giving only two localities (Pentlow, c1930, and Bath Side, Harwich, 1971), compared to Gibson's Halstead, near Borley, Kelvedon, Inworth and near Dedham. The only recent record was 1978, when it occurred in the garden of Colchester Natural History Museum. Its origin was unknown and it did not subsequently reappear.

Garden Catmint
Nepeta mussinii
Jermyn found this garden escape had naturalised in gravel pits, at Heybridge Basin, 1966, but it was not refound.

Marjoram
Origanum vulgare [6]
Marjoram is a native on calcareous soils but an introduction or escape in other areas. Of our six records, we consider two may be native (Great & Little Henny) but certainly the remaining four are garden escapes.

Cut-leaved Selfheal
Prunella laciniata
Jermyn gave two records - East Donyland, 1928 and Boxted Hall Farm, cart track in Mill Field, 1933-34. As there have been no other records for this plant in north east Essex it is probable that these were casual

occurrences, perhaps as a contaminant of seed.

Selfheal
Prunella vulgaris [523] M
Common in lawns, churchyards, woodland rides and tracks over the whole area.

Salvia reflexa [1]
This garden plant was recorded growing at Maldon rubbish tip in 1989.

Wild Clary
Salvia verbenaca [7]
Still decreasing as it has been lost from some of Jermyn's sites although it can still be found in the vicinity of some others. It

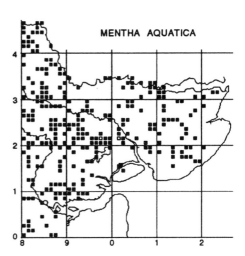

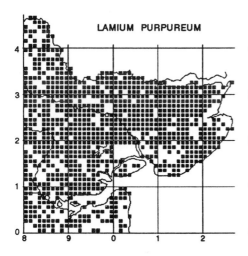

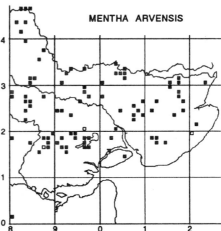

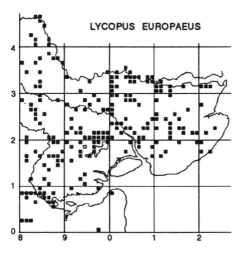

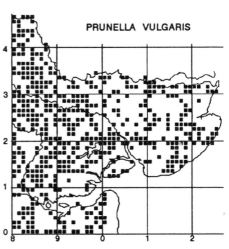

199

grows on dry banks and verges which receive the full benefit of the sun. It is most plentiful on a protected verge at St Osyth but otherwise just a few plants are found at each site. These include: Manningtree Station; the Valley Walk, near Sudbury; Harwich; and Fordham and Aldham churchyards.

Whorled Clary
Salvia verticillata [1]
Very rarely occurs as a garden escape. We found it naturalised on an old wall.

Salvia viridis
A casual noted by Jermyn from the rubbish tip at Hythe Quay.

Common Skullcap
Scutellaria galericulata [30] M
Decreasing and now infrequent in the bankside vegetation of ponds, streams and rivers. It also occurs at Abberton Reservoir where it grows in the cracks in the concrete. Gibson described it as common at Halstead but it now occurs nowhere on the Colne. It has also been lost from the upper reaches of the Blackwater and much of the Stour.

Lesser Skullcap
Scutellaria minor
Rare and decreasing, according to Jermyn, his sites included: Ulting, marsh by canal; Goldhanger, marshy area by brook, scarce; Abberton Reservoir, marsh; Donyland Wood, marsh by Roman River. We have not found this plant during our survey

Field Woundwort
Stachys arvensis [17] M
Regarded both by Gibson and Jermyn as rare, it is pleasant to report an increase in the number of records. However, we do not think it is because of an increase in its distribution but more as a result of the intensive coverage of our survey. We have found **Field Woundwort**, usually in small quantity mainly in the Tendring peninsula, in the edges of arable fields, farm tracks, a cemetery and a gravel drive in urban Clacton.

Stachys byzantina [1]
Recorded from a road verge where it had established itself after being discarded.

Betony
Stachys officinalis [15] M
Another plant whose decline can be tracked through the comments of Gibson and Jermyn - from common, to frequent, and now uncommon. Never more than one or two plants, it is associated with heathy soils and our observations have revealed that it only survives on old grass verges. It appears that once the verge is disturbed and the coarser grasses given the opportunity to colonise, then **Betony** is unable to compete.

Marsh Woundwort
Stachys palustris [95] M
Reasonably frequent, although no longer common, it occurs along our river banks, streams and associated marshy areas, as well as wet ditches. It will creep into arable fields if they are badly drained.

Stachys palustris X sylvatica
Gibson gave four sites in north east Essex where this hybrid had been found, but none have been recorded since. It is possible that it has been overlooked.

Hedge Woundwort
Stachys sylvatica [915] M
Very common in hedgerows, ditchbanks, woodland edges and rides.

Wood Sage
Teucrium scorodonia [287] M
Still common on the light free draining brick-earths and sand and gravels where it occurs in woods, hedgerows, roadside banks and heaths.

Wild Thyme
Thymus praecox ssp arcticus [2]
Once native in our area, we have found it as a garden escape and in a garden lawn where it was imported with the turf.

Large Wild Thyme
Thymus pulegioides [1]
Another native that can now only be found as a garden escape. Gibson describes it as growing in "pastures and stiff cold soils"; his sites were: Felix Hall Park, Kelvedon; Tiptree Heath and West Bergholt.

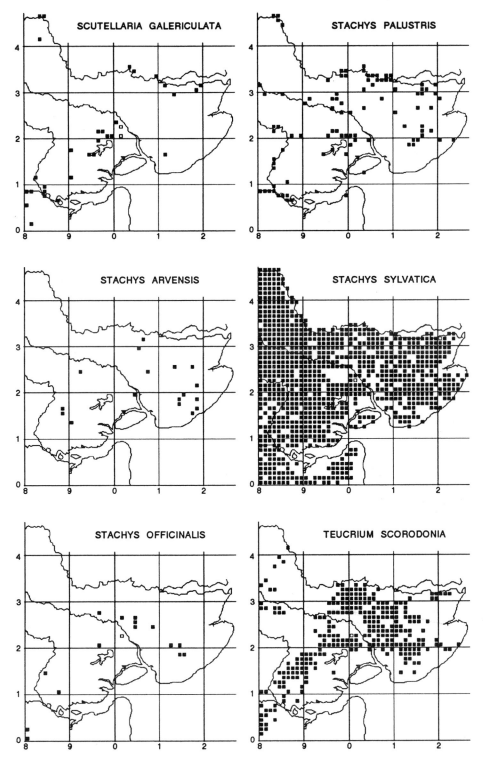

SCUTELLARIA GALERICULATA

STACHYS PALUSTRIS

STACHYS ARVENSIS

STACHYS SYLVATICA

STACHYS OFFICINALIS

TEUCRIUM SCORODONIA

PLANTAIN FAMILY
PLANTAGINACEAE

Plantago arenaria [1]
Recorded by Jermyn as a casual from Alresford and Hythe Quay, and recently as a bird seed alien, Colchester, 1985.

Buckshorn Plantain
Plantago coronopus [269] M
Gibson's description of its habitat requirements are particularly apt "gravelly soils, especially near the sea". The distribution map clearly shows its preference not only for the coast, but also for the gravel soils around Colchester.

Ribwort Plantain
Plantago lanceolata [1231] M
Very common in all kinds of grassland as well as waste places. A 'miscellaneous' piece of information gathered during the survey was that **Ribwort Plantain** overwinters as a basal rosette, but the **Greater Plantain** does not, it waits for the warmer weather before showing itself above ground.

Greater Plantain
Plantago major ssp intermedia [19] M
Plantago major ssp major [1234]
Very common on any disturbed bare soils, particularly in gardens, farmyards, tracks, cracks in paving slabs and waste ground. **Greater Plantain** has, only recently, been divided into two subspecies; *ssp major* is the usual Plantain met with, and *ssp intermedia* a coastal form. The latter is, as yet, under-recorded but to date has been found scattered around most of our coast. It has also been recorded at Abberton where it has probably been brought in by the wildfowl.

Sea Plantain
Plantago maritima [143] M
Still common on many of our saltmarshes, it seems to be more frequent on the more sheltered areas of marsh.

Hoary Plantain
Plantago media [69] M
Common in grassland on calcareous soils, it becomes more scattered where there is only a chalky influence. The odd site at

Clacton was from the grounds of a chapel where it was abundant. As none could be found in the surrounding area it was, therefore, probably imported with the turf.

BELLFLOWER FAMILY
CAMPANULACEAE

Clustered Bellflower
Campanula glomerata
A native plant on calcareous soils, it is also grown as a garden flower and can occur as an escape. Jermyn gave a record which he considered of native origin for factory grounds at Liston where it grew with **Viper's Bugloss**. Neither of these now occur there (at least within view of the perimeter fence). His other site for a naturalised garden escape, near houses at Mount Bures, could not be refound either.

Canterbury Bell
Campanula medium [1]
The only record during our survey was as a bird seed alien in 1981.

Spreading Bellflower
Campanula patula
Gibson records it as having been found once in a meadow near Halstead. There are no other records.

Creeping Bellflower
Campanula rapunculoides [19] M
A garden escape that quickly becomes naturalised and is extremely persistent (unless you **really** like it, never introduce it into your garden!). We have found it at several additional sites to those given by Jermyn as well as refinding his locations on a roadside at Alresford, and road bridge over the railway at Great Bentley.

Rampion Bellflower
Campanula rapunculus [1]
It has been known from Kelvedon railway station since c1850. Jermyn found that it was on the railway bank west of the station in 1961, and in 1964 it was plentiful on both railway banks. Two years later it had spread to a roadside bank near the bridge where it still occurred in 1970. It is still present at Kelvedon but British Rail has dumped rubbish and ballast on part of the

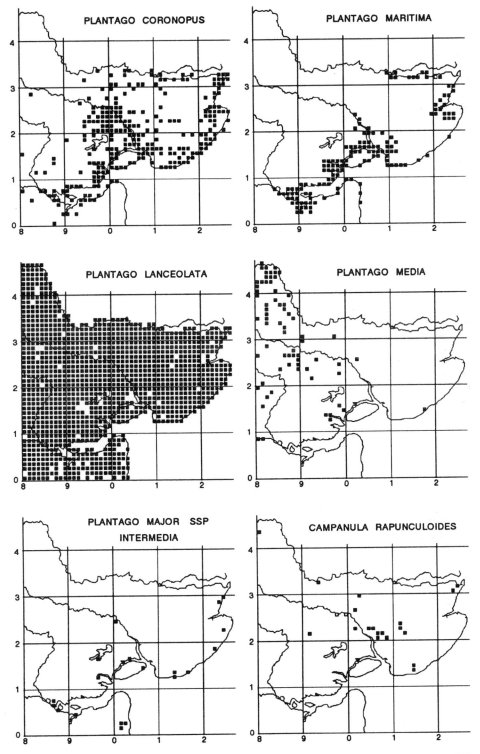

site.

Harebell
Campanula rotundifolia [28] M
Infrequent and usually in small quantity on dry banks and heathy grassland on gravel soils. Its range has contracted and it is decreasing.

Nettle-leaved Bellflower
Campanula trachelium 12] M
Known by Gibson from the chalk outcrop west of Sudbury, he gives records for Pentlow, Henny, between Bulmer Hills and Sudbury. It still occurs in this area today on ditchbanks. There were mostly three or four plants at each site, making a fine show, if they had been missed by the verge mowing. It has also at some time in the past been introduced to St Peter's churchyard in Colchester.

Sheepsbit
Jasione montana
Gibson noted several records for our area; gravel pit at Braxted; Blackheath, Colchester; between Langham and the Gun, and elsewhere near Dedham. There have been no other records in north east Essex and it has since been lost to the county as a whole.

Venus' Looking Glass
Legousia hybrida [17] M
An arable weed of the lighter soils, which has declined over the years and is now rare. It appears to be more frequent some years than others (in 1980 & 1988 it was found at 4 and 5 sites respectively, whilst in 1983, 1986 & 1987, it was not found at all) but whether this is indicative of a dependency on certain weather conditions is not known. It is certainly dependent upon the crop grown; certain sprays cannot be used on some crops allowing **Venus' Looking Glass** to grow and flower.

BEDSTRAW FAMILY
RUBIACEAE

Asperula arvensis [1]
A bird seed alien that Jermyn recorded from Woodham Mortimer, 1963. During our survey it occurred, as a result of feeding wild birds during the winter, in a garden in Colchester in 1985.

Upright Hedge Bedstraw
Galium album
This Bedstraw occurs mostly on calcareous soils and, as such, would always have had a limited distribution in our area. Jermyn gave a record, which was not refound during our survey, for a chalky roadside and cutting between Gestingthorpe and Bulmer.

Goosegrass or Cleavers
Galium aparine [1237] M
Very common over the whole area, in all sorts of habitats.

Crosswort
Galium cruciata
This yellow-flowered Bedstraw is associated with a calcareous soil but Gibson gives a record for Great Oakley which is far removed from the main chalk soils but could have been on a calcareous brick-earth or a soil derived from the shelly Red Crag. It is the only time this plant has ever been noted in north east Essex.

Great Marsh Bedstraw
Galium elongatum
When Jermyn was conducting his survey, this species was regarded as a subspecies of *G palustre* and its distribution was imperfectly known. He did give records for a ditch by Weeleyhall Wood, a marsh at Langham and Holland Brook, but we have been unable to locate, either his, or any other sites during our survey.

Hedge Bedstraw
Galium mollugo [443] M
It is more common on the chalky boulder clays, but it also occurs on other soil types, which may indicate that the availability of suitable habitat also plays a part in its distribution. As its name implies, it is found scrambling up and through hedges, and more often than not, in the older hedgerows.

Sweet Woodruff
Galium odoratum [7]
This woodland species was far more widespread in Gibson's day, as he notes

several woods where it occurred near Maldon, Totham, Layer Marney and Colchester. He states that it was not uncommon around Halstead, and indeed, Jermyn found sites at Greenstead Green, Moat and Broadfield Woods in that area. He was, however, unable to locate **Sweet Woodruff** in Chalkney Wood, another of Gibson's sites. Additionally Jermyn found it growing in the Stour and Copperas Wood complex. During our survey we were able to confirm the sites at Moat, Broadfield, Stour and Copperas Woods, but were unable to find his Greenstead Green site. Additionally it grows in Fordham churchyard, but this is probably the result of an introduction.

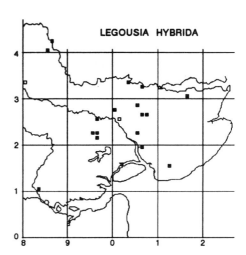

LEGOUSIA HYBRIDA

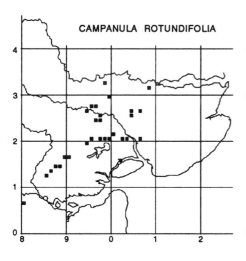

CAMPANULA ROTUNDIFOLIA

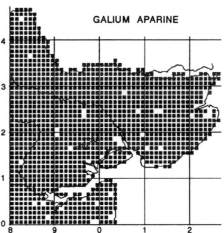

GALIUM APARINE

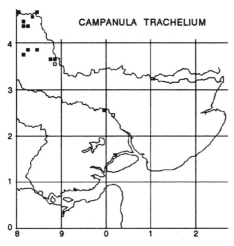

CAMPANULA TRACHELIUM

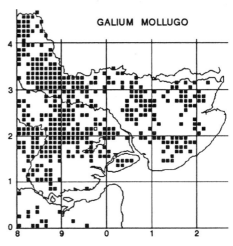

GALIUM MOLLUGO

Marsh Bedstraw
Galium palustre [93] M
Scattered in marshy ponds and occasionally wet ditches, but most common in damp woodland rides and flushes.

Heath Bedstraw
Galium saxatile [34] M
Although we have more sites than given by Jermyn, we feel that this is due to the intensive coverage, and, in actual fact, that **Heath Bedstraw** is probably decreasing with the loss of acid grassland. It is still present at Tiptree, Layer Breton and Fordham Heaths as well as several places in the Roman River Conservation Zone, however, it could not be found at Thorpe Green, Bures or the woods at Markshall. The latter site is a large complex of woods and it may well still occur there.

Rough Corn Bedstraw
Galium tricornutum
Even to Gibson, this cornfield weed was rather local; Halstead - rare, Coggeshall, Kelvedon and Rivenhall, and they were the last records for north east Essex. Jermyn found it to be very rare in the county as a whole.

Fen Bedstraw
Galium uliginosum [1]
We have only one record for this Bedstraw - it was in a very boggy hollow which would have been impenetrable without a wet suit if the surveying had not been carried out during the drought of 1989. It was a short distance from Chalkney Wood (a Gibson location). Gibson also cites Kelvedon and Jermyn found it in this vicinity (gravel pits at Silver End and between Rivenhall and Kelvedon) but we were unable to refind it in this area, or at Jermyn's other locations of Birch and West Bergholt.

Lady's Bedstraw
Galium verum [155] M
No longer common and plentiful, it can, however, still be found reasonably frequently in dry grassy places which are

relics of old pastures and grassland, including churchyards and some road verges. It was surprisingly found in the completely arable desert at the very tip of the Dengie peninsula, possibly because the whole area was, until comparatively recently, grazing, of which fragments remain at field and track edges.

Field Madder
Sherardia arvensis [121] M
Reduced from Jermyn's "common and well distributed" to reasonably frequent and scattered. It is more easily seen when it occurs as an arable weed but it can quite often be found in lawns and other areas of mown grass where it is difficult to see unless in flower. At a derelict hotel site at Clacton it was abundant, growing in great patches over the rubble.

HONEYSUCKLE FAMILY
CAPRIFOLIACEAE

Leycesteria formosa [2]
Of casual occurrence, it either arises as a bird seed alien or as a garden escape. It is grown in Castle Park, Colchester, and seedlings turn up in nearby gardens and on a building in the town.

Perfoliate Honeysuckle
Lonicera caprifolium [1]
A garden plant that had escaped even in Victorian times, as Gibson recorded it from Markshall Woods and Rivenhall. Not fully recorded.

Honeysuckle
Lonicera periclymenum [564] M
Common in hedgerows and woods over most of the area although tending to avoid the extreme coastal strip.

Fly Honeysuckle
Lonicera xylosteum [2]
Not previously recorded for north east Essex but as a garden plant it was bound

to turn up in our hedgerows some time.

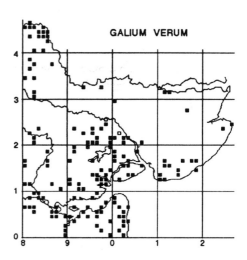

Dwarf Elder or Danewort
Sambucus ebulus
Although Gibson quoted several sites
(Alphamstone, Maldon, Kelvedon, Frinton
churchyard, lane near Harwich), Jermyn
was unable to locate this plant in north east
Essex. This is confirmed by our survey.

Elder
Sambucus nigra [1189] M
Very common in hedgerows, scrub, woods,
waste places and rough ground. Gibson
noted that a planted variety (*var laciniata*)

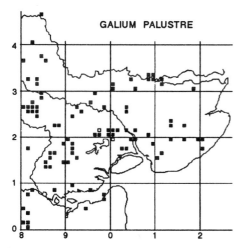

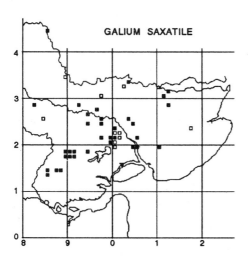

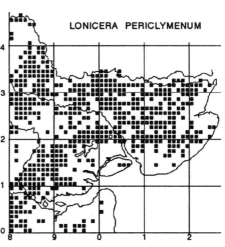

had been found near cottages at Kelvedon and also at Ardleigh.

Snowberry
Symphoricarpos rivularis [113] M

ALBUS - Stace

Introduced originally about 1817 it is now reasonably frequent with a wide but scattered distribution. Mainly found in hedgerows, but forming quite dense thickets when no longer kept in check.

Wayfaring Tree
Viburnum lantana [3]
Native on calcareous soils, but an introduction elsewhere. Jermyn's location in a roadside hedge on the Gestingthorpe-Bulmer road has not survived - the hedge has been grubbed out. However, another site was found further north at Liston where one tree was growing in a hedge. Other records obtained during the survey relate to obvious introductions.

Guelder Rose
Viburnum opulus [57] M
Infrequent and scattered in damp hedges and woodland margins. Some fine specimens grow in the Roman River Valley, they were found in dense scrub during conservation work being carried out by the CNHS. The shrubs themselves were coppiced and, with the clearance of the surrounding **Blackthorn** scrub, have developed into large bushes, red with fruit in the autumn.

MOSCHATEL FAMILY
ADOXACEAE

Moschatel
Adoxa moschatellina [83] M
The detailed survey has revealed more sites than those given by Jermyn, but has also shown that many of his sites have gone. It is found in damp woods, often near streams and growing through leaf litter, as well as copses and shady places.

VALERIAN FAMILY
VALERIANACEAE

Red Valerian
Centranthus ruber [21] M
Introduced. It has been naturalised for

many years on the Roman Wall at Colchester, at its best on the south face in Priory Street car park. Otherwise it occurs on dry banks, the cliffs at Clacton, Frinton and Walton and other scattered walls.

Marsh Valerian
Valeriana dioica
A plant of damp and boggy meadows that was common in Gibson's day. He recorded it from meadows near Halstead and Kelvedon and the banks of the Colne near Colchester. Jermyn was unable to refind any of these sites and found that in the intervening years it was becoming increasingly rare through loss of habitat. His only site, of a brookside near the sewage works at Great Maplestead, could not be refound, leaving us to report the loss of this plant in north east Essex.

Common Valerian
Valeriana officinalis [13]
The downward trend can be traced from Gibson's "common", through Jermyn's "frequent", to the current state of "becoming rare". It no longer occurs at any point on the Colne or Roman River, and is found only at Rivenhall End on the Blackwater (with an out-lying site along Domsey Brook), leaving the bulk of the population on the Stour. Even here, there are gaps, it is no longer found between Boxted Mill and Great Henny where, according to Jermyn, it used to occur at several spots and has even gone from Wormingford Mere where it was once plentiful. **Elder-leaved Valerian** (*V sambucifolia*) was recorded separately by Jermyn but it is now only regarded as a variety of the **Common Valerian** and has not been recorded separately in the present survey.

Keeled Corn Salad
Valerianella carinata
Very local in Gibson's time, he had records from hedgebanks and fields at Kelvedon, Inworth and Berechurch, but it has not been seen since.

Narrow-fruited Corn Salad
Valerianella dentata
Apparently common according to Gibson but Jermyn found only one location - an old gravel pit at Bradwell-on-Sea. There have

been no records of this plant during our survey and it must be regarded as lost to the area.

Corn Salad
Valerianella locusta [9]
The commonest of the Corn Salads in the Victorian era, like the two previous species it has suffered a decline, which has continued since Jermyn's recording - his only location that we have been able to refind is Colne Point. Many of his sites were on dry sunny railway banks but this habitat has changed greatly in the intervening years and in many instances these have now become scrubbed over. Our few records were found either as an arable weed on

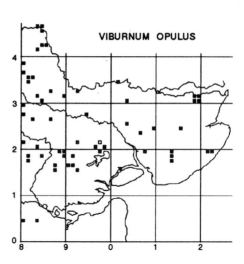

VIBURNUM OPULUS

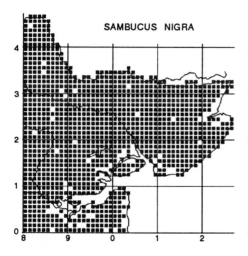

SAMBUCUS NIGRA

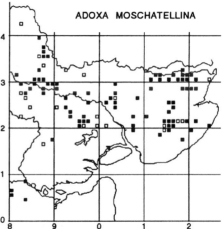

ADOXA MOSCHATELLINA

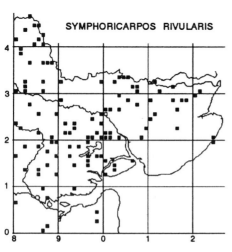

SYMPHORICARPOS RIVULARIS

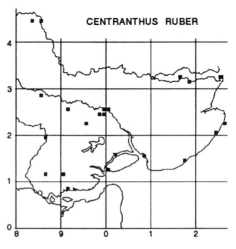

CENTRANTHUS RUBER

light soils or on dry sandy banks, often associated with rabbit disturbance.

Broad-fruited Corn Salad
Valerianella rimosa
Gibson had records for this Corn Salad from old walls at Colchester but there have been none since.

TEASEL FAMILY
DIPSACACEAE

Wild Teasel
Dipsacus fullonum
ssp sylvestris [434] M
Still common over much of the area in damp grassland, ditches, stream and riverbanks, but it has a scattered distribution east of Colchester.

Small Teasel
Dipsacus pilosus [7]
Although now rare, it survives in two of the sites given by Gibson - Halstead, where it was frequent, and Berechurch, where it was abundant. It is still scattered along the Roman River through Friday Wood to Chest Wood but not in as many sites as given by Jermyn. At Halstead (where Jermyn did not record it) there are a few plants along the bank of the Colne. Two other sites have been found - by the Colne west of Fordstreet and on private land at Pebmarsh. We were unable to refind it at Jermyn's sites at Liston Pits, on the Blackwater at Coggeshall or Bradwell where it was also known to Gibson.

Field Scabious
Knautia arvensis [240] M
Still frequent on the soils with a chalky influence but becoming very scattered elsewhere. It is found in mature grassland and roadside verges and banks on the lighter soils. The flowers being full of nectar are beloved by butterflies, often three or four can be seen sharing the same flowerhead.

Small Scabious
Scabiosa columbaria
The only record for our area is from the Roman Wall at Colchester where it was recorded by Gibson. There have been no sightings since.

Devilsbit Scabious
Succisa pratensis [9]
Devilsbit Scabious is a plant of damp old pastures and grassland, a habitat which has all but vanished. This is reflected in the decline of this plant, "common" to Gibson, it was still "frequent and locally common" to Jermyn and his records show its distribution as being over most of north east Essex (he had records for thirteen 10km squares). Indeed, neither he, nor Gibson, considered it worthwhile giving specific locations as there were so many. We have found it along the Valley Walk west of Sudbury, Tiptree Heath, a damp bridleway at Layer Marney, a couple of places in the Roman River Valley Conservation Zone, a further two sites at Crockleford Heath and at Lexden.

DAISY FAMILY
COMPOSITAE

Yarrow
Achillea millefolium [1217] M
Very common in grassland, road verges, hedgerows and waste ground.

Sneezewort
Achillea ptarmica [6]
A rare flower of heathy grassland. It still occurs at Fordham Heath, where Jermyn recorded it, but has been lost from his other sites at Tiptree and Layer Breton Heaths as well as Bath Side, Harwich. We have found additional sites in the Roman River Valley Conservation Zone, Copford, Crockleford Heath and Chigborough Lakes but there are only a few plants at each location.

Achillea serrata
The only record for our area comes from Gibson, who recorded it as a casual escape from Lethe Grove near Berechurch Hall, Colchester.

Ragweed
Ambrosia artemisiifolia
A rubbish tip casual that Jermyn found at Hythe Quay tip and waste ground nearby in 1965. There have been no further records.

210

Corn Chamomile
Anthemis arvensis [60] M
Scattered and not often found in any quantity at the edges of arable fields or fields that have not been cultivated (perhaps awaiting development). It is most frequently found around Thorpe and, more especially, Dovercourt.

Stinking Chamomile
Anthemis cotula [133] M
More frequent than the previous species, growing in similar habitats, it can also be found on bare ground along the road verges and by lay-bys. Depending upon the crop grown it can be locally plentiful, appearing as a white swathe along the

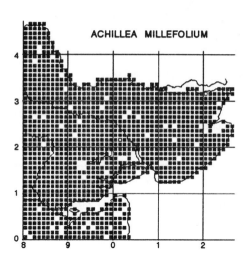

ACHILLEA MILLEFOLIUM

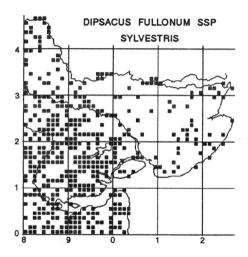

DIPSACUS FULLONUM SSP SYLVESTRIS

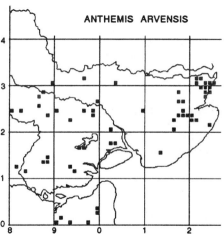

ANTHEMIS ARVENSIS

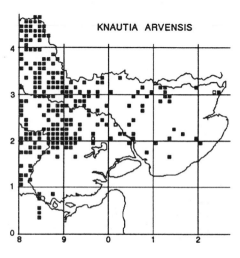

KNAUTIA ARVENSIS

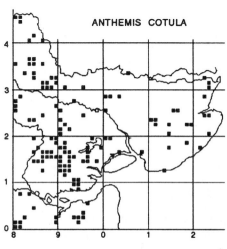

ANTHEMIS COTULA

edge of the field.

Greater Burdock
Arctium lappa [182] M
This Burdock has a preference for damp places and can often be found close by rivers and streams and, less frequently, by ditchbanks. There is an interesting loss of sites east of Colchester, where Jermyn had records for the four 10km squares where we have none. Here there are fewer streams and very intensive agriculture and as a result it has become very scarce. Jermyn also mentions *var foliosum* which he recorded in water meadows at Bures, but this variety no longer merits such distinction and is included in the species.

Lesser Burdock
Arctium minus ssp minus [565] M
Common over the whole area in varying habitats - farm tracks and especially gateways, bare patches on road verges and woodland rides, as well as rough areas beside lay-bys.

Arctium minus ssp nemorosum [17] M
Apparently uncommon and scattered in hedgerows and by woodland edges but possibly under-recorded due to difficulties in identification - it may sometimes have been confused with the previous subspecies.

Arctium minus ssp pubens [13]
A cluster of records occur on the sand and gravel ridge of the Dengie peninsula, but it is otherwise very uncommon.

Lamb's Succory
Arnoseris minima
Gibson gives records for a cornfield near Halstead and near a farmhouse by Lawford Mill wood, but it has not been recorded since.

Wormwood
Artemisia absinthium [26] M
Common in waste places in and around Colchester, but very scattered elsewhere.

Sea Wormwood
Artemisia maritima [101] M
A plant of the higher zone saltmarsh, whose habitat is truncated by sea walls,

resulting in **Sea Wormwood** usually growing along the base of the sea wall itself. It also grows on the cliffs at Clacton. Whilst still common in many parts of our area it has been lost, since Jermyn's recording, from the whole length of the Stour estuary, Beaumont, and the cliffs between Holland and Frinton.

Mugwort
Artemisia vulgaris [1014] M
Very common on road verges, especially rough ground by lay-bys, as well as hedgerows, woodland edges and waste areas.

Michaelmas Daisy
Revised criteria for the identification of this complex group of garden escapes makes direct comparison with earlier work impossible. The following species were recorded on the usual waste ground, road verges and tip sites:
Aster lanceolatus [2]
Colchester, old cattle market, 1978; Shrub End Tip, Colchester, 1983; waste ground near Colchester station, 1983.
Aster X salignus [3]
Tiptree Heath, 1980-85; Clacton, 1989.
Aster X versicolor [1]
Marks Tey, 1978-81.

Sea Aster
Aster tripolium [226] M
A common saltmarsh plant that occurs in two forms: one with mauve rayed florets

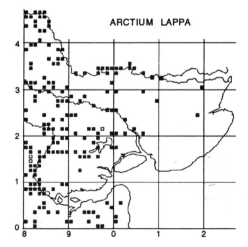

ARCTIUM LAPPA

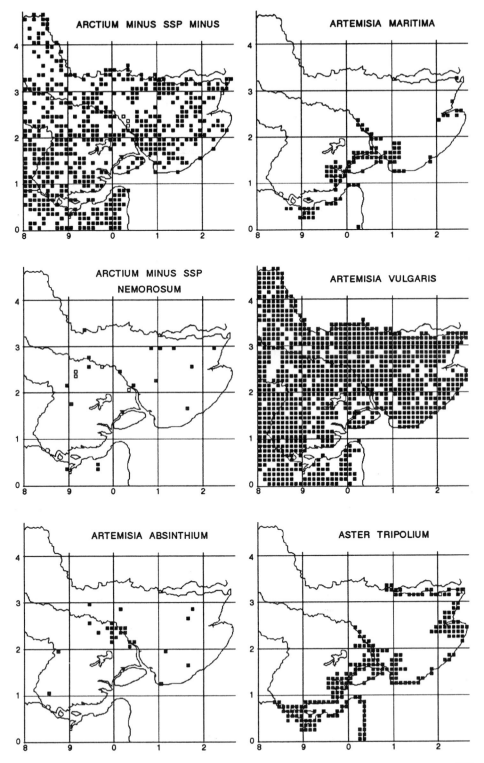

and one without. The latter (*var discoideus*) is by far the commoner of the two. The two forms have not been separated in our recording.

Daisy
Bellis perennis [959] M
Very common - there are very few garden lawns where it cannot be found! It also occurs in other grassy places.

Nodding Bur Marigold
Bidens cernua [5]
Decreased since Jermyn's time and now very rare. It occurs at pond edges on a wet platform of mud that dries out in summer. We have records from Cattawade, Mistley, Colchester and Tolleshunt Major. At no site was it present in any quantity.

Trifid Bur Marigold
Bidens tripartita [30] M
As with the previous species, **Trifid Bur Marigold** has also decreased, although not to such an extent, however, this is little consolation as it was the commoner of the two to start with. It requires wet and marshy places by ponds, lakes, reservoirs and streams. It is plentiful around some parts of Ardleigh Reservoir.

Field Marigold
Calendula arvensis
A casual, found by Jermyn from waste ground near Witham Station in 1957, it was not recorded during our survey.

Pot Marigold
Calendula officinalis [6]
A garden escape that can occasionally be found where garden rubbish has been dumped. Not fully recorded.

Welted Thistle
Carduus acanthoides [127] M   Crispus (Stace)
Reasonably frequent along the river valleys and flushes occurring where the clays and gravels meet but scattered elsewhere. Its main habitat is along river and streambanks.

Musk Thistle
Carduus nutans [34] M
Scattered and in small quantity on the sand and gravels around Colchester. It has been

known from a roadside at Stanway since the 1860s and can still be found there today. There is also a cluster of records around Mistley as well as on the chalk around Liston where it occurs on cart tracks and at Liston Pits.

Slender Thistle
Carduus tenuiflorus [39] M
Locally reasonably frequent on banks, sea walls, cliffs, gravelly car parks and other such areas close to the sea. In Gibson's time there were some inland sites; he mentions Witham, Kelvedon and Feering. It was only recorded from the coast by Jermyn and has now disappeared from many of the areas where he found it - he gives no specific sites but it was not refound in five of his thirteen 10km squares.

Carline Thistle
Carlina vulgaris [1]
The only place where this Thistle can now be seen is the Essex Naturalists' Trust Reserve at Great Holland Pits. We have been unable to find it anywhere else. Gibson gives records for Tiptree Heath, Rivenhall and Donyland Heath in the Roman River Valley, whilst Jermyn had recorded it from the golf course at Woodham Walter, Liston gravel pits, Maldon Wood, a gravel pit at St Osyth, the Naze cliffs as well as the Great Holland Pits site. Whilst at no time common, historically it was found over the whole of our area, frequently on sandy or gravelly soil.

Carthamus lanatus
A casual of rubbish tips and other such places. Jermyn gives a record for Colchester (before 1930) but there have been no sightings since.

Carthamus tinctorius [2]
Another casual of rubbish tips which was found at Maldon and Colchester's Shrub End tips during our survey.

Star Thistle
Centaurea calcitrapa
A very rare casual that has not been seen in the area since 1968, when it was found in a builder's yard at Walton. Previous records include Hythe Quay, c1927,

Witham, c1901, and a Gibson record from cultivated fields at Halstead.

Cornflower
Centaurea cyanus [1]
Common as a cornfield weed in Gibson's day, it had decreased dramatically, due to agricultural changes, by Jermyn's time, when he found it very rarely as a cornfield weed and more often as a garden escape or rubbish tip casual. He gives records for: old railway at Kelvedon, near the mill at Wickham Bishops, roadsides at Bulmer and Belchamp Walter, cornfield at Ardleigh. He also found it at Thorpe Cross but gives no habitat. During 1983 quite extensive patches of this plant were found

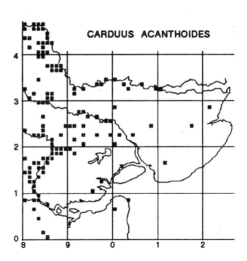
CARDUUS ACANTHOIDES

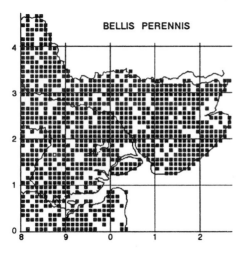
BELLIS PERENNIS

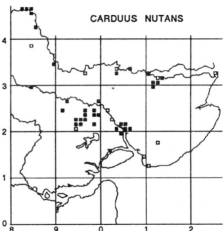
CARDUUS NUTANS

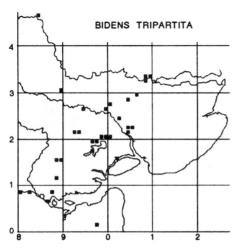
BIDENS TRIPARTITA

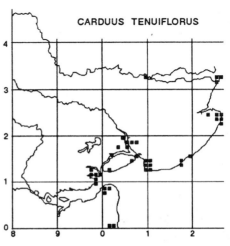
CARDUUS TENUIFLORUS

by Mrs Jane Chave in a corn field opposite Wickham Hall Cottages and along the side of the Langford road nearby after deep ploughing of the land the previous winter.

Knapweed
Centaurea nigra [1001] M
Common in Gibson's time, it makes a change to report that this plant, at least, is still common today. It occurs in almost any kind of grassland and can invariably be found on road verges, ditchbanks, woodland rides and hedgerows. The only major type of grassland where it is not always found is that along our sea walls. At the time Jermyn was recording this species was split into two, but it is now regarded as one variable species.

Greater Knapweed
Centaurea scabiosa [29] M
Reasonably frequent on the chalk outcrop to the west of Sudbury but scattered elsewhere. It is found on grass verges and banks as well as old pits.

St Barnaby's Thistle
Centaurea solstitialis
Gibson had records from cornfields at Halstead and Berechurch. He considered that it had been introduced with **Lucerne** and other seed and disappeared with the crop. Jermyn gives a record for Witham, before 1930. It has not been seen since.

Chamomile
Chamaemelum nobile
Not found during our survey, it was apparently frequent in Gibson's time. He gave records for Tiptree Heath, Great Totham, Bromley Heath, Langham Moor and Bergholt Heath. By Jermyn's time it had become very rare and he considered some of the remaining sites to be introductions. He had found it at Berechurch Common, 1954, on shingle by the sea wall at East Mersea, 1964, and the lawn of St Osyth Priory in 1962.

Corn Marigold
Chrysanthemum segetum [14]
A common cornfield weed in Gibson's time

- his sites range from Sudbury to Kelvedon and Halstead to Colchester. It had, however, subsequently decreased so that Jermyn found it to be uncommon. He gave only two sites: Great Maplestead (up to 1959) and a cornfield near Manningtree Station. It was still present at this latter site in 1981 where it appeared as a yellow border to the field. It was common in the early 1980s around Stanway, Colchester, where some fields were not cultivated prior to being built on. Other records are of a very scattered, casual nature, and it must now be considered rare.

Cicerbita bourgaei
Jermyn gives a record of this casual from a roadside hedge near Woodham Mortimer Place, 1953 and 1956-7.

Endive
Cichorium endivia [1]
A bird seed alien that has occurred just the once during our survey, Colchester, 1985.

Chicory
Cichorium intybus [25] M
Infrequent and scattered on road verges, along bridleways and tracks. It was cultivated as a crop at Alresford in the early 1980s.

Dwarf Thistle
Cirsium acaule
A thistle chiefly of calcareous soils, it was never common in our area; Gibson gives only three sites - two from the Halstead area and the third from Felix Hall Park near Kelvedon. There have been no further sightings.

Creeping Thistle
Cirsium arvense [1300] M
This thistle has the dubious pleasure of being the most common plant in our area. We visited 1,313 1km squares and it was found in all but 13 of them.

Woolly Thistle
Cirsium eriophorum [1]
A thistle of chalky soils that had not

previously been recorded for our area, the nearest record was from Gibson - near Yeldham towards Clare. In 1988, two plants were found growing in a hedgerow by a footpath near Pentlow, only a few kilometres east of Gibson's site.

Marsh Thistle
Cirsium palustre [197] M

No longer common everywhere, it is still reasonably frequent and can be locally plentiful in damp woodland rides and damp areas near rivers and streams. Its decrease is a result of the conversion of its grassland habitat into arable.

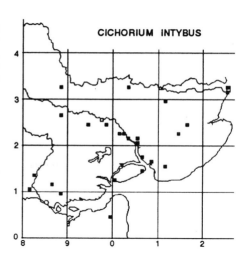

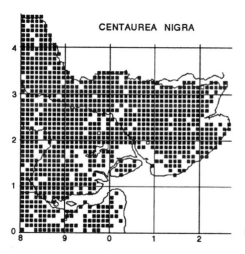

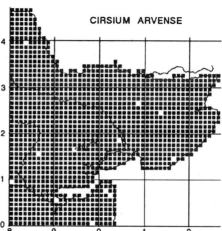

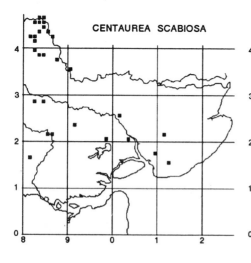

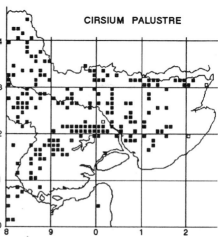

217

Spear Thistle
Cirsium vulgare [1254] M
Very common in all sorts of habitats.

Cosmos bipinnatus
A garden flower that occurs as a casual of rubbish tips and garden refuse. Jermyn had recorded it from Hythe Quay, Colchester and Lawford tip. As it is of a short-lived nature, sightings were not included in our survey.

Rough Hawksbeard
Crepis biennis
A rare plant in Essex, occurring on dry chalky banks. Gibson found two specimens in newly disturbed ground at Kelvedon and Jermyn gives a record for Birch, near Colchester. It was not found during our survey.

Smooth Hawksbeard
Crepis capillaris [615] M
Common in grass verges, particularly where mown by householders. It also occurs in other grassy places and as a weed of disturbed ground.

Stinking Hawksbeard
Crepis foetida
Jermyn considered that it was extinct in the county, as the last record was from Colchester in 1890. Our survey has not changed this position.

Crepis nicaeensis
Jermyn gave two records for the early part of this century (Tollesbury, c1938, and Colchester, c1930), and one for the latter part of the last (Inworth, 1880). He considered that it was introduced as a contaminant of seed - it is a native of the Mediterranean region. These are the only records for our area.

Bristly Hawksbeard
Crepis setosa
Another Mediterranean Hawksbeard that has occurred as a casual introduction in the past. Gibson gave a sighting from fields near Colchester station, 1849, and Jermyn one from the Dedham district, c1939.

Beaked Hawksbeard
Crepis vesicaria
ssp haenseleri [410] M
Not recorded in Britain until 1713, it was first found in Essex in 1843 at Purfleet. Two further sites were found (Thurrock and Leigh) by the time Gibson published his Flora in 1862. Within a hundred years it had become common and widely distributed throughout the county, and the situation has not changed, in north east Essex, in the last two decades. It occurs on dry banks and rough grassy places, such as the grass triangles forming traffic islands at the junctions of country roads.

Globe Artichoke
Cynara cardunculus
Either planted or a casual of garden refuse tips. Jermyn gives records for West Mersea sea front where it was planted, and for St Osyth tip. Not recorded during the survey.

Greater Leopardsbane
Doronicum pardalianches
A garden plant that can become naturalised. Jermyn gives sites for Dynes Hall at Great Maplestead and a wood at Little Bromley. He also found it as a casual at St Osyth. Not recorded during our survey.

Leopardsbane
Doronicum plantagineum
Similar status to the previous species. Jermyn gives a site for a ditchbank at Pebmarsh where it had become naturalised in 1968. Again not recorded during our survey.

Blue Fleabane
Erigeron acer [22] M
Decreased and now infrequent. It occurs in gravel pits and other dry and gravelly places such as car parks.

Canadian Fleabane
CONYZA
(Erigeron) canadensis [275] M
Gibson states that this was a well naturalised plant near London which seemed to be

extending itself into Essex, and, at that time, there were no records for the north east of the county. It is now a relatively common weed over much of our area, only being absent from the chalky and boulder clay soils. It is generally found in dry situations such as cracks in pavements, the bottom of walls and fences, gravel car parks, as well as a garden weed.

Hemp Agrimony
Eupatorium cannabinum [77] M
Decreasing and now generally restricted to the banks of the major rivers and larger tributary streams. It is still locally plentiful

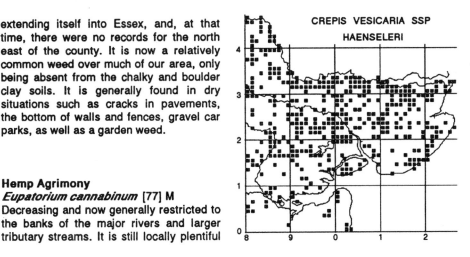

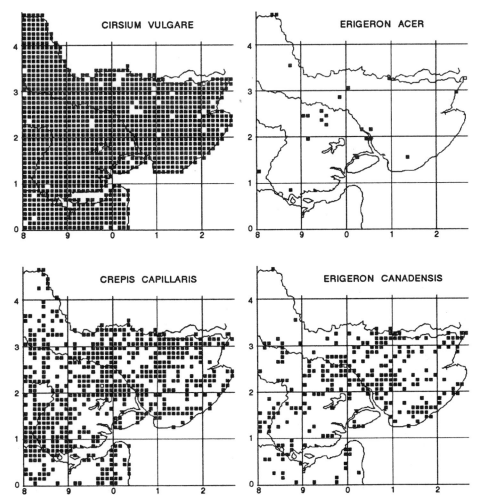

on the Stour between Cattawade and Boxted.

Narrow-leaved Cudweed
Filago gallica
According to the **Atlas of the British Flora**, 1962, there were only three localities in the British Isles where this tiny Cudweed had been recorded since 1930; one site was at Berechurch, Colchester. It was first discovered here by Rev W L P Garnons in 1842 and found to be plentiful in 1848. In 1861 it was found in several fields on the road from Berechurch towards Layer de la Haye. Jermyn had a specimen in his herbarium dated 1882 and goes on to give a very detailed account of its occurrences since then: "It was plentiful after the last war for a short period, but gradually declined as the area became overgrown with little disturbance to the ground. It would appear to have benefited from the war time use of the area as a training ground for tanks and heavy vehicles, which kept the ground disturbed and the brambles and coarser vegetation in check. In 1954 three plants were found in a small partly grassed over gravel pit. Only one small plant could be found the following year and despite many regular searches since, over the whole of Berechurch Common, it could not be refound." We too have been unable to find it. However, part of the area where *F gallica* has occurred in the past and which had become scrubbed over is, in the spring of 1990, being cleared by bulldozer. We think it is safe to say that a very sharp eye will be kept on this area in case seeds of this extremely rare Cudweed have survived the passage of time and produce a further generation of this interesting plant.

Red-tipped Cudweed
Filago lutescens
A rare Cudweed, even in Gibson's time, he had records for Braxted, a field near Kelvedon, Great Totham, the road from St Osyth to Colchester and Berechurch. Jermyn found it was still present at this latter site in 1954 and had additionally found it on a gravelly bank of the railway at Wrabness in 1962-63 and again in 1970. It has not been found during our survey.

Slender Cudweed
Filago minima [27] M
Although infrequent, it can be plentiful where it occurs and even abundant forming a grey carpet, particularly in gravel pits where the extraction has been completed almost down to the clay layer. Although usually found in sand and gravel pits it can also occur in other sandy places.

Broad-leaved Cudweed
Filago pyramidata
Gibson gathered a specimen of what he thought was a variety of **Common Cudweed** in 1843, but when it was re-examined five years later it was found to be a new species for Britain. Apparently it had not escaped the notice of earlier botanists as they mention a Cudweed that could be this plant, however, it had not then been recognised as a distinct species. Contemporaries of Gibson subsequently found it in our area at Kelvedon, Inworth and Berechurch. Jermyn was able to refind it at Berechurch Common from 1951-55, but that was the last time it was sighted.

Common Cudweed
Filago vulgaris [50] M
In similar situations to **Slender Cudweed** although more frequent and with a wider distribution.

Galactites tomentosa
An introduction from Malta that Jermyn recorded from the garden of Daymens Hill Farm, Tolleshunt Major, 1968.

Shaggy Soldier
Galinsoga ciliata [6]
An introduced weed that occurs as a casual on verges and waste places close to houses. It appeared en masse at a building site when the soil was disturbed, only to be lost as the development progressed.

Gallant Soldier
Galinsoga parviflora [4]
In similar situations to the previous species.

Wood Cudweed
Gnaphalium sylvaticum [2]
A rare Cudweed of woods and heaths that has decreased. Gibson's records show that

it was reasonably well distributed: Tiptree Heath, woods at Braxted and Layer Marney, a plantation behind Birch Woods at Dedham, Little Bentley and Kirby. Jermyn could not refind it at any of these sites, his only records coming from Berechurch Common and also a field near Colchester. We, in turn, have been unable to find it here but have found one new location, Chalkney Wood.

Marsh Cudweed

Gnaphalium uliginosum [251] M

Still reasonably frequent, occurring in damp woodland rides, cart tracks and ruts, especially where water is retained in winter.

Guizotia abyssinica [1]

A casual of short-lived duration that Jermyn recorded from Hythe Quay in 1965 and we found at Old Heath, Colchester, as a bird seed alien in 1989.

Annual Sunflower

Helianthus annuus [6]

A casual that we have found in two distinct habitats: at rubbish tips, as were most of Jermyn's records, (Maldon, Great Totham and Colchester's Shrub End), or, growing on the drift line on sandy beaches at Mersea, Dovercourt and Harwich.

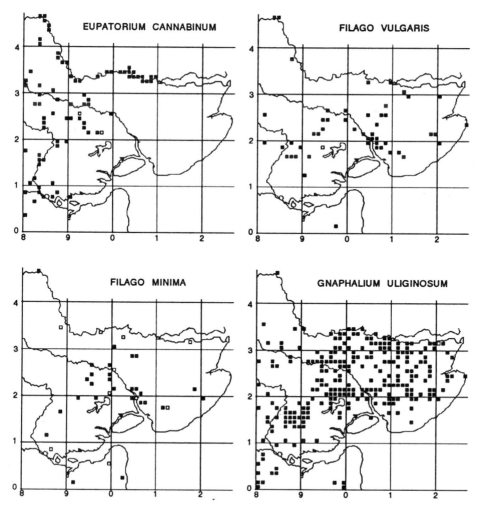

Perennial Sunflower
Helianthus decapetalus
Jermyn had several records for this casual escape but we have found no sites during our survey.

Perennial Sunflower
Helianthus rigidus [1]
Very occasionally found where garden refuse has been discarded. Not fully recorded.

Hawkweeds
It is unfortunate that Jermyn's specimens of this group are all in America so cannot easily be checked against modern criteria. The species listed below are the only ones for which we have definite records. Of the species given by Jermyn, doubts exist as to the identify of *H calcaricola* and *H tridentatum* from Tiptree Heath and his records for *H trichocaulon* (Tiptree Heath and Mill Hill, Lawford) have not been refound. We are grateful to Jim Bevan and Ken Adams for undertaking the determination of the true Hieracia for us.

Orange Hawkweed
Hieracium brunneocroceum [9]
An invasive garden plant that can escape and become naturalised on dry grassy banks but is also equally at home on the Roman Wall in Colchester.

Hieracium eboracense
One record from just before our recording period from a verge on Layer Road, Colchester, 1979. The verge has now been cleared and the plant lost.

Hieracium perpropinquum [53] M
The commonest species in our area on light, free draining soils, found mainly on verges, heathland or open woodland rides.

Mouse-ear Hawkweed
Hieracium pilosella [117] M
Common in the Roman River Valley Conservation Zone but scattered elsewhere, usually on the better drained gravels. It is generally found in short turf in the sun, such as on banks, or where the turf is kept short by grazing. It is also frequently found in churchyards where the lawnmower acts as a surrogate grazing animal. The group has been recorded in the aggregate sense and not split, so here is retained under *Hieracium* and not placed in *Pilosella*. Much work remains to be done in Essex on this group.

Hieracium salticola
Recorded from Berechurch Common in 1978 but not refound during our survey.

Hieracium umbellatum [2]
Tiptree Heath is the main remaining site for this Hawkweed (1978-81 and 1984) but a single specimen was also seen in the Roman River Valley (TL 9720) in 1983. It could not be refound at Jermyn's other sites of Layer Breton Heath, Colchester and Little Oakley.

Spotted Catsear
Hypochaeris maculata
Spotted Catsear is a rare plant of chalk downland. Jermyn gives a record for the sea wall at Mistley, 1953. He was unable to confirm the identity and considered it an unlikely habitat, but due to the proximity of Mistley's grain mills and maltings, thought, that if the record was genuine, it was remotely possible for it to have originated from these sources. We feel that he was correct to doubt the record.

Catsear
Hypochaeris radicata [749] M
Common in grassland over most of the area but avoiding the heavy clay soils. This is demonstrated particularly well by its occurrence on the gravel ridge on the Dengie peninsula and absence from the surrounding clays.

Ploughman's Spikenard
Inula conyza [1]
Gibson gave this as "not uncommon" at Halstead as well as records for Messing and Thorrington. Jermyn's only site for our area was on a chalky bank near Gestingthorpe where it no longer occurs. One plant was found in 1985 growing by the fence to the car park at Marks Tey station.

Golden Samphire
Inula crithmoides [85] M
Primarily a Mediterranean plant, it is reaching its northern limit on the east coast

of Britain; there are a few plants in Suffolk, just across the water at Shotley and Trimley. **Golden Samphire** grows on sandy spits and bars in the saltmarshes, as well as the upper saltings. Where these have been truncated by sea walls, the plant has colonised its base. At Stansgate on the Blackwater, it forms a green and yellow ribbon for over a kilometre growing in the cracks between the concrete slabs of the wall. It has, however, been lost from the whole length of the Stour in the last twenty years.

Elecampane
Inula helenium [2]
A garden throw-out that naturalises in ditchbanks and along road verges where it can survive mowing.

Least Lettuce
Lactuca saligna
Now very rare and confined to one locality in south Essex, however, it was recorded from wet places near the road between Maldon and Mundon prior to 1739 and was found at St Osyth in 1912.

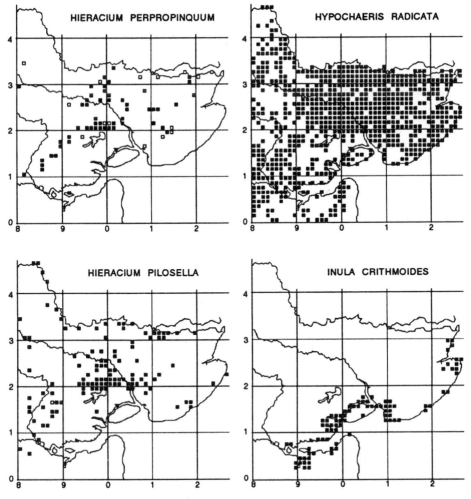

Prickly Lettuce
Lactuca serriola
forma integrifolia [509] M
Lactuca serriola forma serriola [80] M
Common on bare patches of road verges, edges of fences, car parks, other waste places and sea walls. There are two forms: *forma integrifolia*, with an entire leaf, which is much the commonest, and *forma serriola*, with an indented leaf.

Wild Lettuce
Lactuca virosa [150] M
Other than concentrations at the tidal reach of the estuaries (at Maldon, Colchester and Manningtree), it is scattered over much of the area. It is generally found where there is some sort of bank, such as a sea wall, or trunk roads where they pass through a cutting, and sand and gravel pits. Although associated with grassland it seems to require some disturbance to the soil.

Nipplewort
Lapsana communis [1002] M
Very common where there is any bare soil which receives some shade, such as hedgerows, bottom of fences and walls. It appears to be absent only from the estuarine grazing marshes and saltings.

Autumn Hawkbit
Leontodon autumnalis [750] M
Common in most types of grassland including churchyards, verges and sea walls.

Rough Hawkbit
Leontodon hispidus [9] M
A plant requiring calcareous soils it is restricted in north east Essex to the west of our area. All our records come from grass verges showing indications of being of old mature grassland. Jermyn gives it for the whole of our area but we feel that it must have been over-recorded in the past.

Lesser Hawkbit
Leontodon taraxacoides [66] M
Decreasing with the loss of old grazing. This is clearly demonstrated by the clusters of records from Old Hall Marshes and around Hamford Water, particularly on Horsey Island. Otherwise it is scattered, often a few plants being found in horse paddocks.

Shasta Daisy
Leucanthemum maximum [12]
A reasonably frequent garden escape that becomes naturalised in hedges and on waste ground from discarded garden rubbish.

Ox-eye Daisy
Leucanthemum vulgare [261] M
No longer common it is still widely distributed although scattered. Found in old grassland and on dry grassy banks, it can almost invariably be found in churchyards, where it indicates their relic status.

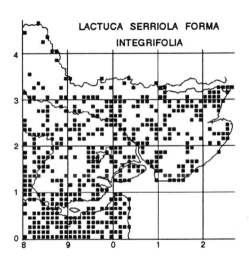

LACTUCA SERRIOLA FORMA INTEGRIFOLIA

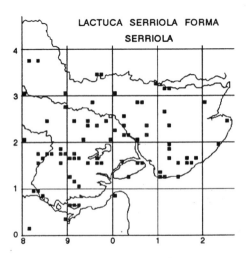

LACTUCA SERRIOLA FORMA SERRIOLA

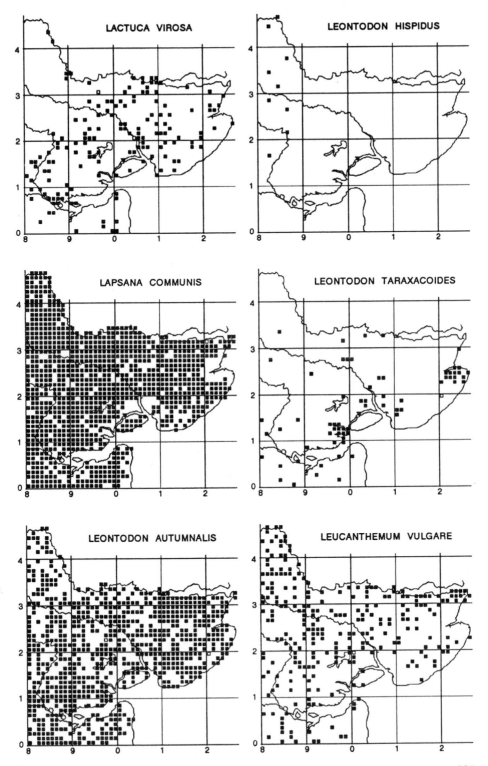

LACTUCA VIROSA

LEONTODON HISPIDUS

LAPSANA COMMUNIS

LEONTODON TARAXACOIDES

LEONTODON AUTUMNALIS

LEUCANTHEMUM VULGARE

Pineapple Weed STACE - DISCOIDEA
Matricaria matricarioides [1013] M
Considering that it was first recorded in Britain in 1871 and only sporadic in Essex up to the early 1930s, this plant has proliferated since. It is now a very common weed of gardens, arable, farm tracks and paths.

Scented Mayweed
Matricaria recutita [900] M
A very common arable weed that also occurs on any bare disturbed soils. Jermyn notes that it had increased considerably since Gibson, presumably reflecting the change from pasture to arable that had taken place in the intervening years. On this basis it must now be even commoner with the further loss of grazing.

Wall Lettuce
Mycelis muralis
The only records for our area date from Gibson: Donyland Heath near Colchester, and the bank of the Stour at Nether Hall.

Scotch Thistle
Onopordum acanthium [27] M
A widespread and scattered distribution that one would expect from a garden escape.

Cottonweed
Otanthus maritimus
Recorded by Gerard (1597) from a sandy sea shore at Mersea Island.

Winter Heliotrope
Petasites fragrans [52] M
Introduced to English gardens in 1806, Jermyn described it as "generally uncommon, but often forming large patches where it occurs". The latter is certainly true, and our survey has revealed that it has now become a frequent garden escape.

Butterbur
Petasites hybridus [26] M
Infrequent, but often in quantity where it occurs. It is generally found on river or streambanks but can occasionally be associated with a damp ditch and road verge as at Ramsey (TM 23).

Creamy Butterbur
Petasites japonicus [1]
A rare introduction. Jermyn gives only one site where it had naturalised in a wood at Thorpe Hall, 1970, (we were unable to check whether it has survived at this site). However, it has also occurred on the bank of the Colne at Middleborough, Colchester, for very many years.

Bristly Ox-tongue
Picris echioides [894] M
Very common over most of the area, although thinning out in the north. It grows anywhere where the soil is partially disturbed such as lay-bys, roadworks, edges of car parks, as well as rough disturbed grassland.

Hawkweed Ox-tongue
Picris hieracioides [35] M
Most frequent on the soils with a chalky influence, it is occasionally found elsewhere on the better drained ground. Whilst present in mature grassland it can also occur on disturbed soils.

Common Fleabane
Pulicaria dysenterica [344] M
No longer common, it is still frequent in damp situations on the London Clay. Most

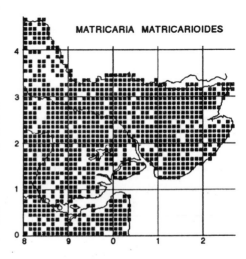

MATRICARIA MATRICARIOIDES

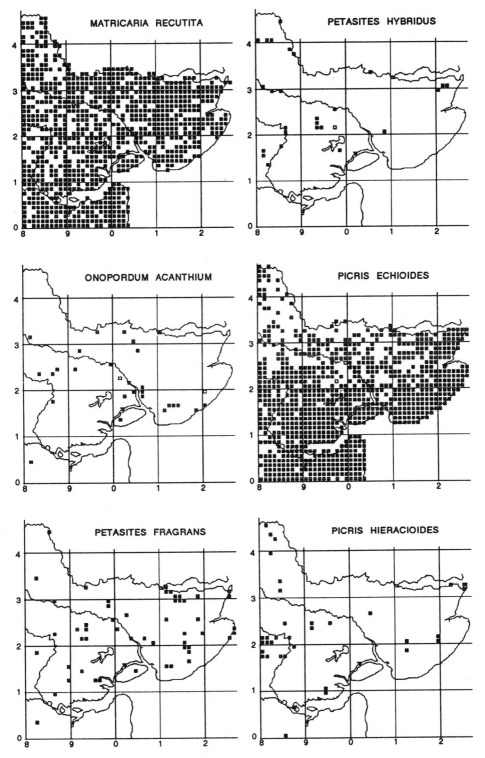

MATRICARIA RECUTITA

PETASITES HYBRIDUS

ONOPORDUM ACANTHIUM

PICRIS ECHIOIDES

PETASITES FRAGRANS

PICRIS HIERACIOIDES

often found in ditches and damp areas of verges, it also occurs where there is a wet flush seeping out on the clay.

Small Fleabane
Pulicaria vulgaris
A very rare plant nationally now, but Gibson's records show that it was once far more widespread: Tiptree Heath; between Layer Marney and Layer Breton; Langham Moor, Ardleigh and other places near Dedham; Great Clacton; Kirby; between Thorpe and Walton. Not refound by Jermyn or during our survey.

Marsh Ragwort
Senecio aquaticus [17]
Still decreasing - it was common in Gibson's time, infrequent but still locally common to Jermyn, and is now very infrequent and always in small quantity. Of Jermyn's sites: it was not refound at Langford and Ulting by the canal, the water meadows by the Blackwater at Wickham Bishops and Great Braxted, from Feering, Hepworth Hall, Great Maplestead, Liston Pits, Abberton Reservoir, Lexden, meadows by the Stour at Bures, marsh by Salary Brook Colchester, Black Brook Langham and the Harwich and Dovercourt area. It still remains at Earls Colne. New sites have been found on the canal around Maldon, Bulmer, Belchamp Walter, Roman River Valley, High Woods Colchester, Little Oakley and Walton.

Hoary Ragwort
Senecio erucifolius [464] M
No longer common over the whole area it is, however, still so near the coast on the grasslands around our sea walls and roadside verges, particularly where these are on the clays. Elsewhere it is scattered on dry verges and banks.

Common Ragwort
Senecio jacobaea [893] M
Very common where there is any sort of ground disturbance, particularly on the lighter soils. It occurs in a wide variety of habitats: lawns, woodland rides, grass verges and waste ground.

Oxford Ragwort
Senecio squalidus [201] M
Oxford Ragwort originally escaped out of the Oxford Botanic Gardens in 1799 and then, with the advent of railways, spread to London by the turn of the last century. Jermyn gives a detailed account of its distribution and spread through Essex since then. He considered that there were several mechanisms by which this could have been achieved but the main one that would affect us in north east Essex was via the railway network. It is interesting to note that we have found clusters of records around Colchester, Clacton and Harwich, with smaller clusters at Maldon and Manningtree - all towns on the railway network (either past or present).

Senecio squalidus X viscosus
A hybrid between Oxford Ragwort and Sticky Groundsel which Jermyn found growing abundantly with both parents in the old station yard at Maldon in 1967-8. This site has been redeveloped since.

Heath Groundsel
Senecio sylvaticus [92] M
No longer frequent as it was with Jermyn, it is now scattered mainly on the free draining brick-earths. It appears to have contracted its range to what must have been its stronghold. Usually just a few plants are found growing in hedgerows or dry gravelly places including sand and gravel pits.

Sticky Groundsel
Senecio viscosus [187] M
Reasonably frequent in and around sand and gravel pits, sand and shingle beaches and waste places in industrial sites.

Groundsel
Senecio vulgaris [1044]
Very common as a garden weed and on any bare disturbed soils. Jermyn recorded a variety with large ray florets (*forma radiatus*) to be plentiful at Manningtree tip and from waste ground by the mills at Mistley. This form has not been found during our survey.

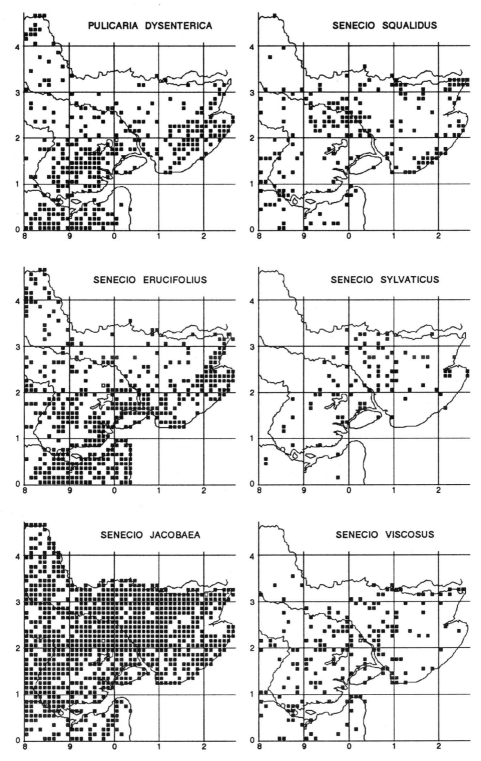

PULICARIA DYSENTERICA

SENECIO SQUALIDUS

SENECIO ERUCIFOLIUS

SENECIO SYLVATICUS

SENECIO JACOBAEA

SENECIO VISCOSUS

Milk Thistle
Silybum marianum [9]
As Jermyn found, it is infrequent and in small quantity. He gave eight sites and we, with our intensive coverage, have nine. With the exception of his records for Fingringhoe Wick Nature Reserve and St Osyth, none of our sites are in the vicinity of his. It can be found at field edges and waste places.

Canadian Golden Rod
Solidago canadensis [8]
Still found as a garden outcast developing from dumped garden rubbish, but most colonies do not persist.

Early Golden Rod
Solidago gigantea ssp serotina [5]
As in Jermyn's day the less frequently found of the introduced Golden Rods with recent records from Woodham Mortimer, Maldon, Witham, Pentlow and Colchester. It was not refound at any of Jermyn's localities.

Golden Rod
Solidago virgaurea
It appears that this native has now been lost to our area. Gibson had records from Tiptree Heath and Chalkney Wood. Jermyn was able to confirm its survival at Tiptree Heath, and found another site at Berechurch Common. We have not found it during our survey.

Corn or Perennial Sow-thistle
Sonchus arvensis [788] M
Common in edges of cornfields, road verges, as well as in reeds and rushes at the edges of ponds and reservoirs.

Prickly Sow-thistle
Sonchus asper [1164] M
Very common in any kind of grassland as well as disturbed ground such as rough areas by lay-bys.

Smooth Sow-thistle
Sonchus oleraceus [1043] M
Very common as a garden weed and other disturbed ground in or near habitation. A basal rosette can often be found growing at the very edge of a country road, where it doesn't usually survive to maturity.

Marsh Sow-thistle
Sonchus palustris [2]
Introduced into Fingringhoe Wick Nature Reserve in 1970, it is still doing well there.

Feverfew
Tanacetum parthenium [160] M
Our findings correlate exactly with Jermyn - scattered over most of the area, usually in small quantity except on the south face of the Roman Wall, Colchester. It is generally found on roadsides and waste places near houses. The double-flowered form is occasionally found.

Tansy
Tanacetum vulgare [205] M
Common on the gravels of the Roman River Valley and the lighter soils around Dedham and Manningtree, but scattered elsewhere. Generally found on grassy verges or field borders where a hedge remains.

Dandelion
Taraxacum [1129]
To the layman this is a widely distributed plant found on roadsides, wet meadows, banks, gravel pits, gardens and other disturbed sites hence the high level of records shown above. There are many species of **Dandelion** and therefore, to the specialist, this group provides much of interest and some anomalous distributions. The species are dealt with alphabetically under the sections into which the group is divided. This list would not have been possible without the help of the late Chris Haworth who, with John Richards, has determined many specimens for us. All the records are from specimens held in the Colchester Natural History Museum and only include those identified to species level.

Section *CELTICA*
Species in this section are more common in the west country and only a few species have been discovered in our area.
bracteatum Dt
Two records from ditchbanks at Birch and Bures.
duplidentifrons Dt (*raunkiaerii* Wiinst)
A widespread species, two records: Malting Green and Thorrington Cross.

lucidum Dt

One occurrence only, at Lawford.

nordstedtii Dt

One record from old wet grassland at Abberton Manor.

subbracteatum A J Rich

Another plant with only one record, from the same site as *T nordstedtii*. This **Dandelion** is normally found in the north and west of Britain.

Section *ERYTHROSPERMA*

The species in this section are mostly native and usually found in natural habitats.

argutum Dt

A distinctively flowered species; two

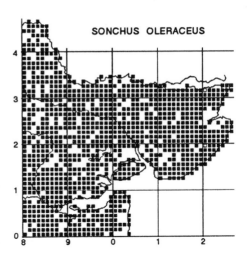

SONCHUS OLERACEUS

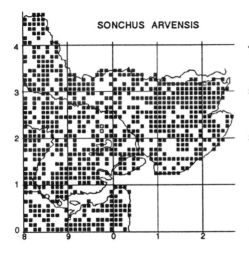

SONCHUS ARVENSIS

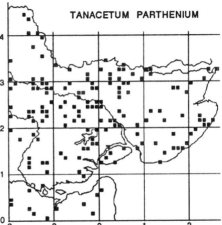

TANACETUM PARTHENIUM

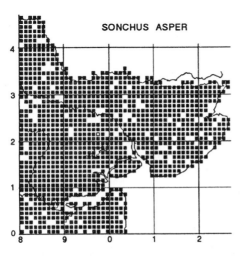

SONCHUS ASPER

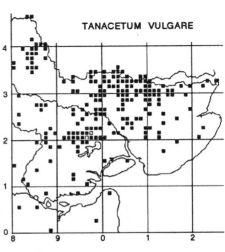

TANACETUM VULGARE

records: Bures and the Roman Wall, Colchester.

brachyglossum (Dt) Raunk
Two records: from Blackheath, Colchester and Great Totham.

fulviforme Dt
Two records: Abberton and Old Hall Marshes.

glauciniforme Dt
Only one record of this distinctively leaved species from Great Braxted churchyard.

lacistophyllum (Dt) Raunk
The commonest species in this group with twelve records, usually on light soils.

oxoniense Dt
One of the commonest and most widespread species at a national level; three records: Roman Wall, Colchester; Great Totham and Old Hall Marshes.

proximum (Dt) Raunk
Three records: Colchester, Great Bentley and Wivenhoe, all on light soils.

simile Raunk
The taxonomic status of this species is still under discussion and we have only one accepted record, from Thorpe le Soken.

wallonicum VS
Elsewhere known only from a few sites in the London area, it has been found at Rowhedge.

Section *HAMATA*

Most species in this section are introduced, often found in 'weedy' habitats.

atactum C I Sahlin & VS
Two records: Weeley and Layer Breton.

boekmanii Borgvall
One specimen from Halstead.

hamatiforme Dt
Common, nine records, mostly from road verges.

hamatum Raunk
Common, eight records, one of the few native species in this section.

hamiferum Dt
Frequent, five records.

lamprophyllum M P Chr
One record from Liston.

pseudohamatum Dt
Possibly a native species, very common, twenty records, mainly road verges.

quadrans H Ollg
A frequent weedy species, three records: Colchester, Layer de la Haye and Thorpe le Soken.

Section *NAEVOSA*

The species in this section typically have spotted leaves and are northern plants of upland habitats. They are thus rare in Essex where they are confined to old damp meadows.

euryphyllum (Dt) M P Chr
Found only at Birch

richardsianum ined
An endemic British species that we have found only at Abberton Manor.

Section *RUDERALIA*

Most **Dandelions** in this section are probably introduced. They are the large weedy dandelions of waste ground, road verges, newly seeded grassland, etc. Some are common and widespread, whilst others are known from perhaps only one site. Any one of a large number of continental species may turn up from time to time.

aequisectum M P Chr
One record from Abberton.

alatum H Lb f
A possible native species, one record from Stanway.

chloroticum Dt
One record from Colchester.

circumiens ined
One record for Rowhedge.

cophocentrum Dt
This native species has been found at six sites.

cordatum Palmgr
A common native species for which we have five records.

croceiflorum Dt
A common species that we have found at four sites.

dahlstedtii H Lb f
A common native species, five records.

dilaceratum M P Chr
One record from Great Braxted.

ekmani Dt
A common weedy plant of waste places, under-recorded, twelve records.

exacutum Markl
Two records, Wivenhoe and St Osyth.

expallidiforme Dt
Another common and probably under-recorded species, ten records.

hemicyclum Hagl
One specimen from Bures.

heulphersianum Dt
One record from Wivenhoe.

insigne M P Chr & Wiinst
A widespread native species, one record: Copford churchyard.
laciniosifrons M P Chr & Wiinst
Two records from Copford and Great Totham.
laeticolor Dt
A native species, three records: Bures, Abberton and Great Holland.
latens ined
One record of this rare species from Copford.
laticordatum Markl
A common species with seven records.
latissimum Palmgr
One specimen from Layer Marney.
leucopodum Hagl
One record from Little Horkesley.
lingulatum Markl
A common species, five records.
longisquameum H Lb f
One record from Colchester.
necessarium H Ollg
Two records, Rowhedge Pits and Fingringhoe Ranges.
obliquilobum Dt
One record from Liston.
oblongatum Dt
A common plant, five records.
ostenfeldii Raunk
A native species with one record from Wivenhoe.
pachymerum Hagl
Five records for this common species.
pallescens Dt
One record from Great Horkesley.
pallidipes Markl
One record from Abberton.
pannucium Dt
Two records, Little Horkesley and Berechurch.
piceatum Dt
Four records.
planum Raunk
One record from Lawford.
polyodon Dt
A common species probably under-recorded, eight records.
rhamphodes Hagl
Three sites: Colchester, Rowhedge and Harwich.
scotiniforme Dt
One record from Kelvedon.
sellandii Dt
This common species is probably under-

recorded with only two records from Little Horkesley and Lawford.
stenacrum Dt
This British endemic has been recorded from four sites.
sublaeticolor Dt
One record only: Great Holland.
subundulatum Dt
Two records: Great Braxted and Liston.
undulatiflorum M P Chr
Two records: Rowhedge and Bures.
undulatum H Lb f & Markl
One record from Little Totham.
xanthostigma H Lb f
One record from Copford.

Salsify
Tragopogon porrifolius [53] M
Scattered and infrequent. Inland records are from road verges and rough grassland but on the coast it grows along the sea walls. It occurred in tremendous quantity in 1989 along the verge on the road into Ramsey (TM 23).

Tragopogon porrifolius
X *pratensis ssp minor*
A hybrid between **Salsify** and **Goatsbeard**, Jermyn found one plant with intermediate characters, growing on the sea wall at Bradwell-on-Sea, 1965. We have not found this hybrid during our survey.

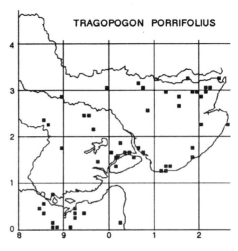
TRAGOPOGON PORRIFOLIUS

Goatsbeard
Tragopogon pratensis [466] M

Common and well distributed, road verges, sea walls, rough grassland and waste places. It is sometimes called **Jack-go-to-Bed-at-Noon** as the flower closes up in the afternoon. Jermyn mentions three sub-species: he found *ssp minor* to be the common plant; had only one site for *ssp pratensis*, Coggeshall churchyard, 1970; and considered the earlier records for *ssp orientalis* to have been in error. Our survey has revealed only *ssp minor*.

Scentless Mayweed
Tripleurospermum inodorum [910] M

Very common as an arable weed and on any bare disturbed ground on roadsides, farm yards and waste places.

Sea Mayweed
Tripleurospermum maritimum [32] M

A plant of sandy and shingly sea shores, it appears that **Sea Mayweed** has increased since Jermyn. There is a possibility that this is due to beach improvements made at Dovercourt and Clacton where sand has been imported. Sand from these beaches could be swept from these areas and deposited further down the coast in the areas where **Sea Mayweed** has increased. The only area where it has decreased is at Walton where erosion has taken place - this sand too could be being deposited further along the coast.

Coltsfoot
Tussilago farfara [432] M

Common and widespread. Its traditional habitat is where there is a seepage of water over clay, such as Walton cliffs; however, it is a quick coloniser of other habitats including gravel pits where the soil has been disturbed. Presumably it is able to do this as it flowers early in the year before the ground dries out. It is also found on sea walls, road verges and waste places.

Spiny Cocklebur
Xanthium spinosum

A casual that used to be found near maltings and mills or where shoddy is used as manure. Jermyn gives records for Hythe Quay, with malting refuse, c1927, and with

shoddy (the debris that is left after a sheep's fleece is cleaned) in a field at Jupes Hill, Dedham, 1958.

Cocklebur
Xanthium strumarium [1]

Jermyn gives a record for malting refuse at Hythe Quay, c1927, and we found it in mill refuse at Fingringhoe Mill in 1983.

WATER PLANTAIN FAMILY
ALISMATACEAE

Narrow-leaved Water Plantain
Alisma lanceolatum [3]

In Gibson's day this had not been recognised as a separate species and was considered to be a variety of the **Common Water Plantain**. Jermyn, found it to be uncommon, but fairly widespread, however, our survey has revealed so few records that it has either declined drastically or been over-recorded in the past. Our records all come from shallow ponds at Colne Engaine and Tiptree.

Common Water Plantain
Alisma plantago-aquatica [157] M

No longer common, but still reasonably frequent and widespread. Not only found, as one would expect, at the edges of ponds, lakes, reservoirs and flooded gravel pits, but also in deep wheel ruts where the water has lain in winter and occasionally along very slow-moving parts of rivers.

Lesser Water Plantain
Baldellia ranunculoides

Not known from the county since Gibson's time. It occurred then in a swampy place near the river at Kelvedon, and, when the mill at Braxted was undergoing repair, growing in the empty channel of the river.

Arrowhead
Sagittaria sagittifolia [27] M

Now found only in the major river systems of our area, Gibson gives its habitat as including ditches. Even Jermyn includes streams and flooded gravel pits. Whilst it is still found over the length of the Blackwater, it has been lost from the upper parts of the Colne and from long stretches of the Stour.

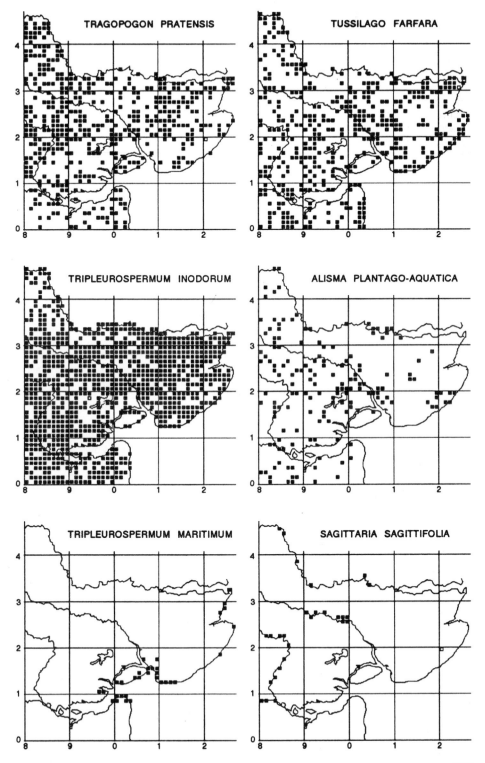

FLOWERING RUSH FAMILY
BUTOMACEAE

Flowering Rush
Butomus umbellatus [18] M
Native on the river systems, but introduced into village ponds. It was obviously more frequent in Gibson's time as he gives several records including "in the Colne at several places near Halstead", and "ditches near the Stour, not uncommon". It is still common in the Chelmer-Blackwater canal where Jermyn recorded it, but otherwise it is found in small quantity, sometimes just single plants, growing a little way out from the bank in slightly deeper water.

FROGBIT FAMILY
HYDROCHARITACEAE

Canadian Pondweed
Elodea canadensis [11]
The only species recorded by Jermyn, it does not appear to be so abundant as in his day (we have not refound the species in 60% of his 10km squares). Some of his records may refer to *E nuttallii* which was not recognised during his recording period. Both this and the following species can be found in rivers, ponds, lakes and gravel pits.

Elodea nuttallii [11]
Probably under-recorded, this recently recognised species has been found in the same habitats as *E canadensis*. Both species are sold by garden centres and aquarium supply shops.

Frogbit
Hydrocharis morsus-ranae [1]
Recorded in Victorian times from ditches by the Stour, near Bures, Sudbury and Dedham, Jermyn could only relocate it at Dedham in 1951. Our one record comes from Chigborough Lakes where it was introduced (1988, it apparently did not reappear in 1989).

Lagarosiphon major [6]
A waterweed used in aquariums that has been introduced into the wild, either deliberately or as a result of discarding surplus weed. So far it has been found at Rowhedge Pits, ponds at Great Bentley and Dedham, and plentifully in a reservoir at Tiptree.

Water Soldier
Stratiotes aloides [3]
Native further north in East Anglia, it is probably introduced in north east Essex. Gibson's single record for our area was in a pond near Pattiswick Hall, where it was abundant, but he continues "where it may possibly have been introduced, though this is not known to have been the case". All our records come from ponds where it has so obviously been planted that it has not been fully recorded.

ARROW-GRASS FAMILY
JUNCAGINACEAE

Sea Arrow-grass
Triglochin maritima [191] M
Common on our saltmarshes. It is found on the higher zone of the marsh, usually close to the sea wall. Where there is seepage through the wall, it can also be found along the edge of the borrow dyke.

Marsh Arrow-grass
Triglochin palustris [2]
Gibson's sites show that it was reasonably frequent in marshy places over much of our area: near the Colne, Halstead; meadow by the river at Pattiswick; Feering Moors; Salcott; Dedham, by the footpath to Manningtree. Jermyn found it gone from all these locations and could only add a record for Witham in 1901. It has, however, been found at two nature reserves during our survey - Brightlingsea Marsh and Howlands Marsh.

EEL-GRASS FAMILY
ZOSTERACEAE

As a family they are very under-recorded due to their late maturing and unfavourable (to botanists) habitat - the inter-tidal mudflats. Much more study is needed on this group in our area. The few records we have result from one search of the mudflats below the Stour/Copperas woods complex at the appropriate time of year when we found both **Narrow-leaved Eel-grass** (*Zostera angustifolia*) and **Dwarf Eel-grass** (*Z noltii*) in four 1km squares. This latter species was also recorded, along with **Eel-grass** (*Z marina*), in a further 1km square by Nature Conservancy Council staff on the Dengie Flats SSSI.

PONDWEED FAMILY
POTAMOGETONACEAE

Opposite-leaved Pondweed
Groenlandia densa
Recorded once by a contemporary of Gibson's from Middleton, south of Sudbury, but not seen since.

Reddish Pondweed
Potamogeton alpinus
Gibson gave records from a pond near Coggeshall and from Kelvedon. There have been no records since.

Small Pondweed
Potamogeton berchtoldii [2]
Rare, but possibly over-looked. Jermyn also considered it to be rare but had several records for our area, all from reservoirs, lakes and flooded gravel pits. Our records also come from large areas of still water at Copford and Old Hall Marshes.

Grass-wrack Pondweed
Potamogeton compressus
Recorded by Jermyn in 1970 from a gravel pit at Foxearth [Liston Pits]. Not refound during our survey.

Curled Pondweed
Potamogeton crispus [23] M
Generally distributed in ponds, old gravel pits and slow-moving rivers.

Shining Pondweed
Potamogeton lucens [7]
Confined to the Chelmer-Blackwater canal and a few sites on the Colne at Colchester. It has not been refound at Jermyn's sites on the Stour.

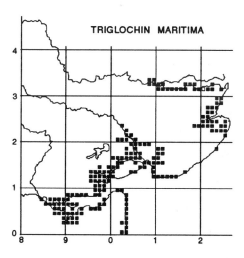

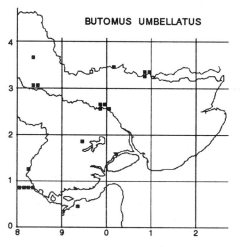

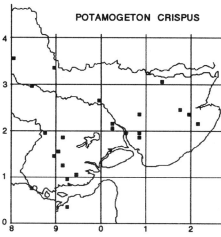

Broad-leaved Pondweed
Potamogeton natans [27]

We have a scattering of records for this once common Pondweed from ponds, gravel pits, and farm reservoirs. Its true distribution has become obscured by introductions.

Blunt-leaved Pondweed
Potamogeton obtusifolius

On checking some historical records Jermyn found that this had been recorded from Goldingham Hall, Bulmer, in 1711, and a pond near Stanway Hall in 1905. There have been no other records.

Fennel Pondweed
Potamogeton pectinatus [91] M

Common in coastal borrow dykes but less so in rivers and streams inland, occasionally found in farm reservoirs and ponds. It has not been refound on the Stour where it was known to both Gibson and Jermyn.

Perfoliate Pondweed
Potamogeton perfoliatus [4]

Rare, Gibson gave three localities; near Heybridge, in the Colne at Lexden and Colchester. It has been refound in the Colne at Colchester and additionally found in the Chelmer-Blackwater canal at Ulting and the Roman River. Jermyn's site in Abberton Reservoir, 1966, was not refound but it could still be present as it is a large area to search.

Bog Pondweed
Potamogeton polygonifolius

Gibson gives records for stagnant peaty water at Kelvedon and Tiptree Heath. It was still present at this latter location in 1920 but has not been seen since. It had also been recorded from Abberton in 1887.

Long-stalked Pondweed
Potamogeton praelongus

Known from Maldon and Kelvedon in Gibson's time, it has not been recorded since.

Lesser Pondweed
Potamogeton pusillus [1]

Rare. Jermyn found on examining Gibson's herbarium specimens that some of Gibson's records for this species related to the

Small Pondweed, and Jermyn himself mentioned that some of his records for the two species may have been confused. We have only one definite record (south of Maldon) for **Lesser Pondweed**, but it has possibly been over-looked.

TASSEL PONDWEED FAMILY
RUPPIACEAE

Spiral Tasselweed
Ruppia cirrhosa [4]

As Jermyn found, it is still scattered and in small quantity in coastal borrow dykes. It has also been found in Brightlingsea boating lake which has a saline influence.

Beaked Tasselweed
Ruppia maritima [4]

In similar habitats to the preceding species.

HORNED PONDWEED FAMILY
ZANNICHELLIACEAE

Horned Pondweed
Zannichellia palustris [17]

This Pondweed occurs in both brackish borrow dykes as well as freshwater streams and rivers, on the upper reaches of which it can be found in fairly fast-flowing water over a gravel bed. Jermyn also recorded *Z pedunculata* but this is no longer regarded as a separate species and is now included with *Z palustris*.

LILY FAMILY
LILIACEAE

Chives
Allium schoenoprasum [1]

Commonly grown in gardens as a herb it is surprising it has not been found more often as an escape.

Ramsons
Allium ursinum [50] M

Particularly on the boulder clays **Ramsons** forms large patches in shady places where there is a wet flush seeping from between the clay and gravel soils. It can also be found in damp woods and copses as well as by rivers or streams. Unlike most of the plants of damp places it can still be found in many of the localities given by both Gibson and Jermyn. It is often first noticed by the strong smell of onions.

Crow Garlic
Allium vineale [53] M
Infrequent and scattered, it appears to occur more often in grassland on the heavier soils, such as on road verges and along sea walls. Two varieties occur, one with bulbils only (*var compactum*) and one with flowers as well as bulbils (*var vineale*). The latter variety has been found only once during the survey, near Maldon.

Asparagus
Asparagus officinalis [36] M
The scattered distribution is typical of a garden escape, it is also grown as a crop in a few places. **Asparagus** is often bird sown and can, therefore, turn up almost anywhere. According to Gibson it appears to have been restricted to the coast and saltmarshes; it was found at Harwich in 1667, and Gerard (1597) wrote "in a meadow adjoining a mill beyond a village called Thorp[e]; likewise it groweth in great plenty near unto Harwich, at a place called Bandamar lading [Landermere?]".

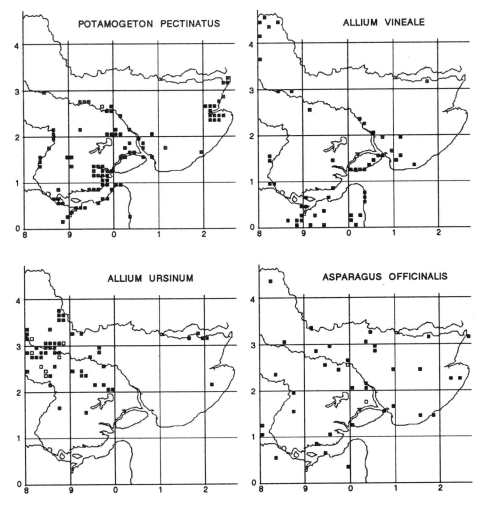

Lily of the Valley
Convallaria majalis [4]
Rare, occurring in ancient deciduous woodlands on the better drained soils. Its stronghold in this area has obviously been the Markshall complex of woods; Gibson gives it as plentiful in a wood near Burton's Green and it had also been found in Monks and Nunty's woods. Jermyn refound it in the latter two woods as well as Lily wood. During our survey we found it only in Monks wood but with the size of the woodland complex other sites could have been missed. Gibson also gives a location for Berechurch and one small patch still survives in Friday Wood. We were unable to confirm whether it was still present at Jermyn's location at Parsonage Wood, Bulmer, but did find further sites in Wivenhoe and Stour Woods.

Spanish Bluebell
Hyacinthoides hispanica [5]
Larger and more showy than the native **Bluebell** it is usually this species that is grown in gardens. As with so many other garden plants that are discarded in ditches and hedgerows it readily becomes established and is probably more frequent than our records show.

Hyacinthoides hispanica
X non-scripta [1]
This hybrid between the two previous species has not been fully recorded. Further field work is required before its full distribution can be ascertained.

Bluebell
Hyacinthoides non-scripta [363] M
Frequent in woods and hedgerows on the better drained soils. Although generally found in clumps here and there throughout the woodland, we are fortunate in having some woods in our area where it forms a magnificent blue carpet in the spring as in the Essex Naturalists' Trust reserve at Weeleyhall Wood.

Grape Hyacinth
Muscari armeniacum [1]
Muscari neglectum [1]
We have not fully recorded these species. They usually originate from garden waste and can become naturalised as had *M armeniacum* on tipped soil in an old gravel pit at Fingringhoe in 1982 where many plants were present, and *M neglectum* on a road verge near Ardleigh Reservoir.

Common Star of Bethlehem Angustifolium
Ornithogalum umbellatum [20]
An introduction with a scattered distribution. Jermyn's location at Tiptree Heath where it was "well established and appearing native, twenty clumps in a grassy track" was refound during our survey, with over fifty clumps present now.

Herb Paris
Paris quadrifolia [5]
A rare plant of ancient woodlands. Gibson knew it from the Markshall complex of woods, as did Jermyn, but we were unable to refind it here, although, with the size of the area, it could still survive. It is still present at Jermyn's location of Broadfield Wood, but not at Big Wood, Dyne's Hall. There are sizeable patches in Chalkney Wood, where it was known to Gibson, but we were unable to refind his site in Hickmore Fen Wood, a short distance to the east. Gibson also mentions Lady Wood, Tey, but this wood no longer appears on the maps and it is possible that it has been grubbed out. In 1910 it was found at Alphamstone and although this particular site was not refound, it was recorded nearby on the border between Alphamstone and Pebmarsh. In 1985 a single plant was found by the warden at Stour Wood, it was growing on the very edge of the wood by the railway line. At the same time British Rail discovered that the embankment was subsiding, and pumped liquid concrete into the bank in order to stabilise it. The concrete, unfortunately, found its way up through the cracks in the embankment and, within a fortnight of its having been discovered, this single plant was encased in concrete.

Common Solomon's Seal
Polygonatum multiflorum
Jermyn notes that this plant was introduced into Copperas Wood in 1972, but it has not been refound.

Butcher's Broom
Ruscus aculeatus [53] M
Infrequent in woods and occasionally found in hedges on the free draining soils. It seems to have maintained its distribution and can still be found in some areas mentioned by Gibson - Braxted, Wickham [Bishops] and Donyland in the Roman River Valley.

RUSH FAMILY
JUNCACEAE

Sharp-flowered Rush
Juncus acutiflorus [16] M
The distribution seems to be centred around Colchester but this probably reflects the residences of the recorders. It has not been refound on a few sites where it was noted in the late 1970s and may well be decreasing.

Jointed Rush
Juncus articulatus [65] M
Possibly over-recorded, a few sites may refer to misidentified *J acutiflorus*. The loss of damp grasslands is reducing the habitat for this species.

Toad Rush
Juncus bufonius [338] M
Frequent on the lighter soils, in wheel ruts, country road edges, and similar depres-

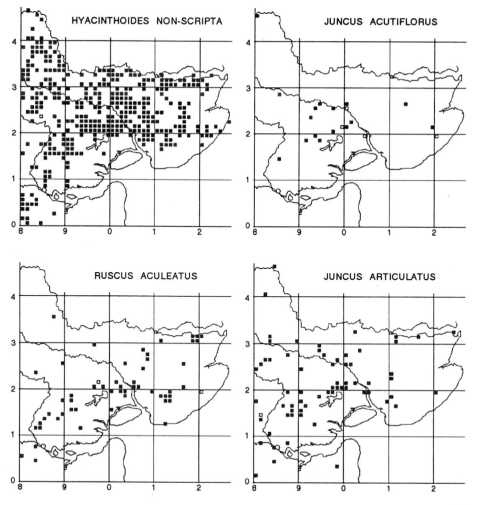

sions, where the water lies in winter. It can also be found growing in between pavements and concrete slabs.

Bulbous Rush
Juncus bulbosus [5]
Rare in wet, boggy places, usually under the shade of trees. In 1983 it was found in two places in the Roman River Valley, and, in 1986, in a very damp woodland ride at Braxted - it was known to Gibson in both these areas. He also had records from Tiptree Heath, where Jermyn also recorded it, but we have been unable to find it here - it is possible that it may still occur. Gibson's site at Bergholt Heath, and Jermyn's of Spratt's Marsh, where it was plentiful, have been lost as these locations are now arable. Jermyn also mentions Layer Breton Heath, but this tiny heathland has changed over the years and its habitat is no longer suitable for Bulbous Rush. We have additional records for High Woods and adjacent to Ardleigh Reservoir.

Round-fruited Rush
Juncus compressus [1]
It appears that in the past this Rush has been confused with the Saltmarsh Rush; all Gibson's sites were maritime, but Jermyn was able to confirm the locality at East Mersea where it was growing by the side of a marsh drainage dyke. Our only record comes from a relic piece of marshy meadow at Belchamp Walter, where it was growing with large stands of Southern Marsh Orchid.

Compact Rush
Juncus conglomeratus [85] M
From our findings we believe that this Rush has been over-recorded in the past, there was possibly some confusion with forms of Soft Rush. In north east Essex, Compact Rush is clearly an indicator of acid soils, and only becomes frequent where habitat and soil requirements coincide, such as around Tiptree. It can be found in roadside ditches, rough grassland, damp woodland rides and heathy places.

Soft Rush
Juncus effusus [757] M
Common in ditches, ponds, marshy places, wet grassland and damp situations in woods, indeed, anywhere where it is damp.

Juncus effusus X inflexus
This hybrid between Soft and Hard Rush was not found during our survey, but could have been overlooked. Jermyn had no records for our area, however, Gibson gave the following localities : Halstead, Rivenhall Park and Tiptree Heath. At that time it was thought to be a distinct species but he comments "As this plant usually occurs in very small quantity only, and amongst abundance of J inflexus and effusus, the possibility of its being a hybrid is suggested."

Saltmarsh Rush
Juncus gerardi [133] M
Still frequent around our coasts, it is a plant of estuarine marshes above the high tide mark. As the majority of this habitat is now arable it is most commonly found on the inside of the sea wall where there is seepage of salt water through the wall. The map clearly shows the remaining estuarine marshes at Old Hall, Langenhoe, Brightlingsea and Hamford Water. It has been lost from much of the Stour estuary in the last twenty years.

Hard Rush
Juncus inflexus [452] M
Common over much of the area, in damp places such as ditches and pond edges. It quickly colonises newly cleaned ditches. As Hard Rush is unpalatable to both ducks and cattle, it is often the only vegetation left at pond edges.

Sea Rush
Juncus maritimus [66] M
Infrequent and usually in small quantity. A plant of the high saltmarsh, it can often be found growing beside the borrow dykes on the inside of the sea walls. It still occurs in all the areas mentioned by Gibson, except Clacton.

Heath Rush
Juncus squarrosus [2]
Rare, due to lack of habitat. It occurs on wet heaths and is now restricted to Tiptree Heath and one site in the Roman River Valley Conservation Zone - it was known to Gibson at both these sites. It has occurred

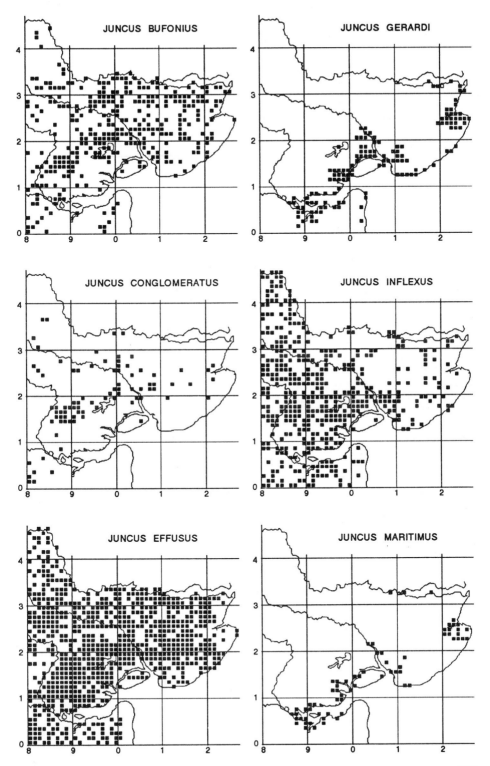

in the past on Bergholt Heath and Spratt's Marsh neither of which still exist.

Blunt-flowered Rush
Juncus subnodulosus
A rush associated with base rich fens, north east Essex is an unlikely area for this rush to occur. However, Gibson gave a record for Bergholt Heath and Jermyn recorded it from a marsh near Belchamp Brook at Gestingthorpe, gravel pits at Foxearth and Fordham Heath. It has not been found during our survey.

Slender Rush
Juncus tenuis
Common in other parts of the country, particularly south west Scotland, this American rush, that was first recorded in Britain in 1883, was found, in 1951, at Stour Wood, but has not been seen since.

Field Woodrush
Luzula campestris [137] M
No longer common, this little Woodrush has declined with the loss of habitat. It can still be plentiful in old grassland including churchyards and lawns.

Heath Woodrush
Luzula multiflora [35] M
Another Woodrush which has declined due to loss of habitat, it is now infrequent in acid grassland and heathy woodland rides. The subspecies with the clustered flower head, *ssp congesta*, has also declined; during our survey it was only found with any frequency around Tiptree.

Hairy Woodrush
Luzula pilosa [28] M
Again, this Woodrush has decreased, which is a little surprising for a woodland plant as such plants seem to have held their own in recent years. However, Jermyn does mention it occurring in shady hedgebanks and this is not a habitat where we have found it during our survey. Its decrease therefore appears to be due to the loss of its secondary habitat, as it is now entirely restricted to damp woods on gravels.

Great Woodrush
Luzula sylvatica [9] M
Occurring only in ancient woodlands this rare plant survives in the Markshall complex of woods where it was known to both Gibson and Jermyn. Gibson also mentioned Colchester, where we have found it in High Woods, East Wood (where it survives in Tesco's car park) and West House Wood. We also refound Jermyn's site in Chalkney Wood and additionally found it at Hyde Wood at Woodham Mortimer and Riddles Wood at St Osyth.

DAFFODIL FAMILY
AMARYLLIDACEAE

Snowdrop
Galanthus nivalis [18]
An introduction that has not been fully recorded.

Summer Snowflake
Leucojum aestivum
A garden plant Jermyn found naturalised in a wood at Thorpe le Soken in 1970.

Wild Daffodil
Narcissus pseudonarcissus [1]
The native **Wild Daffodil** is very rare in north east Essex, and perhaps always has been for Gibson gave only one site - meadows at Bradwell. The next record comes from Little Bentleyhall Wood in 1913, and Jermyn gives Thrift Wood at Woodham Mortimer where it was scarce. In 1988 it was abundant in Thrift Wood and it is perhaps worth further searching the other woods to see if it has survived.

IRIS FAMILY
IRIDACEAE

Gladiolus
Gladiolus communis ssp byzantinus
A garden flower Jermyn recorded from a derelict cottage garden near the station at Thorpe le Soken in 1971.

Stinking Iris
Iris foetidissima [14]
Both native and occurring as a garden escape where it has been discarded in the

hedgerows. We consider it to be of genuine native origin at only one of our sites - a single plant in an old hedge beside a bridleway at St Osyth Heath.

Flag Iris
Iris germanica
A garden outcast that Jermyn found occasionally but which we have not recorded during our survey.

Yellow Flag
Iris pseudacorus [217] M
No longer very common or plentiful, it is still widely distributed. It occurs in shallow water at the edge of ponds, streams and occasionally rivers, as well as in damp

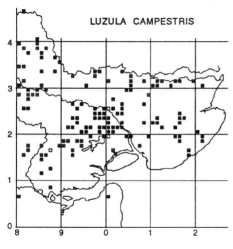

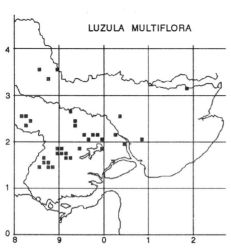

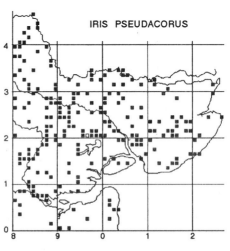

marshy places. Its native distribution has become obscured over the years as **Yellow Flag** is commonly planted.

Montbretia
Tritonia X crocosmiflora
Jermyn had recorded this garden escape from Birch Hall, where it had become naturalised.

YAM FAMILY
DIOSCOREACEAE

Black Bryony
Tamus communis [420] M
Climbing in hedgerows and at woodland edges, this plant is common on the boulder clay, but it can clearly be seen to be absent from the valley bottoms of the upper parts of the Blackwater, Colne and Stour. It is scattered elsewhere.

ORCHID FAMILY
ORCHIDACEAE

Man Orchid
Aceras anthropophorum
There are three historic records for this orchid, all on the chalk outcrop to the west of Sudbury: borders of cornfields at Belchamp St Paul, 1696; Ballingdon, 1715; Belchamp Walter Parish, on a little hillock in the corner of a ploughed field adjoining the way leading from Goldington [Goldingham?] Hall by the lime kiln towards Gestingthorpe, 1738 (see also **Military Orchid**).

Pyramidal Orchid
Anacamptis pyramidalis [1]
Jermyn's record for Tiptree Heath is the only previous sighting of this orchid in our part of the county. We were unable to locate it at this site during our survey. However, it was found at Borley by staff of the Essex Naturalists' Trust in 1984.

Common Spotted Orchid
Dactylorhiza fuchsii [43] M
Infrequent and in small quantity in damp grassland and woodland rides. It also occurs in gravel pits where, occasionally, when conditions are ideal, there is a

profusion of blooms, however, as the natural succession of the vegetation takes place this is only a transient occurrence. Gibson stated that this orchid was common and gave widespread locations in our area except for the Tendring peninsula. The intensive coverage of our survey has revealed more sites over a wider area than that given by Jermyn, but it is our opinion that the plants are becoming fewer and more scattered.

Dactylorhiza fuchsii X praetermissa [3]
Its occurrence at Chigborough Lakes and Loshes Meadows Nature Reserves are mentioned under **Southern Marsh Orchid**. This hybrid was also found at Layer Marney in 1989, where neither of the parents were present.

Early Marsh Orchid
Dactylorhiza incarnata
There have been no records since Gibson - meadow by the Colne at Halstead; marshes or wet meadows at Kelvedon and Braxted.

Heath Spotted Orchid
Dactylorhiza maculata
ssp ericetorum [1]
Recorded by Jermyn from Tiptree Heath, 1969-71, and a small valley in the Langham-Boxted area. It was present at Tiptree Heath in 1989 but plants were subsequently dug up and removed.

Southern Marsh Orchid
Dactylorhiza praetermissa [3]
Jermyn's site in Liston Pits could not be refound, but it occurs at Chigborough Lakes and Loshes Meadows, both Essex Naturalists' Trust nature reserves. At both sites just a few spikes of the **Southern Marsh Orchid** grow with a quantity of **Common Spotted Orchids**, with which it hybridises. The **Southern Marsh Orchid** was further found in a relic meadow at Belchamp Walter in 1988, where over sixty flowering spikes were counted.

Broad-leaved Helleborine
Epipactis helleborine [4]
A plant of ancient woodlands, it is very rare, as it was in Gibson's day. He gives records from Kelvedon, Inworth, Braxted

and a steep bank beyond Mistley Quay. There appear to have been no further published records but it must have been present at the sites where we have found it all along, the locations either being overlooked or kept secret. Three sites where it occurs are Sites of Special Scientific Interest, two of which are also nature reserves, the fourth locality is on private land. At each site, just a few spikes are present.

Marsh Helleborine
Epipactis palustris
Gibson mentioned a record for Parnassus Mount near Long Grove, Halstead, but Jermyn was unable to refind it, and there have been no records since.

Violet Helleborine
Epipactis purpurata [2]
Known to Gibson from Chalkney Wood, it is still present there, but we have been unable to refind it in any of the Markshall complex of woods, where it is mentioned by both Gibson and Jermyn. Our only other site is at Gestingthorpe.

Common Twayblade
Listera ovata [14]
This plant was common in woods and thickets in Victorian times, and even Jermyn found it to be plentiful in damp woods, especially on the boulder clay. Other than one wood, where it is still plentiful, all our other sites hold only a few plants.

Birdsnest Orchid
Neottia nidus-avis
Gibson gives records for Kelvedon, Stour Wood and for the Markshall complex of woods. Jermyn does not mention finding it at Markshall, although he did locate it in a border ride in the adjacent Broadfield and Belchers woods, this is the only recent record. Despite several visits we have been unable to refind Jermyn's site.

Bee Orchid
Ophrys apifera [6]
The **Bee Orchid** is transient in nature, it can occur on banks in small quantity year after year, or in large numbers in old gravel pits, dying out as the habitat matures. In keeping with this pattern we have been unable to refind it at any of Jermyn's sites, but have found others - Bulmer, Gestingthorpe, Aldham, Kelvedon, Messing and Crockleford Heath. Locations where it has previously been recorded include: (Gibson) Halstead, rare; Ballingdon; clay pits, Kelvedon, not common; Braxted; Rivenhall; Felix Hall Park, with white flowers, 1850: (Jermyn) a wood at Messing; pasture at Pattiswick; gravel pits, Alphamstone; Loshhouse Barn, Great Henny; Fingringhoe Wick Nature Reserve; St Osyth, old gravel pit (which has subsequently been used as a council refuse tip); Naze Cliffs.

Fly Orchid
Ophrys insectifera
Recorded once by a contemporary of Gib-

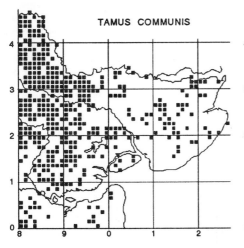
TAMUS COMMUNIS

DACTYLORHIZA FUCHSII

son's from Kelvedon.

Early Spider Orchid
Ophrys sphegodes
Found by Ray in the borders of cornfields at Belchamp St Paul with **Man Orchid** (1696) and at Ballingdon, in an old gravel pit (c1700).

Early Purple Orchid
Orchis mascula [20]
It was common in Gibson's time, but has since declined and continues to do so. Although normally in ancient woodlands it has also been found growing on road verges. It is most frequent on the chalky boulder clay in the west of our region but also occurs in Stour Wood.

Military Orchid
Orchis militaris
The only occurrence was recorded in 1738 in the parish of Belchamp Walter where it grew with **Man Orchid**.

Green-winged Orchid
Orchis morio [15] M
The **Green-winged Orchid** grows in meadows and pastures but with the loss of this habitat or its conversion to 'improved' grassland, this orchid has declined greatly. Gibson recorded that it was abundant in a pasture near Grinstead Green Hall. If this refers to Greenstead Green, near Halstead, then there have been no further records for this vicinity since. He also knew it to be common near Colchester, and Jermyn subsequently found it in a meadow at Berechurch which was later ploughed. However, it still occurs at several places in the Roman River Valley Conservation Zone, although sparingly at any one site. In 1985 this orchid made the national headlines; it grew in large numbers (estimated at 15,000 spikes in 0.4 ha) in an old pasture at West Mersea which the landowner wished to develop, and, when local opposition arose because of the flora of this meadow, it was sprayed with weed killer. We have also found it at Thorpe, near Parkeston (close by Jermyn's location) and Dedham. However, the most remarkable story is that of Iron Latch Meadow, now an Essex Naturalists' Trust nature reserve. It is rather like a modern

version of Sleeping Beauty with CNHS member Dave Baker making a rather reluctant prince! Forty years ago it was a flower-rich meadow which became neglected, and for the next three decades the hawthorn scrub gradually encroached year by year until there was no meadow left. Dave Baker whilst out for a walk discovered the last few orchids still struggling to flower before they too were finally overwhelmed by the scrub. It was his drive and enthusiasm which resulted in the land being first leased and then purchased by the ENT and the commencement of cutting back the thorn. It took eight years to return the whole site to a meadow but by the third year over 120 spikes of **Green-winged Orchid** flowered.

Lesser Butterfly Orchid
Platanthera bifolia
There have been no records since Gibson, when it occurred at Tiptree Heath and Braxted.

Greater Butterfly Orchid
Platanthera chlorantha [3]
We have records from only two sites, both from woods on the chalky boulder clay. At one site it is present in good quantity and at the other there are well over a hundred plants. Gibson gave it as frequent at Halstead which could refer to the Markshall complex and adjacent woods where it was found in several places by Jermyn. We have had unconfirmed reports that it still occurs there but that the plants are eaten by deer, and we have, so far, been unable to refind it in these woods. Gibson's other records show that it was once more widespread, although generally on the chalky boulder clay soils - Felix Hall wood, Rivenhall, Feering, Messing; the exception is his record for woods at Colchester. Jermyn also recorded it away from these soils at Lawford.

Autumn Lady's Tresses
Spiranthes spiralis [2]
Now very rare. It appears that only two sites are left, both are garden lawns. We understand that it is still preserved at Baytree Cottage, Great Horkesley, and it was also found in 1983 at Frinton in another lawn, where it had probably been

imported with the turf from an old meadow site as there was also **Adderstongue** and **Common Thyme** with it. Jermyn's other sites for a meadow north of Cook's Wood, Birch, and the green near Lower Houses, Maltings Green, 1961, could not be refound.

ARUM FAMILY
ARACEAE

Sweet Flag
Acorus calamus [12]
Still frequent along the Chelmer-Blackwater canal, but otherwise only four sites have been found at very scattered locations: Thorpe le Soken, pond at Bradfield, stream at Kelvedon, pond near Halstead.

Italian Lords & Ladies
Arum italicum
Jermyn's site in the border of Tarecroft wood, 1972, could not be refound.

Cuckoo Pint or Lords & Ladies
Arum maculatum [718] M
Common in hedgerows and shady banks.

DUCKWEED FAMILY
LEMNACEAE

Fat Duckweed
Lemna gibba [23] M
Scattered in coastal and estuarine areas in borrow dykes, ditches and slow-moving rivers and also all along the Chelmer-Blackwater canal.

Lemna miniscula [5]
A very recent introduction found for the first time in 1984 at Distillery Pond, Colchester. It was subsequently found in ponds at Fordham, Birch and Fingringhoe Wick Nature Reserve and a ditch at Langford.

Common Duckweed
Lemna minor [312] M
Common and widely distributed, it can

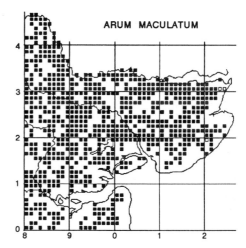

ARUM MACULATUM

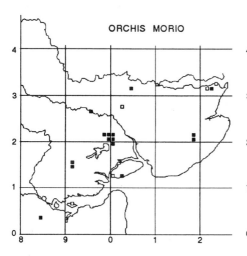

ORCHIS MORIO

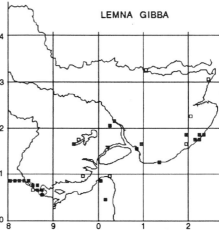

LEMNA GIBBA

occur in almost any body of water from wet ruts, cattle drinking troughs, and garden ponds to large lakes and rivers.

Great Duckweed
Lemna polyrhiza [4]
Apparently reduced in distribution since Jermyn's day but easily overlooked. It is still present in Holland Brook where it had been recorded by Jermyn.

Ivy Duckweed
Lemna trisulca [36] M
Still reasonably frequent but easily overlooked as its submerged life style conceals it from casual observation, particularly in murky waters.

BUR-REED FAMILY
SPARGANIACEAE

Unbranched Bur-reed
Sparganium emersum [3]
This plant appears to have suffered a serious decline. Gibson recorded that it was abundant at Halstead in several places, and also present on the Blackwater at Kelvedon. Jermyn, too, found it present in the Colne at Halstead, at several places on the Blackwater as well as the Chelmer-Blackwater canal, Roman River, a pond at St Lawrence and a ditch near Weeleyhall Wood. During our survey we have not recorded it from any of the major river systems mentioned above, but have done so from the Stour at two sites at Liston. It was also found in a borrow dyke at Mundon.

Branched Bur-reed
Sparganium erectum [192] M
Still reasonably frequent at the edges of the main rivers and tributary streams as well as lakes and reservoirs. Four subspecies of **Branched Bur-reed** occur in Britain, but the current survey has not recorded these separately and the distribution of each subspecies is therefore unknown. However, Jermyn found that *ssp erectum* was the normal subspecies, but that there had been a few records of *ssp neglectum* - Nayland, 1887; Layer Breton, 1889; Little Clacton, 1912; he also found it in flooded gravel pits at Bradwell and at Abberton

Reservoir.

REEDMACE FAMILY
TYPHACEAE

Lesser Reedmace
Typha angustifolia [61] M
Infrequent but widespread, although commonest close to the coast. It prefers deeper water to the **Greater Reedmace** and is often found in borrow dykes and flooded gravel pits.

Greater Reedmace
Typha latifolia [398] M
Common in ponds, large ditches, flooded gravel pits, edges of lakes and reservoirs as well as shallow water at the edge of slow-moving rivers.

SEDGE FAMILY
CYPERACEAE

Flat-headed Sedge
Blysmus compressus
Gibson gave a record for "near the Colne below Colchester" but it has not been found since.

Slender Tufted Sedge
Carex acuta [1]
A sedge of wet marshy places and flood meadows beside streams, Gibson's records show that it occurred along the Blackwater at Kelvedon and the Stour at Dedham. Jermyn found it in a marsh at Belchamp Walter. This marsh, beside Belchamp Brook, used to cover an extensive area but there now remains just one small remnant - the sedge was not present in this area. However, a few plants were found in the late 1970s in Bull Meadow, an ancient flood meadow beside the Colne in the centre of Colchester. This tiny relic is now a local nature reserve managed by the Colchester Natural History Society, and so the future of this site seems assured.

Lesser Pond Sedge
Carex acutiformis [65] M
Declining and now no longer frequent or as widespread as Jermyn found, it can still be plentiful where it does occur at the edges

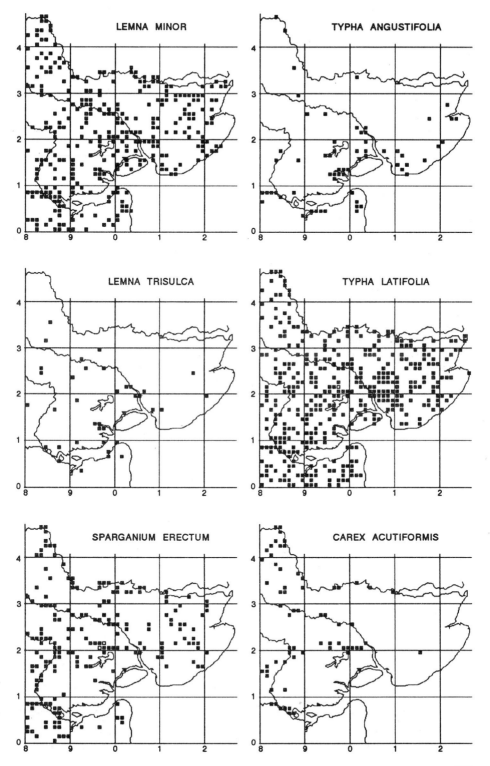

of streams and rivers. Also found in marshy places, it occurs in the plantations of **Cricket-bat Willows** and **Poplars**, which are often planted in this habitat in our area.

Sand Sedge
Carex arenaria [15] M
A sedge of sandy places by the sea, its distribution has remained remarkably constant to that given by Jermyn, the only site not refound being at Osea Island.

Ribbed Sedge
Carex binervis [3]
Gibson's sites include Tiptree Heath, Birch Wood (Dedham), West Bergholt Heath and Harwich. It was still present at Tiptree Heath according to Jermyn, but his only other site was from grassland between Kirby and Walton. We have not been able to refind it at any of these locations except Tiptree Heath. However, it was found in East Wood, Colchester, in 1981 (now part of the High Woods housing development), and on a fragment of relic heathy grassland by the river in the centre of Colchester (soon to be built on).

Spring Sedge
Carex caryophyllea [1]
Previous records include: Gibson - Halstead, not common; Tiptree Heath and Dedham, whilst Jermyn found it at Fordham Heath. Our single record comes from Greenstead Green churchyard where it was growing in the turf, 1981.

Common Yellow Sedge
Carex demissa [2]
Jermyn's sites include Great Monks Wood, where we have been unsuccessful in relocating it (it is possible it still occurs here), and Tiptree Heath, where it was refound in 1984. An additional site was found during the survey; a few scattered plants along an overgrown marshy bridleway in Squeakinggate Wood, south of Maldon.

Distant Sedge
Carex distans [4]
Much declined due to loss of habitat. Gibson's sites include Witham; banks of the canal at Heybridge; marshy ground between Witham and Colchester, and Harwich. Jermyn's locations were similarly widespread in the area: Earls Colne; Fordham Heath; by a saltmarsh pool at St Osyth; marshes between Frinton-Holland and Kirby-Walton, and by the side of a brackish dyke at Dovercourt. Our survey has only found it at Old Hall Marshes, Point Clear and Frating.

Brown Sedge
Carex disticha [2]
A sedge of marshy places and margins of ponds it is now reduced to just two sites in our area: Bull Meadow, Colchester, and another flood meadow in the Roman River Valley. Historical records indicate its previous distribution: Gibson - Maldon, Kelvedon, Feering and Walton; Jermyn - by the canal at Mundon, Tiptree Heath, waste ground near Halstead, a marshy plantation at Great Maplestead, Fordham Heath, Wormingford and Bradwell-on-Sea.

Divided Sedge
Carex divisa [24] M
Divided Sedge is found in coastal grassland and Jermyn's records show it used to occur all round our coast, including the Blackwater, Colne and Stour estuaries. It is still present on the Colne but is now very scattered elsewhere. Traditionally a sedge of estuarine grazing marshes, sea walls and borrow dykes, we have found it at seaside caravan sites indicating the grassland was derived from the original marshland turf. It is possible that some plants have been overlooked in rough grassland as it tends to blend into the background.

Grey Sedge
Carex divulsa ssp divulsa [97] M
Usually in small quantity but still reasonably frequent and widespread in road verges.

Carex divulsa ssp leersii [1]
Generally regarded as a sedge of limestone areas, it was found in 1983 growing from the mortar of the railway bridge at Copperas Wood. This bridge was subsequently demolished and rebuilt when the line was electrified, however, plants from this site were introduced to the car park at Stour Wood nearby. Jermyn gives a record for Goldhanger in 1956 but we have been unable to refind it in this area.

Star Sedge
Carex echinata
Not refound during our survey, it is a sedge of wet and boggy places. Gibson's sites include Tiptree Heath, Pods Wood and Bergholt Heath, and Jermyn found it in the Langham-Boxted area in 1968.

Tufted Sedge
Carex elata [1]
Regarded by Jermyn as lost to the county, two plants were found in a pond near Bulmer in 1987.

Elongated Sedge
Carex elongata
First recorded for the county in 1844 from Chalkney Wood, it was subsequently found during the last century in Markshall woods. It has not been refound at these sites since.

Long-bracted Sedge
Carex extensa
Previous to Gibson this sedge had been recorded once from marshy ground near Harwich. There have been no further records.

Glaucous Sedge
Carex flacca [37] M
Generally restricted to old grassland, woodland rides and glades on the chalky boulder clays.

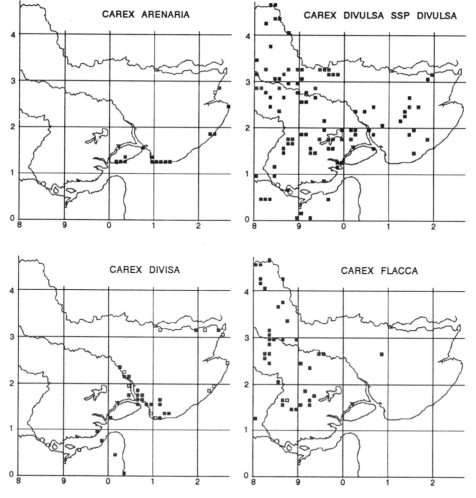

Large Yellow Sedge
Carex flava
Gibson gave a record for Kelvedon for this sedge, but in view of the revisions that have taken place in the taxonomy of all the Yellow Sedges, the identification of old records such as this cannot be relied upon. In all probability it was likely to have been *C demissa*, but this is pure conjecture.

Hairy Sedge
Carex hirta [194] M
Frequent over much of the area. It is found in grass verges, cart tracks, damp woodland rides and other damp grassy places. It is a persistent and determined sedge - it can often be seen pushing its way up through tarmac pavements and road edges, it seems to survive being trampled, and can withstand being mown.

Smooth Sedge
Carex laevigata [5]
A sedge found in the really boggy parts of old woodland. During our survey it was found at Great Totham (a Gibson locality), at three places in the Roman River Valley and at Little Clacton (a Jermyn locality). Gibson also gave locations for Copford, Messing, Inworth and Braxted showing that it had been reasonably frequent in the Tiptree-Kelvedon-Witham area.

Prickly Sedge
Carex muricata
ssp lamprocarpa [48] M
In the past there has been much confusion over the identification of this subspecies with *ssp muricata* and also with *C spicata* and we are, therefore, only commenting on records obtained during our survey and not making comparison to the historical data given by Gibson or Jermyn. Infrequent and scattered on drier verges and quite often on graves in churchyards.

Common Sedge
Carex nigra [8]
A sedge of old wet meadows and boggy places which has declined with the loss of habitat. Although we have found it at locations not mentioned previously, only two of Jermyn's sites have survived; a marsh at Belchamp Walter and Fordham Heath. His other sites included the canal at Ulting, Great Braxted, Cook's Mill at West Bergholt, a marsh by Salary Brook at Colchester and by the Stour at Langham. Additionally it has been found in the Roman River Valley, at a field on the outskirts of Tiptree, Langley Mill on the Colne and at Liston.

False Fox Sedge
Carex otrubae [282] M
The commonest sedge of our area it is found mainly in roadside ditches but also in ponds and occasionally borrow dykes.

Carex otrubae X remota [1]
This hybrid has only been found once during our survey, in a roadside ditch near Chalkney Wood. Both Gibson and Jermyn give several localities indicating that it was not an uncommon hybrid in our area. Our survey has shown that both parents have decreased and the chances of this hybrid occurring now have therefore been reduced.

Oval Sedge
Carex ovalis [21] M
A sedge of damp heathy grassland and heathy woodland rides, its range has contracted mainly to the Roman River Valley and the heathlands running from Layer Breton through to Tiptree, with only odd scattered records elsewhere. Both Gibson's and Jermyn's records show that it was previously frequent and widespread.

Pale Sedge
Carex pallescens [8]
Never common, previous records show that it did occur over the whole of our area, but it is now restricted to damp grassy rides in two localities - the woodland complex of Markshall and around Layer and Pods Woods.

Carnation Sedge
Carex panicea [1]
Evidently always uncommon in our area, Gibson gave sites from moist meadows at Inworth and Messing, and Jermyn from a marsh by Stone Bridge at Earls Colne and Tiptree Heath. We were unable to refind it in any of these locations, but discovered it close by the Stour at Bures in 1984.

254

Greater Tussock Sedge
Carex paniculata [5]
With the loss of wet marshes it is surprising that two of Jermyn's sites have survived - marsh at Cross End, Pebmarsh, and Liston Pits. Even more surprisingly a further site has been found, a marsh at Countess Cross, 1982. It appears, however, that his other locations at Langford Park and Langham have gone. It also occurs at two Essex Naturalists' Trust nature reserves - Loshes Meadows and Fingringhoe Wick.

Pendulous Sedge
Carex pendula [104] M
Very common around Halstead (it was

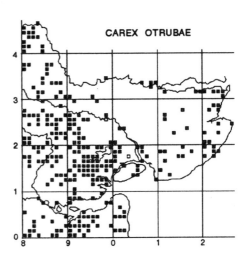

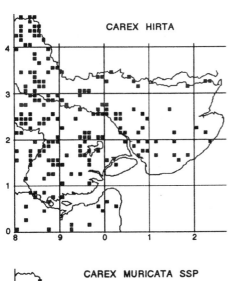

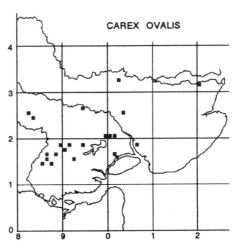

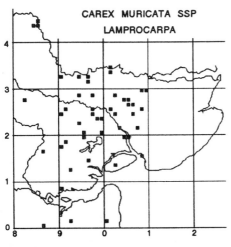

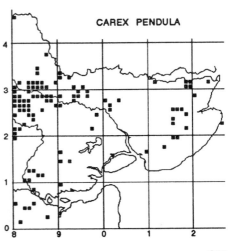

frequent in this locality in Gibson's time), but scattered elsewhere. It is most frequent in wet woodland rides and ditches at the woodland margins. It also occurs in damp shady hedgerows.

Pill Sedge
Carex pilulifera [13]
An uncommon sedge of damp heathy grassland and woods. It occurs on Layer Breton Heath along a damp ride and in several places in Layer, Pods and Coneyfield Woods. Jermyn's location at Great Monks Wood still survives but we were unable to confirm its presence at Fordham Heath or Little Bentleyhall Wood; Spratt's Marsh is now arable. We have found this sedge at Tiptree Heath and nearby in a wood at Braxted, both locations are given by Gibson. Additionally it has been recorded from Roman River Valley, High Woods, Stour Wood and at Aingers Green.

Cyperus Sedge
Carex pseudocyperus [21] M
Considered by Jermyn to be "frequent and locally common", this sedge is now very infrequent in our area. It was always commonest in the woods on the chalky boulder clays such as the Markshall complex but has become very scattered or disappeared completely elsewhere. It occurs in ponds and damp ditches as well as wet places in woods. This sedge is now available from garden centres and it is beginning to be planted in village ponds.

Flea Sedge
Carex pulicaris
Gibson's record for Bergholt Heath, which no longer exists, is the only known sighting in our area.

Remote Sedge
Carex remota [136] M
No longer common, it is still quite widespread and locally frequent in, for example, the Roman River Valley, the Markshall complex of woods and around Layer and Pods Woods. Comparing Jermyn's comments with our findings it would appear that it has maintained its status in these woods but has declined in other habitats such as damp shady places by streams, ditches and ponds.

Great Pond Sedge
Carex riparia [103] M
Still frequent along most of the major rivers and their tributaries. It is also found in marshy places close by where it can withstand some shading as often occurs when these areas become **Cricket-bat Willow** and **Poplar** plantations.

Carex serotina
The only record for this member of the **Yellow Sedge** group is given by Gibson. It was found at Messing Heath which is now part of urban Tiptree.

Spiked Sedge
Carex spicata [20] M
As mentioned previously under *C muricata ssp lamprocarpa* there has been much confusion in the past between these sedges and we are only commenting on our findings. **Spiked Sedge** is usually found in small quantity in varying habitats. It occurs in both wet and dry grassland including grass verges and by streams as well as old gravel pits.

Thin-spiked Wood Sedge
Carex strigosa [7]
A rare sedge of shady, wet ditches and woodland rides. Historically all records have been from the chalky boulder clay in the west of our region but, in 1985, it was found in Copperas Wood by the Stour for the first time. Gibson had records for Kelvedon and Inworth but there have been none from this area since, although it was found during our survey in a wood to the east of Tiptree. Further north, we move into the heart of its distribution. Gibson found it to be "not uncommon" around Halstead, and Jermyn had records from Broadfield, Bungate and Chalkney Woods. We have refound it in both the two former woods as well as another in the Markshall complex, but we have been unable to locate a specimen in Chalkney Wood (it could still be there, somewhere!). Jermyn's sites by the lake at Colne Park and Parkhill Wood, Alphamstone also eluded us, however, it was found in a damp shady roadside ditch at Little Henny.

Wood Sedge
Carex sylvatica [83] M
This is the commonest woodland sedge but it too has declined, although it has maintained its status in the large old woodlands, it has been lost where smaller copses have been removed.

Bladder Sedge
Carex vesicaria
We have been unable to refind it at any of the historical sites mentioned: Gibson - Chalkney Wood; Jermyn - ponds at Stansgate and Maldon Wood and by the lake at Thorpe Hall.

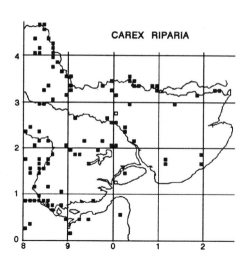

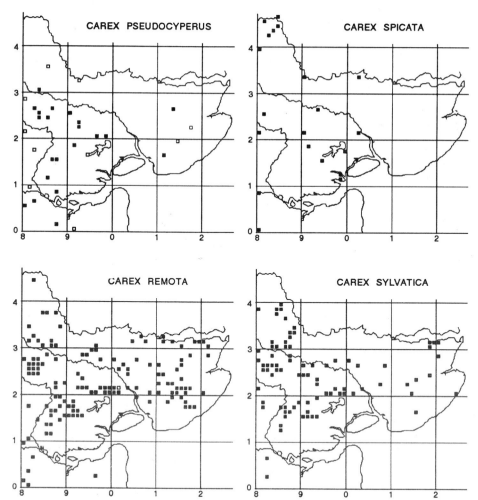

Galingale
Cyperus longus [8]
An introduction that has become natural-ised in places. It still occurs at Jermyn's location at Witham, and has now been found at several scattered sites in the area. It colonises ditches, streams and farm reservoirs.

Many-stemmed Spike Rush
Eleocharis multicaulis
Gibson knew it from marshy ground on Tiptree Heath and from Lawford, but it has not been recorded since.

Common Spike Rush
Eleocharis palustris [37] M
Infrequent at the edges of ponds, ditches, streams and reservoirs as well as in damp areas nearby. In Gibson's time it was frequent around Halstead, and he also gave records for Kelvedon, Messing, Ded-ham and Harwich. Jermyn, too, found it to be frequent and locally plentiful and had records for these areas, but the map reveals how much it has declined.

Floating Scirpus
Eleogiton fluitans
Apparently this plant has always been rare in our area. Gibson's records are from ditches and ponds at Pods Wood, Tiptree and West Bergholt Heaths, whilst Jermyn recorded it from Abberton Reservoir in 1952. It has not been found during our survey.

Broad-leaved Cotton Grass
Eriophorum latifolium
Recorded during Victorian times from Markshall Wood, but there have been no further records.

Bristle Scirpus
Isolepis setacea [6]
Very infrequent, but possibly overlooked, particularly as it sometimes occurs in the same places as Toad Rush. It has been found in damp patches of bare ground,

woodland rides and old gravel pits.

Bulrush
Schoenoplectus lacustris
ssp lacustris [53] M
Generally restricted to the main river sys-tems and the occasional reservoir or large stream. Gibson reported that it had been formerly abundant on the Colne around Halstead but that it was now "nearly extirpated". This implies deliberate digging up or destruction but there is no indication of the reason for this.

Glaucous Bulrush
Schoenoplectus lacustris
ssp tabernaemontani [20] M
Its main habitat is the brackish dykes of estuarine marshes, but in the past it has occurred away from the coast as both Gibson and Jermyn give inland locations; Jermyn considered that these could have been introductions. The historical records show it occurring all round our coast from Maldon to Manningtree, but it is now restricted, in any quantity, to the grazing marshes of Old Hall, Howlands and Bright-lingsea Marshes. It is also found at St Osyth Beach, between Holland and Frinton and at Dovercourt.

Sea Clubrush
Scirpus maritimus [282] M
Common in the borrow dykes around the coast, it also occurs in ditches, ponds and farm reservoirs a little way inland.

Wood Clubrush
Scirpus sylvaticus [4]
Rare in very boggy areas in old woodland. It has been known from Friday Wood since 1841 and it is still present in Chalkney Wood where it was known to Gibson. Gibson also gave sites at Totham and for a wood near Braxted, and in 1977 it was found in a wood situated between Great Totham and Braxted, but unfortunately we have been unable to confirm its continued presence. Of Jermyn's records, we were able to refind **Wood Clubrush** in a marsh near Stone Bridge at Earls Colne, but not at Mundon Furze, Colne Park or Liston.

Deer Grass
Trichophorum cespitosum
Known from Tiptree Heath in the last century but not seen since.

GRASS FAMILY
GRAMINEAE

Brown Bent
Agrostis canina [11] M
A grass of acid heathy places which we feel has been over-recorded in the past. Our survey has revealed only a few scattered sites, mainly on the heathy areas in the Roman River Valley, Layer Breton and Tiptree Heaths.

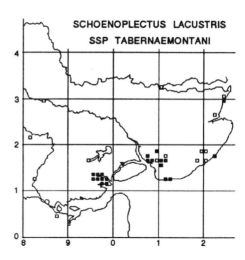
SCHOENOPLECTUS LACUSTRIS
SSP TABERNAEMONTANI

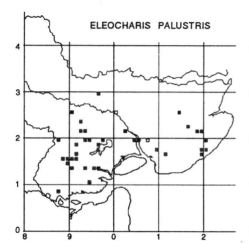
ELEOCHARIS PALUSTRIS

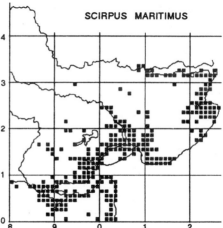
SCIRPUS MARITIMUS

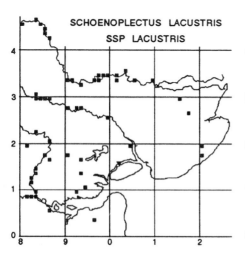
SCHOENOPLECTUS LACUSTRIS
SSP LACUSTRIS

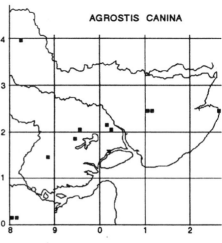
AGROSTIS CANINA

Common Bent
Agrostis capillaris [427] M
Common in the shorter turf on the drier verges and other grassy places.

Black Bent
Agrostis gigantea [95] M
A grass of arable field edges and disturbed waste places, it has decreased, probably due to the more effective sprays used today.

Creeping Bent
Agrostis stolonifera [849] M
Very common in all sorts of grassland as well as urban waste places. It has been under-recorded in the Tendring Hundred during our survey.

Agrostis vinealis [1]
Mis-recorded in the past, it is a very rare grass in our area, the only site where it has been found being Tiptree Heath.

Silvery Hair-grass
Aira caryophyllea [18]
Infrequent and scattered on dry well-drained banks, where it usually grows in small bare patches in the turf.

Early Hair-grass
Aira praecox [97] M
In similar places to the previous species, but generally on banks that are even drier and barer. It is often found in old gravel pits and on sea walls; in suitable areas it will form a thick tufty carpet which remains throughout the summer.

Orange Foxtail
Alopecurus aequalis [2]
Very rare, it has been found at only two locations during the survey; both in ponds by farm houses. The historical data shows that it was never common, but was certainly more widespread: Gibson - Halstead, Earls Colne, Kelvedon, Copford; Jermyn - moat at Twinstead Hall, plentiful in village pond at Wakes Colne Green, plentiful in dyke behind sea wall at St Osyth and near the Haven at Holland Brook.

Bulbous Foxtail
Alopecurus bulbosus
Apparently always rare, Gibson's only

record was for the Hythe, Colchester. Jermyn, despite much searching, could only locate it at Wivenhoe and west of Manningtree, 1951. It has not been found during our survey, but further searches are planned.

Marsh Foxtail
Alopecurus geniculatus [165] M
No longer common, it is still reasonably frequent in the area. Its particular niche is in a depression in grassland where water lays for a time; in these conditions it can be plentiful.

Slender Foxtail (Black Grass
Alopecurus myosuroides [681] M
Still very common as a cornfield weed, despite the many attentions of the farmers and chemical companies - it appears that it is almost impossible to eradicate.

Meadow Foxtail
Alopecurus pratensis [782] M
Very common in many kinds of grassland, particularly on road verges.

Marram Grass
Ammophila arenaria [16]
A grass of sandy beaches and sand dunes it is present at most of the places where these habitats occur: Bradwell-on-Sea, Mersea Island, Dovercourt and Walton as well as Colne Point and St Osyth Beach area where it is most frequent.

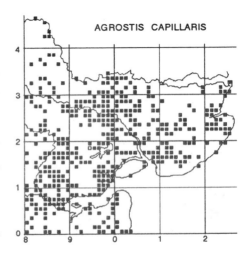
AGROSTIS CAPILLARIS

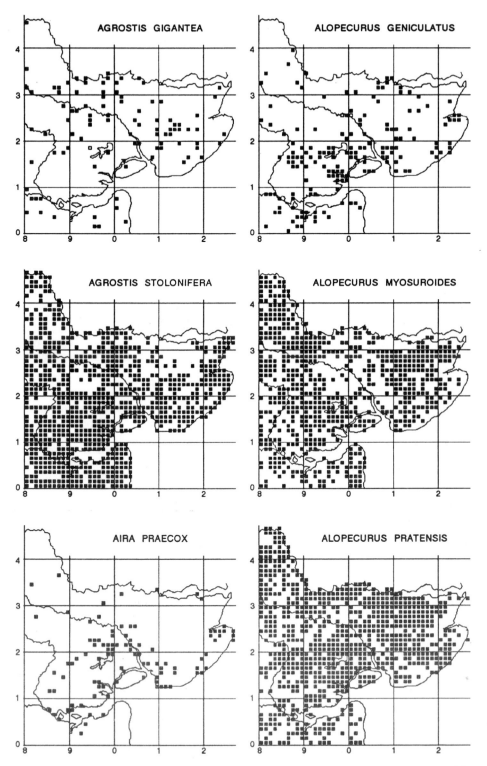

Sweet Vernal Grass
Anthoxanthum odoratum [189] M

A common grass of grazing and old pasture, it has declined with the loss of this habitat. The Roman River Valley still retains much grazing land and this is reflected on the map. Sweet Vernal Grass can usually be found in horse paddocks, the lawns in churchyards and sometimes on road verges where the turf contains the remnants of native grassland.

Dense Silky-bent
Apera interrupta

In 1843 this grass was observed near Marks Tey Station - it had probably originated from impure seed. There have been no other records.

Loose Silky-bent
Apera spica-venti [36] M

On the light soils around St Osyth, this grass is almost a common arable weed. There is also a cluster of records on the gravel ridge of the Dengie peninsula. Elsewhere there have been only scattered sightings.

False Oat-grass
Arrhenatherum elatius [1182] M

A very common grass that can be found as a component of any grassland. On some road verges it is so common that possibly 75% of the grass on the verge is this species.

Wild Oat
Avena fatua [543] M

Common as an arable weed and also on disturbed ground nearby.

Avena sativa [3]

An escape from cultivation - not fully recorded.

Winter Wild Oat
Avena sterilis ssp ludoviciana [89] M

In similar habitats to *A fatua* but not as widespread.

Hairy Oat-grass
Avenula pubescens [2]

A plant of old calcareous grassland, previously there have been no records for north east Essex. During the survey it was found in the churchyard at Great Maplestead and along the Valley Walk near Sudbury.

Slender False Brome
Brachypodium sylvaticum [486] M

Very common on the chalky boulder clay with a rather patchy distribution elsewhere. A grass of shady banks and hedgerows.

Large Quaking Grass
Briza maxima [1]

Grown in gardens as an ornamental grass it can escape and establish itself for a short while.

Quaking Grass
Briza media [1]

Once common throughout the county, it was still frequent in old pastures according to Jermyn, so much so that he did not consider giving specific sites - he had records from six 10km squares in our area. We have found just one site - a few plants were growing on the very edge of a roadside bank on a corner at Wormingford.

Meadow Brome
Bromus commutatus [86] M

This grass is an absolute pest in many of the arable fields on the Dengie peninsula. It is also common in the fields around Tollesbury but elsewhere it occurs only intermittently. The historical data is somewhat confusing: Gibson gives its habitat as "cultivated fields" (the habitat where we

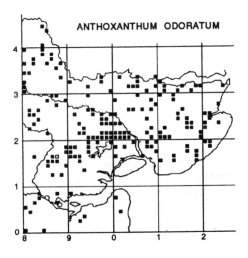

ANTHOXANTHUM ODORATUM

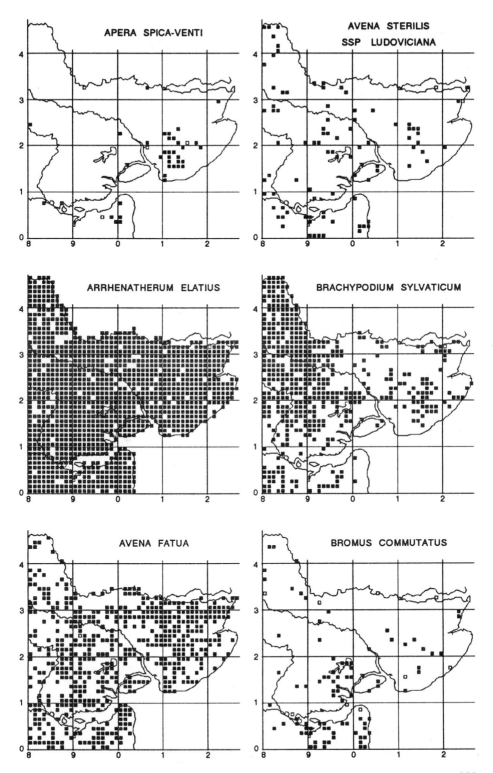

have found it), but Jermyn gives "damp meadows and grassy waste places". However, he goes on to say it was "most frequent in the old grassland of the drained estuarine marshes" and the arable fields, where we have found it to be common, were grazing marshes in his time.

Great Brome
Bromus diandrus [14]
Jermyn gives the habitat of this grass as "rubbish tips and waste ground" and, in the early years of this survey, these were the places where it was found. However, in the latter years it started to turn up as an arable weed.

Upright Brome
Bromus erectus
A grass of calcareous soils, Jermyn's records were from a roadside verge near Broadfield Wood, a roadside near Borley and the unlikely spot of the old airfield at Bradwell-on-Sea. This grass has not been found during the present survey.

Soft Brome
Bromus hordeaceus
ssp hordeaceus [815] M
Very common in most kinds of grassland as well as disturbed ground, it is also a component of seed mixtures and is, therefore, sown beside carriageways and in amenity grassland.

Bromus hordeaceus ssp thominii
The records Jermyn gives for this species are likely to have been *B X pseudotho- minii*. We have no confirmed records for our area.

Hungarian Brome
Bromus inermis [11] M
An introduced grass that was found beside the A12 at Rivenhall End and on the A604 along the Wix bypass. It had obviously been introduced with the seed mixture.

Slender Soft Brome
Bromus lepidus [11]
This grass was either previously mis-recorded or has suffered a drastic decline. We have only found it as a rare arable weed, generally occurring on the lighter soils.

Compact Brome
Bromus madritensis
A casual found at Parkeston railway sidings in 1961, but it has not been recorded since.

Bromus X pseudothominii [11]
This hybrid has occasionally been found in dry grassland, around farmyards and on disused airfields; it has probably been under-recorded during our survey. Jermyn's records of *B thominii* are likely to have been this species.

Smooth Brome
Bromus racemosus
Despite careful searching we have been unable to refind any of Jermyn's sites or indeed any records at all for this grass. Although Gibson gave some localities, he also said that the records cannot be relied upon as a hairless form of **Soft Brome** is frequently mistaken for this grass. Over a century later, Hubbard, in his book, **Grasses** (1984), also comments on the frequency of confusion, this time, with **Meadow Brome!**

Hairy Brome
Bromus ramosus [169] M
Reasonably frequent in damp woodland edges and shady hedgerows and ditchbanks.

Bromus rigidus [1]
A casual of waste ground in Jermyn's time; he had five localities scattered in the area. Our only record comes from St Osyth Beach where a large patch was found on disturbed ground by the side of a track in 1988.

Rye Brome
Bromus secalinus [5]
An uncommon arable weed. Gibson gave records for Halstead, Inworth and Mile End Heath, Colchester. There were no further records for many years and Jermyn thought it had been lost to the county, but our survey has revealed its continued presence. The records are from Layer Marney, Tolleshunt Knights and Peldon.

Barren Brome ANISANTHA
Bromus sterilis [1096] M
Very common in all sorts of habitats including hedgerows, roadsides, field margins, waste ground and gardens.

Bush Grass
Calamagrostis epigejos [11]
Infrequent and very scattered, not only in damp woods and shady places but also roadside ditches.

Water Whorlgrass
Catabrosa aquatica [3]
A rare grass of swampy streams, we have found it on just three occasions; Roman River Valley, 1983, by the Stour at Bures,

1987, and in a stream at Great Horkesley. Previous localities include: Gibson - Halstead, Kelvedon, near Dedham and Walton; Jermyn - stream near Stour at Little Horkesley, a stream and pond in the Alresford Creek area and in the marshes north east of Ramsey (TM 23). We have been unable to refind it at any of these sites but it is a grass that disappears some years, reappearing later.

Bermuda Grass
Cynodon dactylon
An introduced grass that was found at Dovercourt Beach in 1952 but did not persist.

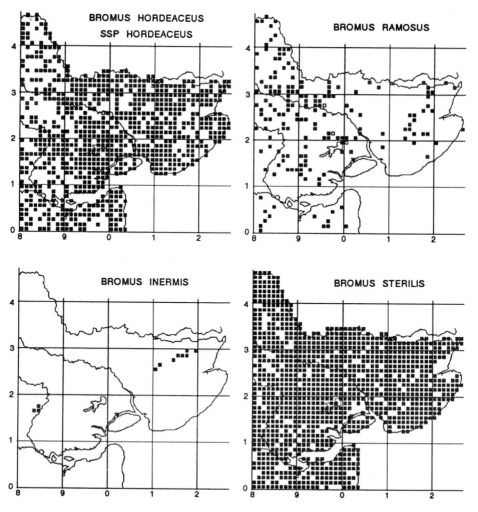

Crested Dogstail
Cynosurus cristatus [322] M
A common grass of grazing lands, it can invariably be found in any horse paddock, and is present in most relic areas of old grassland, including churchyards. It has probably declined with the conversion of grassland to arable indicating how common it must once have been.

Rough Dogstail
Cynosurus echinatus
An introduced grass that does not appear to have colonised north east Essex as it has done adjacent areas; there is just one record from Berechurch which dates from before 1930.

Cocksfoot
Dactylis glomerata [1285] M
Very common in all kinds of grassland, including road verges, sea walls and rough areas.

Heath Grass
Danthonia decumbens [10] M
Very local in heathy grassland and never in any quantity. It is still present at all three localities given by Jermyn: Tiptree Heath, Layer Breton Heath and Berechurch. We have found it at several new sites in the Roman River Valley and additionally at Fordham Heath and adjacent to West Bergholt school.

Tufted Hair-grass
Deschampsia cespitosa [164] M
Reasonably frequent in wet grassland and damp areas in woods occurring on the acid gravels, but scattered elsewhere. It has suffered a decline since last century when it was "common in all districts". Jermyn recorded var parviflora from three sites but this variety has not been separately recorded during the survey.

Wavy Hair-grass
Deschampsia flexuosa [1]
A very rare grass for north east Essex due to lack of suitable habitat. Gibson knew of no sites in his day and our survey has revealed only one location; on the heathlands in the Roman River Valley. We feel that Jermyn may have been mistaken in his records for this grass.

Sea Fern-grass
Desmazeria marina [7] M
A very local grass of sand dunes. Harwich was Gibson's only site, but Jermyn had records from Tollesbury, Colne Point-St Osyth Beach area and Dovercourt. It is still present in these last two localities but we were unable to refind it at Tollesbury. However, it has been found in plenty along the promenade at Clacton.

Fern-grass
Desmazeria rigida [32] M
Infrequent and scattered, **Fern Grass** is usually found at the bottom of or on walls; it can be found all round the Roman Wall at Colchester. Other habitats include the sidings at Parkeston, bare dry patches on the sea cliffs, cracks in concrete paving and in the gardens at Essex County Hospital where some very lush specimens were found (no pun intended!).

Hairy Finger-grass
Digitaria sanguinalis [3]
A bird seed alien that occurs regularly.

Cockspur
Echinochloa crus-galli [3]
A casual of rubbish tips or as a bird seed alien.

Echinochloa frumentacea
As with the previous species, this is a casual of rubbish tips recorded by Jermyn from Ballingdon tip. It has not occurred during our survey.

Bearded Couch
Elymus caninus [5]
A rare grass which was earlier confused with the awned form of the **Common Couch**. The typical habitat for **Bearded Couch** is by a shady stream or ditchside, and our sites include a ditchside at the edge of a wood near Greenstead Green (a few plants only), a shady streamside at Belchamp Walter (several plants), and, rather untypically, a roadside bank at Borley. It was a large bank, dropping down from the fields above to the road, which had recently been completely cleared of all its trees and scrub cover. To confound us further, it was present in good quantity.

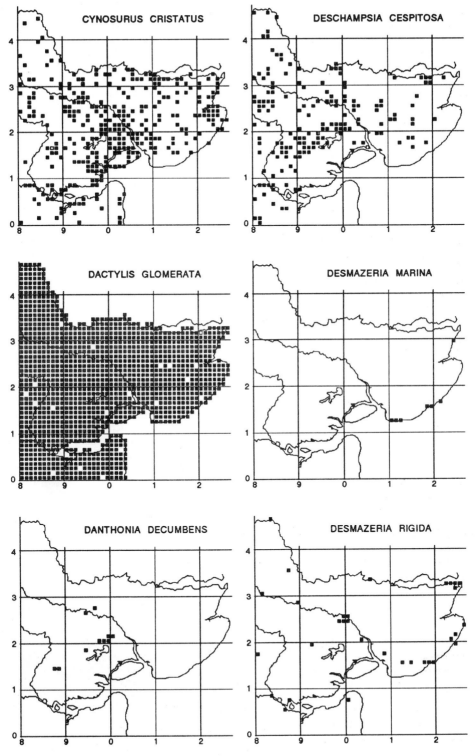

CYNOSURUS CRISTATUS

DESCHAMPSIA CESPITOSA

DACTYLIS GLOMERATA

DESMAZERIA MARINA

DANTHONIA DECUMBENS

DESMAZERIA RIGIDA

Sand Couch
Elymus farctus [34] M

As its name suggests, it is a grass of sand dunes and sandy sea shores. It is still present at all the locations given by Jermyn except for Fingringhoe. During the last century it has been lost from the upper reaches of the Blackwater and Stour where Gibson gave records for both Maldon and Manningtree.

Elymus farctus X pycnanthus [3]

This hybrid between **Sand** and **Sea Couch** only occurs where both parents grow in close proximity. Although **Sea Couch** occurs all round our coast it is often separated from **Sand Couch** by a salt-marsh, thus reducing the opportunity for the hybrid to arise. It still occurs at Walton, where Jermyn recorded it in 1965, but we were unable to refind his sites at Bradwell-on-Sea, 1964, or Dovercourt-Little Oakley area, 1965-66 (there is no reason why it should not occur at this latter site). Additionally it has been found at East Mersea and Lee-over-Sands.

Sea Couch
Elymus pycnanthus [261] M
Elymus pycnanthus var setigerus [22]

Common on the sea walls and upper saltings round the whole of our coast up to the tidal limits on the estuaries. There has been the occasional inland record where it has been found by a roadside. A scattering of the awned form, *var setigerus*, can be found around the coast.

Elymus pycnanthus X repens [2]

Records for this hybrid between **Sea** and **Common Couch** have been confirmed at only two sites, but it probably occurs all round the sea walls where the two grasses meet.

Common Couch   Elytrigia
~~*Elymus repens*~~ [993] M
~~*Elymus repens*~~ var aristatum [261] M

Very common in all kinds of grassland as well as arable fields, bare disturbed ground and waste places. The awned form *var aristatum* occurs scattered throughout the region.

Tall Fescue
Festuca arundinacea [371] M

Common on the clay soils, it is less frequent elsewhere. Its main habitat now appears to be road verges where, as a vigorous grass, it seems to thrive on the mulch resulting from mowing.

Giant Fescue
Festuca gigantea [61] M

Infrequent, it is usually found in damp shady situations, often by streams and ditches.

Rush-leaved Fescue
Festuca juncifolia

Not refound during our survey, the only records are those of G C Brown at St Osyth in 1912 and Jermyn from Crabknowe Spit, 1961. This latter area has been subject to erosion since that date and the site may well no longer exist.

Sheep's Fescue
Festuca ovina [56] M

Usually on light free draining acid soils and banks as well as sometimes in better quality seed mixes or turf. The recent work on this species and the keys to its subspecies came too late to assist our recording and so we have used the **Excursion Flora** to key out our specimens. Of the few specimens examined critically one is ssp *hirtula* but further research is needed before the full picture emerges in our area.

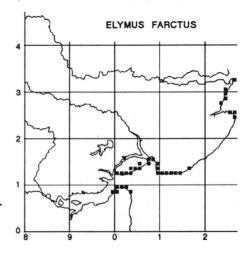

ELYMUS FARCTUS

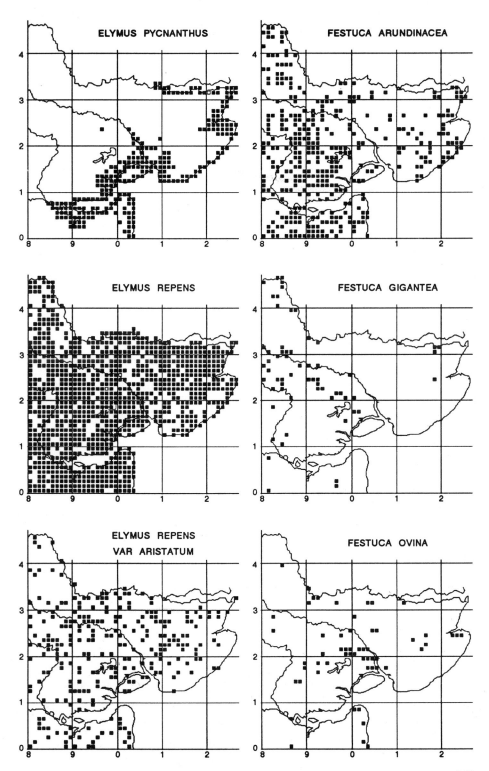

ELYMUS PYCNANTHUS

FESTUCA ARUNDINACEA

ELYMUS REPENS

FESTUCA GIGANTEA

ELYMUS REPENS
VAR ARISTATUM

FESTUCA OVINA

Meadow Fescue
Festuca pratensis [43] M
More frequent in calcareous areas as reflected by the cluster of records on the chalk outcrop to the west of Sudbury. Elsewhere it occurs occasionally in old grassland on road verges.

Red Fescue
Festuca rubra [728] M
Very common in all kinds of grassland including verges, churchyards and sea walls. It is a component of lawn seed and therefore also occurs in modern grassland. The many different subspecies and varieties of **Red Fescue** were not fully recorded during the survey; the following gives an indication of those found in north east Essex. Jermyn had records for *ssp arenaria* from the sand dunes at Colne Point, St Osyth Beach, Walton and Dovercourt - it has been confirmed at Dovercourt, and may still occur at the other sites. A common component of lawn seed, for which we have only one confirmed record, is *ssp commutata*, Jermyn gave several sites scattered throughout our area but, he, too, had not fully recorded its distribution. Records for both *ssp litoralis* and *ssp pruinosa*, which occur in saltmarsh turf, have been made during the survey. Jermyn's records, for St Osyth Beach and Dovercourt, for *var glaucescens*, another saltmarsh variety, could not be confirmed.

Fine-leaved Sheep's Fescue
Festuca tenuifolia [7] M
A rare grass of heathland which has decreased with the loss of this type of grassland. It is now restricted to the Roman River Valley, Layer Breton, Fordham and Tiptree Heaths and a sandy roadside bank at Bulmer. Jermyn's sites where it could not be refound include: an old gravel pit at Bradwell, disused railway line at Tiptree, Spratt's Marsh (now arable), waste ground at Manningtree-Lawford, St Osyth Beach, cliffs at Frinton-Holland and Beaumont Quay area.

Hard Fescue
Festuca trachyphylla [4]
An introduced species found on road verges and other seeded areas.

X *Festulolium loliaceum*
A hybrid between **Meadow Fescue** and **Perennial Rye-grass**, it appears that it was more frequent in our area in Gibson's time when it had been recorded from Halstead, moist meadows at Kelvedon, Dedham and Colchester. Jermyn found it to be infrequent but had recorded it from near Tiptree Heath and near Bures. We have been unable to find this hybrid during our survey.

Nitgrass
Gastridium ventricosum
Last recorded in north east Essex from Hythe Quay, Colchester, before 1930, this casual arable weed was known to Gibson from several localities: Halstead, Kelvedon, Inworth, Braxted, Felix Hall Woods and Berechurch.

Small Sweet-grass
Glyceria declinata [15] M
Uncommon in damp soft ground beside ponds and streams as well as in wet flushes. It has been found in the same vicinity as some of Jermyn's records but many could not be relocated. A few additional records were obtained.

Floating Sweet-grass
Glyceria fluitans [136] M
As with many plants with a watery habitat, it has declined, but it is still reasonably frequent, although scattered, over the whole area. Found in ponds and wet ditches as well as very wet flushes and marshy places.

Glyceria fluitans X plicata
No records for this hybrid were made during the survey. Jermyn sites were: from the lake at Langford Park, mill stream at Wickham Bishops, a pond at Berechurch, a swamp at Gallows Green, a stream near the Stour at Bures, and a freshwater ditch at Bradwell-on-Sea.

Great Water-grass
Glyceria maxima [124] M
A tall grass, beloved by cattle, it is still

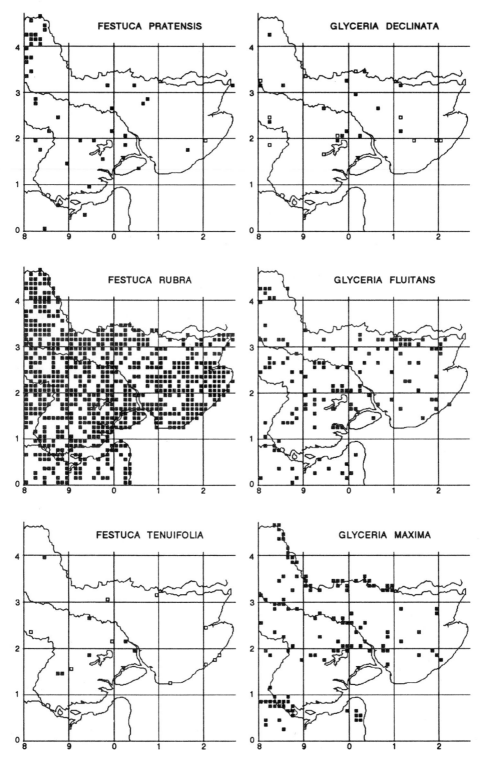

FESTUCA PRATENSIS

GLYCERIA DECLINATA

FESTUCA RUBRA

GLYCERIA FLUITANS

FESTUCA TENUIFOLIA

GLYCERIA MAXIMA

frequent on the edges of the main rivers, their tributaries and large streams. It can occasionally be found in large ponds and farm reservoirs. Both Gibson and Jermyn indicate that its habitat included ditches and marshy places but we have rarely found it in these places during the survey, again indicating the decline in quantity and quality of these habitats.

Plicate Sweet-grass
Glyceria plicata [56]
Neither as widespread nor as frequent as **Floating Sweet-grass** it is generally found in similar places but in slightly drier conditions.

Yorkshire Fog
Holcus lanatus [1069] M
Very common in all kinds of grassland. The gap in distribution running from Silver End to Marks Tey is inexplicable, correlating with neither geology, landuse or recorders.

Creeping Soft Grass
Holcus mollis [461] M
Common on the lighter soils where it occurs in the drier parts of woods and hedgerows as well as under isolated trees on the verges. In damper habitats it is often found on the drier soil of banks.

Wood Barley
Hordelymus europaeus
Known from Chalkney Woods in Victorian times it has not been seen since.

Foxtail Barley
Hordeum jubatum [2]
Introduced when road verges and sea walls have been reseeded.

Sea Barley
Hordeum marinum [112] M
Its range has contracted slightly since Gibson's time but it is still frequent, and locally abundant, in the old grazing marshes and on parts of some sea walls. It often forms a swathe on a bare patch of sea wall, or in the wheel ruts of the track between the borrow dyke and sea wall. In some fields on the Dengie peninsula it was found as an arable weed indicating the recent nature of the change in agricultural practice in this area.

Wall Barley
Hordeum murinum [748] M
Very common by walls, fences and buildings and on disturbed ground.

Meadow Barley
Hordeum secalinum [223] M
It appears this grass has suffered a serious decline on inland habitats. This grass was common to Gibson and he described its habitat as damp meadows; Jermyn, too, gave its habitat as mostly meadowland and pastures, but our findings clearly show that it is now virtually restricted to the old grazing marshes and adjacent sea walls. Other sites include horse paddocks, the odd piece of old grass verge and a few relic meadows.

Crested Hair-grass
Koeleria macrantha [1]
An unusual grass to find in this part of the country, being more frequent on calcareous soils. Jermyn gives records for a grassy bank at Goldhanger and a meadow at Salcott cum Virley. We did not refind these sites but it was discovered at Langenhoe in 1986.

Lyme Grass
Leymus arenarius [5]
A striking grass of sandy shores with blue-grey leaves. It was known to Gibson from Mersea Island but has not been recorded there this century. Jermyn's only site was Walton, where there were two small clumps in 1952 and considerably more in 1967-70. It is still present there, and additional sites have been found between Dovercourt and Little Oakley.

Italian Rye-grass
Lolium perenne
ssp multiflorum [102] M
Naturalised at scattered locations, it has been introduced in sown grass, or planted as a crop for hay and silage.

Lolium perenne
ssp multiflorum X ssp perenne [2]
With the increase in occurrence of **Italian Rye-grass** it was inevitable that the hybrid between this and the **Perennial Rye-grass** would occur in our area. Not fully recorded.

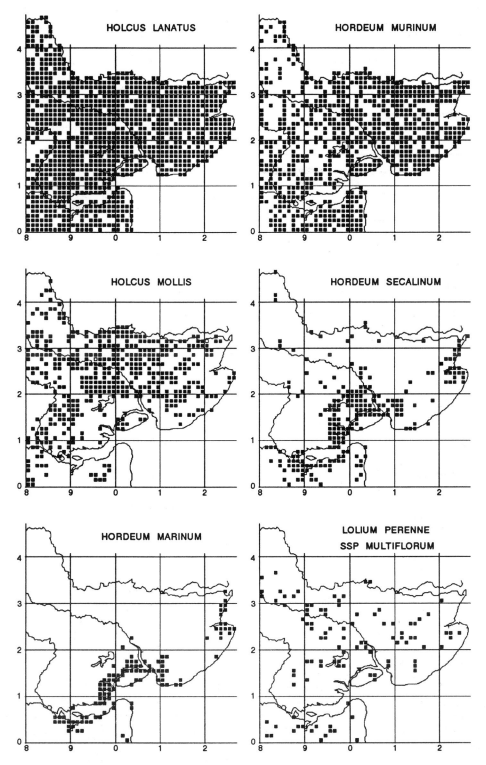

HOLCUS LANATUS

HORDEUM MURINUM

HOLCUS MOLLIS

HORDEUM SECALINUM

HORDEUM MARINUM

LOLIUM PERENNE
SSP MULTIFLORUM

Perennial Rye-grass
Lolium perenne ssp perenne [1211] M
Very common both as a native grass and planted in lawns, parks, resown verges and 'improved' pastures.

Darnel
Lolium temulentum [1]
In the last century this was an arable weed for which Gibson had records from Halstead, Kelvedon, Inworth, Colchester, Thorpe and Dedham. Jermyn found it had become a casual of rubbish tips and waste ground but had no records for north east Essex. In 1980 a few plants were found growing on a farm track near Chalkney Wood.

Wood Melick
Melica uniflora [65] M
Scattered mainly in the west of our region, it grows on dry banks at woodland edges and under shady hedges. No longer "common and well distributed" it has suffered with the loss of many of the hedgerows.

Early Sand-grass
Mibora minima
In 1973 it was noted at Notcutt's Nursery at Ardleigh - it was thought to have come in from their gardens at Woodbridge, Suffolk. There have been no other records for this grass.

Wood Millet
Milium effusum [60] M
No longer common and well distributed, it has become infrequent. Usually found near the woodland edge, it can also occur deeper within the wood. Although most books indicate that it is found in damp woods, we have found that it is more frequent in the woods on the free draining soils and can often be found on the dry banks at the very edge of the wood.

Purple Moor-grass
Molinia caerulea [7] M
Always uncommon in our area due to lack of habitat (wet heaths) it is still present at Tiptree Heath where it was known to both Gibson and Jermyn. Gibson's other sites of Birch Woods, Dedham and Mile End Heath, Colchester have gone as has Jermyn's locations of Spratt's Marsh and

Fordham Heath. It is still present at Layer Breton Heath, a Jermyn locality, and additionally, has been found on a piece of relic heath adjacent to West Bergholt school, in the Roman River Valley, Alresford and Alphamstone. *M caerulea ssp altissima* was recorded from Middlewick by G C Brown in 1924 but we have not found any trace of **Purple Moor Grass** on this site.

Mat Grass
Nardus stricta [3]
A grass found on similar wet heaths as the previous species, it still occurs in the Roman River Valley where it was known to Gibson. However, we were unable to refind it at Tiptree Heath, his other location. Jermyn's sites at Fordham and Layer Breton Heaths were refound but his Spratt's Marsh site has been ploughed. No additional locations were found.

Common Millet
Panicum mileaceum [8]
A bird seed alien that can also occur at rubbish tips and occasionally on waste places.

Curved Hard-grass
Parapholis incurva [13] M
A coastal grass, it is infrequent and found in varying habitats. These include: sandy seafront (West Mersea), the ballast of the old railway line (Brightlingsea), bare patches on sea walls or in the tracks behind the sea wall (St Osyth, Holland, Little Oakley), flowerbed beside putting green (Dovercourt), gravel tracks (Titchwell Marina), the tops of ant hills on grazing marshes (Horsey Island), and lastly, but most abundantly, with **Sea Fern-grass** at the bottom of the cliffs on Clacton promenade. It grows here in the 'pots' in the concrete sea defences. It has not been refound at many of Jermyn's locations including Tollesbury, Bradwell-on-Sea, Colne Point-St Osyth Beach area, Frinton-Walton cliffs, and Ramsey Marsh (TM 23).

Sea Hard-grass
Parapholis strigosa [102] M
Reasonably frequent around the coast, it can usually be found in the wheel ruts in the track between the sea wall and borrow

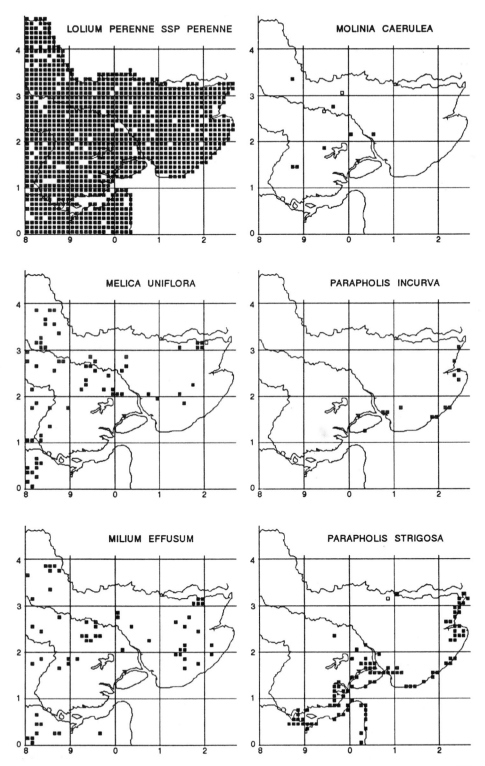

dyke. This is particularly so where saline water has lain for a while making the ground unsuitable for more vigorous competitors and leaving it bare. In these conditions **Sea Hard-grass** will form a swathe along the track. It is occasionally found on road verges which are subject to winter salting.

Phalaris aquatica [5]
A recent introduction that is now planted for cover and food for game birds.

Reed Canary-grass
Phalaris arundinacea [273] M
Common along the edges of the major rivers, their tributaries and large streams. It is also found at the margins of large ponds and increasingly farm reservoirs. The variegated garden form *var picta* is occasionally found planted in village ponds and has survived in a wet hollow in Friday Wood for the duration of the survey.

Canary-grass
Phalaris canariensis [14]
A bird seed alien and casual of waste places, rubbish tips and farm yards.

Lesser Canary-grass
Phalaris minor
Recorded from Hythe Quay, Colchester, in 1913.

Phalaris paradoxa [11]
Previously only known from Hythe Quay, Colchester, 1913, we have found it occurring as an arable weed. It appears that it is a contaminant of seed and once in an area could be spread via the farm machinery - there is a cluster of records on the Dengie peninsula.

Sand Catstail
Phleum arenarium [13] M
A charming little grass of sand dunes. We have records of it from East and West Mersea, Colne Point-St Osyth Beach area and Dovercourt, but have been unable to refind it at the following Jermyn locations: Stansgate, Holland Cliffs and Stone Point, Walton.

Catstail
Phleum pratense ssp bertolonii [915] M
Very common in all kinds of grassland. It is a common component of seed mixes for reseeding verges.

Timothy
Phleum pratense ssp pratense [221] M
Far less common than its close relative above, it is usually associated with 'artificial' grassland.

Common Reed
Phragmites australis [317] M
Both Gibson and Jermyn considered this plant to be common in wet habitats over the whole county. Our survey has shown that whilst it is still very common around our coasts, inland it has become scattered along the main river systems and larger streams. This plant is fairly tolerant of pollution and if the **Common Reed** has suffered a major decline, it is a clear indication of the recent loss and degradation of wetland habitats. Its major habitat is now the borrow dykes behind the sea walls, but it also colonises flooded gravel pits and farm reservoirs.

Narrow-leaved Meadow-grass
Poa angustifolia [27]
This grass is only in flower for a short period and then becomes lost amongst its neighbours. It has, therefore, been under-recorded during our survey; even so, it is not a common grass. When found, it is often on banks and railway embankments.

Annual Meadow-grass
Poa annua [1191] M
Very common, managing to grow wherever there is a patch of disturbed ground. The only area from which it has not been recorded is the closed turf of Langenhoe Marshes.

Bulbous Meadow-grass
Poa bulbosa [1]
Not previously recorded for Essex, it was found for the first time in 1982 at Shoebury in south Essex in short coastal turf and was subsequently found in similar turf at St Osyth Beach in 1987. It rarely reaches the flowering stage and persists and spreads by the bulbils after which it is named.

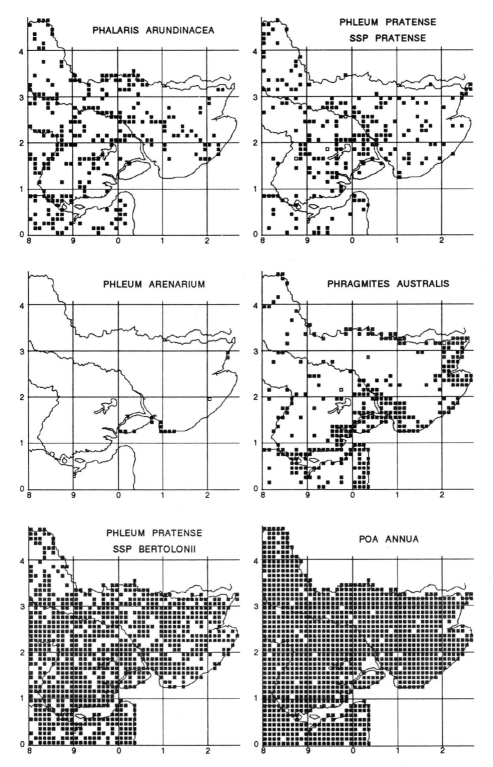

PHALARIS ARUNDINACEA

PHLEUM PRATENSE
SSP PRATENSE

PHLEUM ARENARIUM

PHRAGMITES AUSTRALIS

PHLEUM PRATENSE
SSP BERTOLONII

POA ANNUA

Flattened Meadow-grass
Poa compressa [2]
A rare grass which grows on walls. Despite the historical records indicating that it was not uncommon there have been only two confirmed records during our ten year survey.

Wood Meadow-grass
Poa nemoralis [104] M
A delicate grass of shady hedgebanks and woods. It is reasonably frequent in the Roman River Valley but scattered elsewhere, except in the Lamarsh-Great Henny area.

Smooth Meadow-grass
Poa pratensis [638] M
Very common in all kinds of grassland including road verges, churchyards and sea walls.

Spreading Meadow-grass
Poa subcaerulea [56] M
Probably under-recorded it appears to be present on a number of country roads, growing in a line where the gravel edge of the road meets the grass verge.

Rough Meadow-grass
Poa trivialis [628] M
Another of our very common grasses that can be found in a variety of grassland habitats.

Annual Beard-grass
Polypogon monspeliensis [1]
A casual that was recorded from Hythe Quay, Colchester, 1923-26, and found in a shipyard at Brightlingsea in 1987.

Beardless Beard-grass
Polypogon semiverticillatus
A casual of waste places for which Jermyn had records from Colchester and Frinton-Walton. We have not found this Beard Grass during our survey.

Reflexed Saltmarsh-grass
Puccinellia distans [84] M
A grass of the upper saltmarsh it is often found growing in the wheel ruts on the track behind the sea wall where there is some seepage of salt water. It also occasionally turns up inland on salted roadsides.

Borrer's Saltmarsh-grass
Puccinellia fasciculata [11]
Jermyn found this grass to be widespread although scattered on the coastal and estuarine marshes. Our survey has not revealed many sites but it is possible that it has been under-recorded.

Common Saltmarsh-grass
Puccinellia maritima [207] M
Present and plentiful on all our saltmarshes, it is a major component of this type of plant community.

Stiff Saltmarsh-grass
Puccinellia rupestris [61] M
Reasonably frequent around our coast, it is most prevalent in bare trampled areas, such as the tops of sea walls, or the track at the back of the sea wall where it occurs in the dry wheel ruts. It can occasionally be found on roadsides which are subject to winter salting - on the B1418 about three miles from Maldon it was found to be plentiful for several hundred yards.

Bristle-grasses
Setaria
Several members of this family occur intermittently as casuals of waste places or, more often, as bird seed aliens. Those

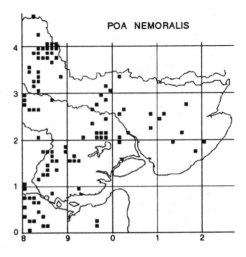

POA NEMORALIS

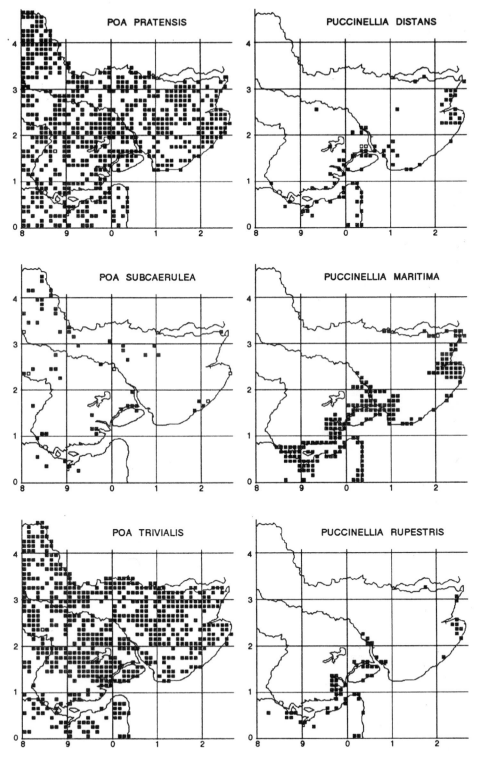

recorded include :
Foxtail Millet - *S italica* [3];
S pumila [3];
Rough Bristle-grass - *S verticillata* [1];
Green Bristle-grass - *S viridis* [4].

Sorghum halepense [1]
Occurring as a casual, two plants were found growing on the railway track at Colchester in 1987.

Smooth Cord-grass
Spartina alterniflora [3]
Introduced to the Blackwater Estuary, it is now well established at three sites.

Common Cord-grass
Spartina anglica [166] M
Our most abundant and variable species on all salt marshes, it is also sometimes found in borrow dykes behind the sea walls. In size varying from small plants a few inches high to others reaching a full three feet. Such diverse specimens can be found growing next to each other.

Small Cord-grass
Spartina maritima [60] M
The original native species, now rare and possibly slightly over-recorded as some forms of **Townsend's Cord-grass** are very similar. The small delicate stature, early flowering and purplish colour are useful identification points but these need to be judged against the ligule length - 0.2mm to 0.6mm in this species and over 1mm for all the others.

Townsend's Cord-grass
Spartina X townsendii [15]
Under-recorded, but rare and often difficult to separate from **Small Cord-grass** and some smaller forms of **Common Cord-grass**.

Yellow Oat
Trisetum flavescens [170] M
Not common, but widely scattered throughout the area. It is usually a component of old grassland and is found on grass verges and in churchyards. It is not often present in the grassland of the sea walls.

Squirrel-tail Fescue
Vulpia bromoides [151] M
Reasonably frequent on the free draining soils, it is usually found on the dry bare patches of banks and sea walls, gravel edges of car parks, rough areas in builders' yards and similar places as well as walls and railway sidings.

Dune Fescue
Vulpia fasciculata [6] M
Recorded from Mersea Island by Dale (1732), this rare sand dune grass is still present at East Mersea today. It also still occurs where Jermyn found it at Colne Point and St Osyth Beach but we have been unable to refind his site at Parkeston, 1964.

Ratstail Fescue
Vulpia myuros [32] M
Less frequent than the **Squirrel-tail**, it is found in very dry habitats including walls, gravel drives, between concrete slabs and around railway sidings.

Matgrass Fescue
Vulpia unilateralis
Not found during the survey, the only record remains that given by Jermyn for Dedham.

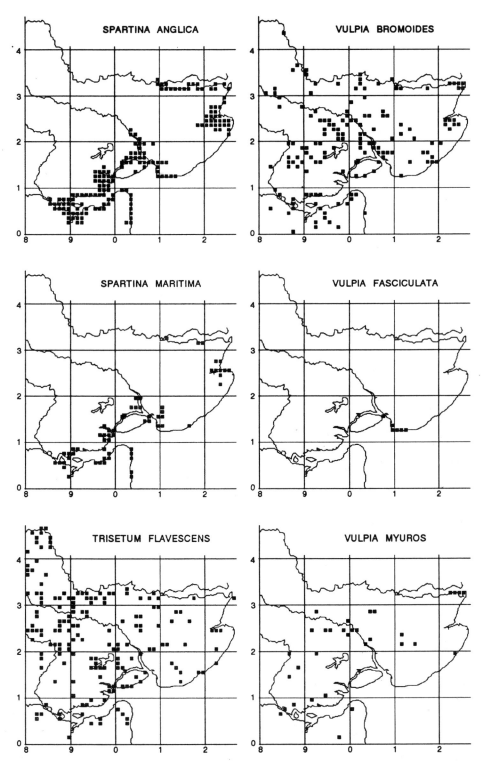

SPARTINA ANGLICA

VULPIA BROMOIDES

SPARTINA MARITIMA

VULPIA FASCICULATA

TRISETUM FLAVESCENS

VULPIA MYUROS

THE 'LOST AND FOUND' PLANTS

Jermyn listed almost 100 species mentioned in Gibson's Flora that he was unable to refind in Essex. Our comparisons are somewhat different as they refer only to our recording area of north east Essex. Due to changes in identification criteria over the last 150 years, absolute comparisons are impossible but an outline of some of the 'native' plants lost and found is given below.

Nearly 1,400 different species, subspecies, varieties or forms of plant have been recorded at some time in north east Essex.

Gibson listed just over 900 species in his Flora that occurred in our area but some of these were historical records so the plants had been lost even by his time - these included such plants as **Man Orchid**, **Military Orchid** and **Early Spider Orchid**. About 80 species listed by Gibson have not been seen since and a further 50 have been lost since Jermyn carried out his recording; approximately 770 being re-recorded during our survey.

Jermyn's list for our area was higher at just over 1,100 but this included many casual and alien species. We too, have recorded just over 1,100 species, again including casuals and aliens but, in many instances, not the same ones as Jermyn found. These types of plant are dependent upon man's activities and as these change so do the species that occur. This is covered in the habitat notes, particularly under Docks and Rubbish tips. We were unable to refind approximately 170 species, varieties and forms listed by Jermyn.

Amongst the 'native' species not refound during our survey were :
Alopecurus bulbosus - **Bulbous Foxtail**
Anthyllis vulneraria - **Kidney Vetch**
Carex echinata - **Star Sedge**
Cerastium arvense - **Field Mouse-ear**
Echium vulgare - **Viper's Bugloss**
X Festulolium loliaceum
Filago gallica - **Narrow-leaved Cudweed**
Genista anglica - **Petty Whin**
Geum rivale - **Water Avens**
Juncus subnodulosus - **Blunt-flowered Rush**
Lathyrus montanus - **Bitter Vetch**
Lysimachia vulgaris - **Yellow Loosestrife**
Minuartia hybrida - **Fine-leaved Sandwort**
Myriophyllum verticillatum - **Whorled Water Milfoil**
Neottia nidus-avis - **Birdsnest Orchid**
Oenanthe silaifolia - **Narrow-leaved Water Dropwort**
Pedicularis sylvatica - **Lousewort**
Samolus valerandi - **Brookweed**
Scutellaria minor - **Lesser Skullcap**
Solidago virgaurea - **Golden Rod**
Valeriana dioica - **Marsh Valerian**
Viola canina - **Heath Dog Violet**
Viola tricolor - **Heartsease**

A high proportion of these plants are associated with water, ancient grassland or heaths, all of which have, and continue, to decrease as quality habitats in our area.

On the credit side we have added approximately 150 species to the list for north east Essex. This number includes seven new County or botanical Vice-County records, or 'firsts' for this century:

Bromus secalinus - **Rye Brome** : 1st record this century
Carex elata - **Tufted Sedge** : 1st record since 1805
Nitella opaca : new County record
Poa bulbosa - **Bulbous Meadow-grass** : new record for Vice-County 19
Polygonum oxyspermum ssp raii - **Ray's Knotgrass** : new County record
Scrophularia umbrosa - **Green Figwort** : new County record
Vicia bithynica - **Bithynian Vetch** : new record for Vice-County 19

There have also been nine other native or well-established species recorded from north east Essex for the first time :

Avenula pubescens - **Hairy Oat-grass**
Cirsium eriophorum - **Woolly Thistle**
Cuscuta europaea - **Great Dodder**
Elodea nuttallii
Fumaria parviflora - **Small White Fumitory**
Fumaria vaillantii - **Small Pink Fumitory**
Helianthemum nummularia - **Common Rockrose**
Oenanthe pimpinelloides - **Corky-fruited Water Dropwort**
Triglochin palustris - **Marsh Arrow-grass**

The remainder are either casuals, aliens, hybrids or the result of the critical examination of difficult groups, although the total does not include the **Brambles** and **Dandelions**.

BIBLIOGRAPHY

Ambrose, J D, (1975), *The Sand and Gravel Resources of the Country East of Colchester, Essex*. Resource Sheet TM 02. Institute of Geological Sciences. (Mineral Assessment Report 14).

Ambrose, J D, (1974), *The Sand and Gravel Resources of the Country West of Colchester, Essex*. Resource Sheet TL 92. Institute of Geological Sciences. (Assessment of British Sand and Gravel Resources No 10).

Ambrose, J D, (1973), *The Sand and Gravel Resources of the Country Around Maldon, Essex*. Resource Sheet TL 80. Institute of Geological Sciences. (Assessment of British Sand and Gravel Resources No 4).

Ambrose, J D, (1973), *The Sand and Gravel Resources of the Country Around Layer Breton and Tolleshunt D'Arcy, Essex*. Resource Sheet TL 91 and Part of TL 90. Institute of Geological Sciences. (Assessment of British Sand and Gravel Resources No 7).

Babbington, C C, (1856), *Manual of British Botany*. 4th ed. London.

Baldwin, S A, (1986), *John Ray Essex Naturalist*. Baldwin's Books.

Benton, E, (1988), *The Dragonflies of Essex*. Essex Field Club. (Essex Naturalist No 9).

Bridgland, D R, (1988), *The Pleistocene Fluvial Stratigraphy and Palaeogeography of Essex*. Proc Geol Ass **99**(4), *291-314.*

Bridgland, D R et al, (1988), *Report of Geologists' Association Field Meeting in North-east Essex, May 22nd-24th 1987*. Proc Geol Ass **99**(4), *315-333.*

Bristow, C R, (1985), *Geology of the County Around Chelmsford*. Memoir for 1:50,000 Geological Sheet 241. British Geological Survey.

Camus, J and Jermy, C, (1987), *The BM Fern Crib*. British Museum (Natural History).

Chapman, J and Andre, P, (1777), *A Map of the County of Essex*. (Reproduction). Essex Record Office Publications, No 11, 1970.

Clapham, A R, Tutin, T G and Moore, D M, (1987), *Flora of the British Isles*. 3rd ed. Cambridge University Press.

Clapham, A R, Tutin, T G and Warburg, E F, (1981), *Excursion Flora of the British Isles*. 3rd ed. Cambridge University Press.

Corke, D, (1984), *The Nature of Essex. The Wildlife and Ecology of the County*. Barracuda Books.

Dale, S, (1732), *The History and Antiquities of Harwich &c* by Silas Taylor; to Which is Added a Large Appendix Containing the Natural History of the Sea Coast &c by Samuel Dale. London.

Dony, J G, Jury, S L and Perring, F H, (1986), *English Names of Wild Flowers*. 2nd ed. Botanical Society of the British Isles.

Doubleday, H A et al (eds), (1903-1963), *The Victoria History of the County of Essex*. Vols 1-3. Constable.

Emmet, A M, (1981), *The Smaller Moths of Essex*. Essex Field Club. (Essex Naturalist No 6).

Emmet, A M and Pyman, G A, (1985), *The Larger Moths and Butterflies of Essex*. Essex Field Club. (Essex Naturalist No 8).

Firmin, J et al, (1975), *A Guide to the Butterflies and Larger Moths of Essex*. The Essex Naturalists' Trust.

Gerarde, J, (1597), *The Herball or Generall Historie of Plants*. London.

Gibson, G S, (1862), *The Flora of Essex*. Pamplin.

Haggard, H J E, (1972), *The Sand and Gravel Resources of the Country Around Witham, Essex*. Resource Sheet TL 81. Institute of Geological Sciences. (Assessment of British Sand and Gravel Resources No 2).

Hey, R W, (1980), *Equivalents of the Westland Green Gravels in Essex and East Anglia.* Proc Geol Ass **91**(4), *279-290.*

Hodge, C A H et al, (1984), *Soils and Their Use in Eastern England.* Soil Survey of England and Wales. (Bulletin No 13).

Hooker, J D, (1884), *The Student's Flora of the British Islands.* Macmillan.

Hopson, P M, (1982), *The Sand and Gravel Resources of the Country Around Sudbury, Suffolk.* Resource Sheet TL 84. Institute of Geological Sciences. (Mineral Assessment Report 118).

Hubbard, C E, (1984), *Grasses.* 3rd ed. Penguin Books.

Jermy, A C, Chater, A O and David, R W, (1982) *Sedges of the British Isles.* 2nd ed. Botanical Society of the British Isles. (BSBI Handbook No 1).

Jermyn, S T, (1974), *Flora of Essex,* Essex Naturalists' Trust.

Lake, R D et al, (1977), *Buried Channel Deposits in the South-east Essex Area; Their Bearing on Pleistocene Palaeogeography.* Institute of Geological Sciences. (Report No 77/21).

Laver, H, (1898), *The Mammals, Reptiles and Fishes of Essex: A Contribution to the Natural History of the County.* Essex Field Club. (Essex Field Club Special Memoirs Vol 3).

Lousley, J E and Kent, D H, (1981), *Docks and Knotweeds of the British Isles.* Botanical Society of the British Isles. (BSBI Handbook No 3).

Meikle, R D, (1984), *Willows and Poplars of Great Britain and Ireland.* Botanical Society of the British Isles. (BSBI Handbook No 4).

Moore, J A, (1986), *Charophytes of Great Britain and Ireland.* Botanical Society of the British Isles. (BSBI Handbook No 5).

Page, C N, (1982), *The Ferns of Britain and Ireland.* Cambridge University Press.

Perring, F H, and Walters, S M, (eds) (1962), *Atlas of the British Flora.* Botanical Society of the British Isles.

Preston, C D and Sell, P D, (1988), *The Aizoaceae naturalized in the British Isles.* Watsonia **17**, *217-245.*

Rackham, O, (1986), *The History of the Countryside.* Dent.

Ransome, A M, (1930), *Swallows And Amazons.* Cape.

Ransome, A M, (1937), *We Didn't Mean To Go To Sea.* Cape.

Ray, J (1724), *Synopsis Methodica Stirpium Britannicarum.* Facsimile of the 3rd edition, 1973. Ray Society.

Rich, T C G and Rich, M D B, (1988), *Plant Crib.* Botanical Society of the British Isles.

Richens, R H, (1983), *Elm.* Cambridge University Press.

Simmons, M B, (1978), *The Sand and Gravel Resources of the Dengie Peninsula, Essex.* Resource Sheet TL 90 and parts of TL 80, TM 00, TQ 89, TQ 99 and TR 09. Institute of Geological Sciences. (Mineral Assessment Report No 34).

Soil Survey of England and Wales, (1983), *Soils of England and Wales.* Sheet 4 Eastern England, 1:250,000. Soil Survey of England and Wales.

Sturdy, R G, and Allen, R H, (1981), *Soils in Essex IV.* Sheet TM 12 (Weeley). Soil Survey of England and Wales. (Soil Survey Record No 67).

Tutin, T G, (1980), *Umbellifers of the British Isles.* Botanical Society of the British Isles. (BSBI Handbook No 2).

Tutin, T G et al (eds), (1964-1980), *Flora Europaea.* 5 vols. Cambridge University Press.

Wake, A J, (1984), *Grasshoppers and Crickets of Essex. A Provisional Atlas.* Colchester and Essex Museum. (Essex Biological Records Centres Publication No 3).

Wigginton, M J and Graham, G G, (1981), *Guide to the Identification of some of the More Difficult Vascular Plant Species.* Nature Conservancy Council.

INDEX TO ENGLISH NAMES

288

290

The scientific names of some plants have changed since Jermyn wrote his **Flora of Essex.** These instances are indicated below within square brackets e.g. Aconitum napellus L *[J as A anglicum].*

295